B&W·HF

Functions of
Several Variables

HARBRACE COLLEGE MATHEMATICS SERIES

Salomon Bochner and W. G. Lister, EDITORS

PUBLISHED TITLES

Calculus, Karel de Leeuw
Linear Algebra, Ross A. Beaumont
Functions of Several Variables, John W. Woll, Jr.

Functions of
Several Variables

JOHN W. WOLL, JR.
UNIVERSITY OF WASHINGTON

Harcourt, Brace & World, Inc.

New York / Chicago / Burlingame

To Patricia, Holly, and Heather

LIBRARY OF CONGRESS CATALOG CARD NUMBER: 66-14924

PRINTED IN THE UNITED STATES OF AMERICA

Foreword

The Harbrace College Mathematics Series has been undertaken in response to the growing demands for flexibility in college mathematics curricula. This series of concise, single-topic textbooks is designed to serve two primary purposes: First, to provide basic undergraduate text materials in compact, coordinated units. Second, to make available a variety of supplementary textbooks covering single topics.

To carry out these aims, the series editors and the publisher have selected as the foundation of the series a sequence of six textbooks covering functions, calculus, linear algebra, multivariate calculus, theory of funtions, and theory of functions of several variables. Complementing this sequence are a number of other planned volumes on such topics as probability, statistics, differential equations, topology, differential geometry, and complex functions.

By permitting more flexibility in the construction of courses and course sequences, this series should encourage diversity and individuality in curricular patterns. Furthermore, if an instructor wishes to devise his own topical sequence for a course, the Harbrace College Mathematics Series provides him with a set of books built around a flexible pattern from which he may choose the elements of his new arrangement. Or, if an instructor wishes to supplement a full-sized textbook, this series provides him with a group of compact treatments of individual topics.

An additional and novel feature of the Harbrace College Mathematics Series is its continuing adaptability. As new topics gain emphasis in the curricula or as promising new treatments appear, books will be added to the series or existing volumes will be revised. In this way, we will meet the changing demands of the instruction of mathematics with both speed and flexibility.

SALOMON BOCHNER

W. G. LISTER

Preface

This book is an exposition of selected topics from the calculus of functions of several variables. It is intended for undergraduate mathematics students in the third or fourth year analysis program, who have had several semesters of the calculus and at least an introduction to linear algebra.

Specifically, the prerequisites include knowledge of the real numbers and functions of one variable plus some introductory experience with multivariate calculus of the type that is usually included in the first two years of college mathematics. The linear algebra needed, which is approximately the content of *Linear Algebra* by Ross A. Beaumont, includes the concept of a finite dimensional vector space, some experience with the idea of a basis for a vector space, and some elementary concepts and properties associated with linear transformations, such as those of rank and determinants. Aside from the fact that the fundamental existence and uniqueness theorem for ordinary differential equations is used without proof, the results used are proved in the body of the text.

The topics treated in this book were selected with two primary objectives: (1) these topics cover the notions usually referred to as "vector analysis," and (2) they cover concepts that can be easily generalized to differentiable manifolds in a relatively coordinate-free manner.

The book divides naturally into three sections. The first two chapters are rather standard, treating respectively the point set topology of $\mathbf{R}^n$ and differentiation on $\mathbf{R}^n$. In the second chapter the inverse function theorem and the theorem on change of variables in multiple integrals are proved and several important implications are discussed in detail. The latter include the concept of local coordinates and the rank of a differentiable map from $\mathbf{R}^m$ to $\mathbf{R}^n$. Basically preparatory, these two chapters constitute the theoretical foundations of the material developed in the remainder of the book.

Chapters Three, Four, and Five constitute the next unit. They are basically manipulative. In Chapter Three the notion of a (tangent) vector at $p \in \mathbf{R}^n$ and the dual notion of covectors at p are developed. With this introduction, Chapter Four is devoted to exposition of the multilinear algebra necessary to construct and verify the properties of exterior multiplication. This chapter actually includes a little more than is needed, however, since the exterior product is constructed by antisymmetrization of multilinear forms rather than by the somewhat more elementary method of giving a multiplication table with respect to a specific basis and showing that the resulting properties of the product imply uniqueness. Chapter Five treats differential forms on $\mathbf{R}^n$, k-chains, Stokes theorem, and some related integral expressions involving the metric, such as Green's identities and Poisson's integral formula for harmonic functions.

Chapter Six treats the concept of a flow with velocity field X and the related derivations on vector fields and differential forms. It includes Frobenius' theorem on completely integrable systems of first-order partial differential equations and Poincaré's lemma that a closed differential form is locally exact.

Chapter Seven shows how the notation and ideas developed earlier can be used in the theory of functions of a complex variable. After a discussion of terminology and of the concept of an analytic coordinate system in the first two sections, the remainder of the chapter is devoted to developing some of the standard material centering around Cauchy's integral formula and power series expansions. The nature of these last two chapters is again somewhat more theoretical than manipulative.

JOHN W. WOLL, JR.

Seattle, Washington

Contents

Functions of
Several Variables

CHAPTER ONE

Topology of $\mathbf{R}^n$

1 Fundamental structure of $\mathbf{R}^n$

n-dimensional euclidean space $\mathbf{R}^n$ is the set of all n-tuples $p = (a^1, \ldots , a^n)$ of real numbers, a^k represents the kth member of the n-tuple (not a to the kth power), and the letters p and q are used to represent elements of $\mathbf{R}^n$. $\mathbf{R}^n$ is a vector space, two points $p = (a^1, \ldots , a^n)$ and $q = (b^1, \ldots , b^n)$ having the sum $p + q = (a^1 + b^1, \ldots , a^n + b^n)$. If λ is a real number, $\lambda p = (\lambda a^1, \ldots , \lambda a^n)$. The length of an element $p = (a^1, \ldots , a^n)$ of $\mathbf{R}^n$ is given by

$$\|p\| = \{\sum_{k=1}^{n} (a_k)^2\}^{1/2}$$

and it satisfies the important relations

$$\|p + q\| \le \|p\| + \|q\|;$$
$$\|\lambda p\| = |\lambda|\,\|p\|.$$

The euclidean distance $d(p, q)$ between p and q is the length $\|p - q\|$.

2 Open sets, closed sets, and neighborhoods

The ε-*ball centered at* q or, equivalently, the *ball of radius* ε *centered at* q is the subset $B_\varepsilon(q)$ of $\mathbf{R}^n$ consisting of those points p for which $d(p, q) \le \varepsilon$.

$$B_\varepsilon(q) = \{p \in \mathbf{R}^n : d(p, q) \le \varepsilon\}.$$

q is an *interior point* of the set A if A contains some ball of positive radius centered at q as a subset. The set of interior points of A is denoted by interior (A). The set U is *open* if $U =$ interior (U), while U is a *neighborhood of* q if $q \in$ interior (U). So a set is open if and only if it is a neighborhood of each of the points it contains. The empty set $\varnothing$ does not contain any points and accordingly is equal to its own interior and open. Every point of $\mathbf{R}^n$ is an interior point of $\mathbf{R}^n$, so that $\mathbf{R}^n$ is also open.

A set F is *closed* if its complement F^c, the set of points in $\mathbf{R}^n$ which are not members of F, is open. For example, the complement of the empty set $\varnothing$ is $\varnothing^c = \mathbf{R}^n$ which is open, so that $\varnothing$ is closed. ($\varnothing$ is both open and closed as is $\mathbf{R}^n$.)

A few of the more important properties of open and closed sets are established below as examples; many other properties are left as exercises. In general, of course, most sets are neither open nor closed.

(2.1) Example. If $U_1, \ldots, U_m$ are open sets, their intersection $U_1 \cap U_2 \cap \cdots \cap U_m$ is open. In fact, if p belongs to $U_1 \cap \cdots \cap U_m$, then for each $i = 1, \ldots, m$ there is a number $\varepsilon_i > 0$ such that $p \in B_{\varepsilon_i}(p) \subset U_i$. The intersection of these concentric balls $B_{\varepsilon_i}(p)$ is the ball $B_\delta(p)$ where $\delta =$ minimum $\{\varepsilon_1, \varepsilon_2, \ldots, \varepsilon_m\}$, so that $p \in B_\delta(p) \subset B_{\varepsilon_i}(p) \subset U_i$ for each i. That is, $B_\delta(p) \subset U_1 \cap \cdots \cap U_m$ and p belongs to interior $(U_1 \cap \cdots \cap U_m)$. Since p was an arbitrary point of $U_1 \cap \cdots \cap U_m$, this intersection is open.

(2.2) Example. The union of an arbitrary class of open sets is open. Let $\{U_\alpha : \alpha \in \Gamma\}$ be a class of open sets and let S be the union of all the sets U_α, $\alpha \in \Gamma$. If $p \in S$, then $p \in U_\beta$ for some $\beta \in \Gamma$, and since U_β is open, $B_\varepsilon(p) \subset U_\beta \subset S$ for some $\varepsilon > 0$. Thus $p \in$ interior (S) and S is open.

(2.3) Example. The intersection of any class of closed sets is closed. Let $\{F_\alpha : \alpha \in \Gamma\}$ be a class of closed sets whose intersection is D. A point belongs to each F_α if and only if it does not belong to any of the sets F_α^c, $\alpha \in \Gamma$. $S = \bigcup_\alpha F_\alpha^c$ is known to be open by Example (2.2) and D is consequently closed.

A subset V of the set D in $\mathbf{R}^n$ is called *relatively open in* D if for each $p \in V$ there is a ball $B_\varepsilon(p)$ centered at p such that $B_\varepsilon(p) \cap V = B_\varepsilon(p) \cap D$. Corresponding to this, a subset F of the set D in $\mathbf{R}^n$ is called *relatively closed in* D if $D \cap F^c$ is relatively open in D. The consequences of these definitions are left to the exercises.

Exercises

2.1 Show that V is relatively open in D if and only if $V = D \cap W$ for some open subset W in $\mathbf{R}^n$.

2.2 Give an example of a set which is neither closed nor open.

A sequence of sets $A_1, A_2, \ldots, A_n, \ldots$ is *monotone decreasing* or just *decreasing* if $A_1 \supset A_2 \supset \cdots \supset A_n \supset A_{n+1} \supset \cdots$.

2.3   Give an example of a sequence of open sets $\{U_n\}$ which is decreasing and has empty intersection, $\bigcap\limits_{n=1}^{\infty} U_n = \varnothing$.

2.4   Give an example of a sequence of closed sets $\{F_n\}$ which is decreasing and has empty intersection, $\bigcap\limits_{n=1}^{\infty} F_n = \varnothing$.

2.5   Show that the intersection of a countable number of open sets can be closed; can be a set which is neither open nor closed; can be open.

2.6   Show that the union of a countable number of closed sets can be a set which is neither open nor closed.

2.7   Show that if $F_1, \ldots, F_k$ are closed subsets of $\mathbf{R}^n$, then so is $F_1 \cup \cdots \cup F_k$. A finite union of closed sets is closed.

2.8   For each subset $F \subset \mathbf{R}^n$ let cl (F) denote the intersection of all the closed subsets of $\mathbf{R}^n$ which contain F. cl (F) is closed by Example (2.3).

(a) Show that cl (F) is the smallest closed subset of $\mathbf{R}^n$ which contains F.
(b) Show cl $(F) = F$ if and only if F is already closed. In particular cl (cl (F)) = cl (F) for any subset F.
(c) Show cl $(F \cup E) \supset$ cl $(F) \cup$ cl (E) for any E and F in $\mathbf{R}^n$.

2.9   Let $B_\varepsilon^{\circ}(q) = $ interior $B_\varepsilon(q) = \{p \in \mathbf{R}^n : d(p, q) < \varepsilon\}$ be the open ε-ball centered at q. $q = (a^1, \ldots, a^n)$ is called a *rational point* if each of its coordinates a^k is a rational number.

(a) Show that the set of rational points of $\mathbf{R}^n$ is countable.
(b) Let $\mathcal{U} = \{B_\varepsilon^{\circ}(q) : \varepsilon$ is a rational number and q is a rational point of $\mathbf{R}^n\}$. Show that the class of subsets $\mathcal{U}$ of $\mathbf{R}^n$ is countable.
(c) If p is an interior point of E, show that there is a set $B_\varepsilon^{\circ}(q) \in \mathcal{U}$ such that $p \in B_\varepsilon^{\circ}(q) \subset E$.
(d) Show that each open set J in $\mathbf{R}^n$ can be expressed as a (countable) union of sets in the class $\mathcal{U}$.

2.10   Show that the class of open subsets of $\mathbf{R}^n$ is not countable.

2.11   (Based on Exercise 2.9.) If $\mathcal{V}$ is a class of open subsets of $\mathbf{R}^n$, let $V = \cup \{W : W \in \mathcal{V}\}$ be the union of all the sets in $\mathcal{V}$. Show that $\mathcal{V}$ has a countable subclass $\mathcal{V}_0 \subset \mathcal{V}$ such that $V = \cup \{W : W \in \mathcal{V}_0\}$.

A set E is called a G_δ ("G-delta") if it can be expressed as the intersection of a countable number of open sets. $E = \bigcap\limits_{k=1}^{\infty} V_k$, where V_k is open.

2.12   Show that the unit ball $B_1((0, \ldots, 0))$ centered at the origin is a G_δ.

For each closed set $F \subset \mathbf{R}^n$ and each $p \in \mathbf{R}^n$ put

$$d(p, F) = \inf \{d(p, q) : q \in F\}.$$

2.13   Show that whenever F is closed and $\varepsilon > 0$ the set $F_\varepsilon = \{q : d(q, F) < \varepsilon\}$ is open.

2.14 (Based on Exercise 2.13.) Show that $F = \bigcap\limits_{k=1}^{\infty} F_{1/k}$. That is, show that each closed subset of $\mathbf{R}^n$ is a G_δ.

2.15 For each subset $A \subset \mathbf{R}^n$ let $U(A) = \{q \in A : B_\varepsilon(q) \cap A$ is at most countable for some $\varepsilon > 0\}$. Show $U(A)$ is a countable subset of A.

A class $\mathfrak{U}$ of subsets of $\mathbf{R}^n$ is a *covering of B* or covers B if $\cup \, \{U : U \in \mathfrak{U}\} \supset B$. $\mathfrak{V}$ is a *subcovering* of the preceding covering if $\mathfrak{V} \subset \mathfrak{U}$ and $\mathfrak{V}$ covers B. $\mathfrak{V}$ is a *finite subcovering* or *countable subcovering* of B if the class $\mathfrak{V}$ is finite or countable, respectively.

2.16 Let $\mathfrak{U}$ be a covering of B and suppose each $U \in \mathfrak{U}$ is open. Show that $\mathfrak{U}$ has a countable subcovering $\mathfrak{V}$ of B. [HINT: See Exercises 2.9 and 2.11.]

3 Sequences

A sequence $p_1, p_2, \ldots, p_k, \ldots$ of points of $\mathbf{R}^n$ *converges* to the point p—in symbols, $\lim_k p_k = p$ or $\lim p_k = p$—if and only if for each neighborhood V of p the set $\{k : p_k \notin V\}$ is finite. In this case p is called the *limit* of the sequence $\{p_m\}_{m=1}^{\infty}$. (The reader is cautioned that the points p_j need not differ for different values of j. It is even perfectly possible that $p_1 = p_k$ for all k.) Since each $B_\varepsilon(p)$ is a neighborhood of p, $\lim p_m = p$ if and only if for each $\varepsilon > 0$, $\|p_k - p\| < \varepsilon$, except possibly for a finite number of k's. Stated alternatively, $\lim p_m = p$ if and only if the limit of the numerical sequence $\{\|p_k - p\|\}$ is zero. The concept of convergence can be phrased in another manner. The sequence $\{p_k\}_{k=1}^{\infty}$ is *ultimately in the set J* if and only if $\{k : p_k \in J\}$ is finite. In this terminology a sequence $\{p_m\}_{m=1}^{\infty}$ converges to the point p if and only if it is ultimately in each neighborhood of p.

$\mathbf{R}^n$ is the space of n-tuples of real numbers, so that a sequence whose kth term is $p_k = (a_k^1, \ldots, a_k^n)$ gives rise to n sequences of real numbers $\{a_k^1, k = 1, 2, \ldots\}, \ldots, \{a_k^n, k = 1, 2, 3, \ldots\}$. The inequalities

(3.1) $\max \{|a_k^1 - a^1|, \ldots, |a_k^n - a^n|\} \leq \|p_k - p\|$

$$\leq n \max \{|a_k^1 - a^1|, \ldots, |a_k^n - a^n|\}$$

show that $\lim p_k = p$ where $p = (a^1, \ldots, a^n)$ if and only if $\lim_k a_k^j = a^j$ for each $j = 1, 2, \ldots, n$. This last observation can be exploited to reduce many properties of sequences in $\mathbf{R}^n$ to corresponding properties for sequences of real numbers.

(3.2) Example. $\{p_k\}$ is a *Cauchy sequence* in $\mathbf{R}^n$ if for each $\varepsilon > 0$ the set $\{j : \text{for some } m \geq j, \|p_m - p_j\| > \varepsilon\}$ is finite. Every Cauchy sequence in $\mathbf{R}^n$ converges. In fact an inequality like the first inequality in (3.1) shows that each of the subsidiary sequences $\{a_k^1\}$, . . . , $\{a_k^1\}$ is a Cauchy sequence of real numbers. Each Cauchy sequence of real numbers converges (this is one of the basic properties of **R**); so $\lim a_k^1 = a^1$, . . . , $\lim a_k^n = a^n$. According to the observation preceding this example, $\lim p_k = p$ where $p = (a^1, \ldots, a^n)$.

The sequence $\{q_m\}$ is a *subsequence* of the sequence $\{p_k\}$ if $q_m = p_{k(m)} (m = 1, 2, \ldots)$ where $m \to k(m)$ is a map which assigns to each positive integer m another positive integer $k(m)$ subject only to the requirement that $k(m + 1) > k(m)$. The point q is an *accumulation point* of the sequence $\{p_k\}$ if for each neighborhood W of q the set $\{k : p_k \in W\}$ is infinite. The sequence $\{p_k\}$ is *eventually in the set J* if and only if $\{k : p_k \subset J\}$ is infinite. In this terminology q is an accumulation point for $\{p_k\}$ when and only when $\{p_k\}$ is eventually in each neighborhood W of q.

As a further criterion: q is an accumulation point of $\{p_k\}$ if and only if $\{p_k\}$ has a subsequence $\{q_m\}$ which converges to q. To see this suppose first that $\{q_m\}$ is a subsequence of $\{p_k\}$, $q_m = p_{k(m)}$, which converges to q. Then for each neighborhood W of q the set $\{m : q_m \notin W\}$ is finite, consequently $\{k(m) : p_{k(m)} = q_m \in W\}$ is infinite. Since this latter set of $k(m)$'s is a subset of $\{k : p_k \in W\}$, it follows that this set too is infinite and by definition q is an accumulation point of $\{p_k\}$. Conversely if q is an accumulation point of $\{p_k\}$, define inductively

$$k(1) = 1, \qquad k(m) = \inf \left\{ j : j > k(m - 1), \|p_j - p\| < \frac{1}{m} \right\}.$$

With this definition $\|p_{k(m)} - q\| < \dfrac{1}{m}$ for each m; so the subsequence $\{q_m\}$, $q_m = p_{k(m)}$, converges to q.

Exercises

3.1 If $\{q_m\}$ is a subsequence of $\{p_k\}$ and q is an accumulation point of $\{q_m\}$, show that q is an accumulation point of $\{p_k\}$.

3.2 If the set D is not closed, show there is a sequence $\{p_k\}$, $p_k \in D$, which converges to a point $p \notin D$.

3.3 Construct a sequence with no accumulation points.

3.4 Construct a sequence in **R** whose set of accumulation points is the unit interval $[0, 1]$.

3.5 If $\{p_k\}$, $\{q_k\}$ are sequences in $\mathbf{R}^n$ with $\lim_k p_k = p$, $\|q_k - p_k\| < 1/k$, show that $\lim_k q_k = p$.

3.6 Let cl (F) be the set of points q which are limits of sequences $\{q_k\}$, $q_k \in F$, chosen from F.

(a) Show that cl (F) is closed.

(b) Show that cl (F) is the smallest closed set containing F.

3.7 Show that the set of accumulation points of a sequence is closed.

3.8 If F is a closed set in $\mathbf{R}$, construct a sequence whose set of accumulation points is F.

A subset $P \subset \mathbf{R}^n$ is *perfect* if (i) P is closed in $\mathbf{R}^n$, (ii) each $p \in P$ is the limit of a sequence $\{q_n\}$ of points $q_n \in P$, $q_n \neq p$, chosen from P with the point p itself removed, (iii) $P \neq \varnothing$, P is not empty.

3.9 Construct examples of perfect and nonperfect closed sets.

3.10 A perfect subset of $\mathbf{R}^n$ is never countable. Suppose P is perfect and countable, $P = \{p_1, p_2, \ldots, p_k, \ldots\}$.

(a) Show for some $\varepsilon_1 > 0$ there is a closed ball B_1 of radius ε_1 which contains infinitely many points of P but does not contain p_1.

(b) Show that if B_k is a closed ball of radius $\varepsilon_k > 0$ which contains infinitely many points of P but does not contain the points $p_1, p_2, \ldots, p_k$, there is a ball $B_{k+1} \subset B_k$ of radius ε_{k+1}, $0 < \varepsilon_{k+1} < \varepsilon_k$, which contains infinitely many points of P but does not contain $p_1, p_2, \ldots, p_{k+1}$.

(c) Suppose the closed balls $B_1 \supset B_2 \supset \cdots \supset B_k \supset B_{k+1} \supset \cdots$ of radii $\varepsilon_1 > \varepsilon_2 > \cdots > \varepsilon_k > \varepsilon_{k+1} > \cdots$ have been constructed inductively satisfying the conditions in (a) and (b) above and that $\lim_k \varepsilon_k = 0$. Show that each sequence $\{q_m\}$, $q_m \in B_m \cap P$, is a Cauchy sequence.

(d) Obtain a contradiction by considering $\lim_m q_m$, $\{q_m\}$ as in (c), and thus show P could not have been countable.

3.11 If F is closed in $\mathbf{R}^n$, show that $F = C \cup P$ where C is countable and P is perfect. [HINT: Put $C = U(F)$ where $U(F)$ is defined as in Exercise 2.15.]

4 Compact sets

If $\{p_k\}$ converges to q then q is the only accumulation point of $\{p_k\}$, but in general a sequence which has just one accumulation point need not converge to that accumulation point. There is, however, one important situation where this last statement is true. A subset D of $\mathbf{R}^n$ is *compact* if every sequence of points $\{p_k\}$ of D has an accumulation point in D. Equivalently a subset D of $\mathbf{R}^n$ is compact if every sequence of points $\{p_k\}$ of D has a subsequence which converges to a point of D.

(4.1) Example. If D is compact and p is the only accumulation point of the sequence $\{p_k\}$ of points of D, then $\lim p_k = p$. Suppose on the contrary that for some neighborhood W of p $\{k : p_k \notin W\}$ is infinite. In this case $\{p_k\}$ has a subsequence $\{q_m\}$ with $q_m \notin W$ for each m. $\{q_m\}$ is still a sequence of points in D and hence $\{q_m\}$ has an accumulation point q which (Exercise 3.1) is an accumulation point of $\{p_k\}$. As p is the only accumulation point of $\{p_k\}$, $p = q$. This gives a contradiction: W is a neighborhood of $q = p$ and $\{m : q_m \in W\}$ is not infinite. In fact it is empty, because $q_m \notin W$ for each m.

(4.2) **Example.** A compact set D is always closed. According to Exercise 3.2 if D is not closed there is a sequence $\{p_k\}$ of points of D which converges to a point $p \notin D$. The only accumulation point of $\{p_k\}$ is p and it does not belong to D; so D is not compact.

(4.3) **Example.** If D is compact there is a number M such that $\|q\| \leq M$ whenever $q \in D$. Otherwise D would contain points p_m such that $\|p_m\| \geq m$ for each $m = 1, 2, 3, \ldots$. The sequence $\{p_m\}$ cannot have an accumulation point q, because if W is the neighborhood $B_1(q)$ of q, every point p of W satisfies $\|p\| \leq \|q\| + \|p - q\| \leq \|q\| + 1$ and consequently the set $\{k : p_k \in W\}$ is certainly finite.

A set F for which there is an M with $\|p\| \leq M$ whenever $p \in F$ is called *bounded*. The preceding examples show that a compact set D is always closed and bounded. More is true.

(4.4) **Theorem.** The set D is compact in $\mathbf{R}^n$ if and only if D is both closed and bounded.

PROOF. Because of Examples (4.2) and (4.3) it is sufficient to show that a closed bounded set F is necessarily compact. As F is closed, it suffices to show that every sequence of points of F has a convergent subsequence. This can be done directly, but it is schematically a little simpler (1) to assume the theorem is true when the dimension $n = 1$ and establish the general result from this, and (2) to establish the result when $n = 1$ separately.

If $\{p_k\}$, $p_m = (a_m^1, \ldots, a_m^n)$, is a sequence of points of F, the sequences of real numbers $\{a_m^1\}, \ldots, \{a_m^n\}$ all belong to the closed bounded interval $[-M, M]$ on the real line. (M is chosen so that $\|p\| \leq M$ when $p \in F$.) Assuming for the moment that Theorem (4.4) is true when $n = 1$, the first of these sequences has a subsequence $\{a_{m(j)}^1\}_{j=1}^{\infty}$ converging to some limit a^1. Now $\{a_{m(j)}^2\}_{j=1}^{\infty}$ may not converge, but it certainly has a convergent subsequence $\{a_{m(j(k))}^2\}_{k=1}^{\infty}$ with limit a^2 and $\lim_k a_{m(j(k))}^1 = a^1$. Passing in this manner to successive subsequences, one obtains after n steps subsequences $\{a_{k(m)}^1\}, \ldots, \{a_{k(m)}^n\}$ converging respectively to $a^1, \ldots, a^n$. The observation following (3.1) then shows that $\lim_m p_{k(m)} = p$ where $p = (a^1, \ldots, a^n)$.

To prove Theorem (4.4) when $n = 1$ suppose $F \subset [-M, M]$ and $\{p_k\}$ is a sequence of points of F. Define q_k by $2Mq_k = p_k + M$ and note that $2M|q_k - q_m| = |p_k - p_m|$, so that a subsequence $\{p_{k(j)}\}$ is a Cauchy sequence and hence converges if and only if $\{q_{k(j)}\}$ converges. $q_k \in [0, 1]$; so without loss of generality one may as well assume from the outset that $\{p_k\}$ is a sequence of points from the closed interval $[0, 1]$. Set $I_m = [(j - 1)/2^m, j/2^m]$ where j is the smallest integer, $1 \leq j \leq 2^m$, for which the set $\{k : p_k \in [(j-1)2^{-m}, j2^{-m}]\}$ is infinite. Note that

$$I_1 \supset I_2 \supset \cdots I_m \supset I_{m+1} \supset \cdots$$

and that length $I_m = 2^{-m}$. Choose $k(m)$ $(m = 1, 2, \ldots)$ inductively so that (1) $k(m) > k(m-1)$ and (2) $p_{k(m)} \in I_m$. This can always be done because $\{k : p_k \in I_m\}$ is infinite. Contention: $\{p_{k(m)}\}$ is a Cauchy sequence and hence converges. In fact $|p_{k(i)} - p_{k(j)}| \leq (\frac{1}{2})^m$ when $i, j \geq m$. This completes the proof of Theorem (4.4). ◆

Exercises

4.1 If $D_1 \supset D_2 \supset \cdots \supset D_m \supset \cdots$ is a decreasing sequence of nonempty compact sets, show that $\bigcap_{k=1}^{\infty} D_k \neq \varnothing$. [HINT: Let $q_k \in D_k, k = 1, 2, \ldots$, and consider $q = \lim_j q_{k(j)}$ for some subsequence $\{q_{k(j)}\}$ of $\{q_k\}$.]

A class $\mathcal{C}$ of subsets of $\mathbf{R}^n$ has the *finite intersection property* if each intersection $A_1 \cap \cdots \cap A_k$ of a finite number of sets in $\mathcal{C}$ is nonempty, $A_1 \cap \cdots \cap A_k \neq \varnothing$, $A_j \in \mathcal{C}$.

4.2 (Based on Exercise 4.1.) If $\mathcal{C}$ has the finite intersection property and is a countable class of compact sets, show that $\cap \{A : A \in \mathcal{C}\} \neq \varnothing$.

4.3 (Based on Exercises 4.1 and 4.2.) If B is compact show that each countable open covering $\mathcal{U}$ of B has a finite subcovering. (For the definition of covering and subcovering see the insert before Exercise 2.16.) [HINT: Let $\mathcal{C} = \{B \cap U^c : U \in \mathcal{U}\}$ and show that $\mathcal{C}$ cannot have the finite intersection property.]

4.4 (Based on Exercises 4.1, 4.2, 4.3, and 2.16.) Show that each open covering $\mathcal{U}$ of the compact set B in $\mathbf{R}^n$ has a finite subcovering. This is the *Heine Borel* property.

4.5 If B is not compact in $\mathbf{R}^n$ show that there is an open covering $\mathcal{U}$ of B which does not have a finite subcovering. That is, the Heine Borel property is equivalent to compactness in $\mathbf{R}^n$.

4.6 (Existence of the Lesbesgue number.) Let $\mathcal{U}$ be an open covering of the compact set D. Show that there is a number $\varepsilon > 0$ such that if $d(p, q) < \varepsilon$, $p, q \in B$, then it is guaranteed that $p, q \in V$ for some $V \in \mathcal{U}$. The largest ε for which this is true is called the *Lesbesgue number* of the covering $\mathcal{U}$.

4.7 Show by an example that if $\mathcal{U}$ is an open covering of a closed set B, there may not be any $\varepsilon > 0$ satisfying the conditions of Exercise 4.6.

The *diameter* of a set $B \subset \mathbf{R}^n$ is the least upper bound of the numbers $d(p, q)$, $q, p \in B$.

4.8 Let $\mathcal{U}$ be an open covering of the compact set D. Show that there is a number $\varepsilon > 0$ such that whenever diameter $(B) \leq \varepsilon$ and $B \subset D$, then $B \subset V$ for some $V \in \mathcal{U}$.

5 Continuity

A map $p \to f(p)$ defined on the subset D of $\mathbf{R}^n$ with values in $\mathbf{R}^m$ is *continuous at* $p \in D$ if whenever $\{p_k\}$ is a sequence of points of D converging to p it is true that $\lim_k f(p_k) = f(p)$, a statement which is usually abbreviated $\lim_{q \to p} f(q) = f(p)$. f is *continuous or continuous on* D if it is continuous at every point of D. As a point of terminology, if $m = 1$ so that the values of f are real numbers, f is called a *real-valued function* or just a function.

Among the most primitive examples of continuous functions on $\mathbf{R}^n$ are the cartesian coordinate functions $x^1, \ldots, x^n$ associated with the underlying product representation of $\mathbf{R}^n$ and defined by $x^j[(a^1, \ldots, a^n)] = a^j, j = 1, 2, \ldots, n$.

Given any map f of D into B, usually described as a map $f: D \to B$, several notations are in common use. If E is a subset of D, $f(E) = \{f(q): q \in E\}$ is used to denote the image of E under f. f is *onto* or a map of D *onto* B if $f(D) = B$. If F is a subset of B, $f^{-1}(F) = \{p \in D: f(p) \in F\}$ denotes the inverse image of F. f is *one-one* if $f(p) = f(q)$ implies $p = q$ and f is *one-one onto* if f is one-one and onto. In this case f has an inverse map f^{-1} mapping the points of B onto those of D and described by: $f^{-1}(b) = p$ if and only if $f(p) = b$. Note that if such an inverse map exists, each of the two meanings attributed to $f^{-1}(F)$ defines the same subset of D.

If $f: D \to B$ and $g: B \to E$ are two maps, their *composition* is the map $g \circ f: D \to E$ defined by $g \circ f(p) = g(f(p))$.

(5.1) Example. The map $f: D \to \mathbf{R}^m$ is continuous$\Leftrightarrow f^{-1}(U)$ is relatively open in D whenever U is open in $\mathbf{R}_m$.

PROOF. ($\Rightarrow$): Suppose $f^{-1}(U)$ is not relatively open in D; then for some open subset U of $\mathbf{R}^m$ there is a $p \in f^{-1}(U)$ such that $p \notin$ interior $f^{-1}(U)$ and

$$B_\varepsilon(p) \cap f^{-1}(U) \subsetneq B_\varepsilon(p) \cap D$$

for any $\varepsilon > 0$. Choose for each k a point $p_k \in B_{1/k}(p) \cap D$, $p_k \notin f^{-1}(U)$. $\lim_k p_k = p$; U is a neighborhood of $f(p)$ and yet $\{k: f(p_k) \notin U\}$ includes each $k > 0$ and is infinite. So $\{f(p_k)\}_{k=1}^\infty$ does not converge to $f(p)$ and f is not continuous at p. ($\Leftarrow$): If $p_k \in D$, $\lim_k p_k = p$; then choosing $\delta > 0$ so that

$$B_\delta(p) \cap f^{-1}(U) = B_\delta(p) \cap D$$

it follows (see Figure 1) that

$$\begin{aligned}
\{k: p_k \notin B_\delta(p)\} &= \{k: p_k \notin B_\delta(p) \cap D\} \\
&\supset \{k: p_k \notin f^{-1}(U) \cap D\} \\
&= \{k: p_k \notin f^{-1}(U)\} \\
&= \{k: f(p_k) \notin U\}.
\end{aligned}$$

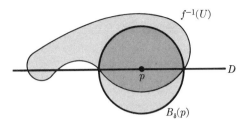

$f^{-1}(U)$

p

D

$B_\delta(p)$

FIGURE 1

The first set above is finite because $\lim_k p_k = p$. The last set is then finite and since U is an arbitrary open neighborhood of $f(p)$, $\lim_k f(p_k) = f(p)$.

(5.2) Example. If $f: D \to \mathbf{R}^m$ is continuous and F is a compact subset of D, then $f(F)$ is compact in $\mathbf{R}^m$. That is, *the continuous image of a compact set is compact*.

PROOF. Suppose that $\{q_k\}$ is a sequence of points in $f(F)$ and for each k choose $p_k \in F$ so that $f(p_k) = q_k$. $\{p_k\}$ has a convergent subsequence $\{p_{k(m)}\}$, $\lim_m p_{k(m)} = p \in F$, and by continuity $\lim_m f(p_{k(m)}) = f(p)$. Thus the subsequence $\{q_{k(m)}\}$ of $\{q_k\}$ converges and $f(F)$ is compact.

(5.3) Theorem. If D is a compact subset of $\mathbf{R}^n$ and $f: D \to B$ is continuous, one-one, and onto, then $f^{-1}: B \to D$ is continuous.

PROOF. Let $\{q_k\}$ be a sequence of points of B converging to the point q. Suppose $\{f^{-1}(q_{k(m)})\}_{m=1}^{\infty}$ converges to p. By the continuity of the map f,

$$f(p) = \lim_m f \circ f^{-1}(q_{k(m)}) = \lim_m q_{k(m)} = q;$$

so $p = f^{-1}(q)$ is the only accumulation point of $\{f^{-1}(q_k)\}$ and by Example (4.1) $\{f^{-1}(q_k)\}$ converges to $f^{-1}(q)$. That is, f^{-1} is continuous.

For the sake of illustrating the possibilities a second proof is given for Theorem (5.3). Let $g = f^{-1}$. It suffices to show according to Example (5.1) that $g^{-1}(U)$ is relatively open in B whenever U is open in $\mathbf{R}^n$. Now

$$g^{-1}(U) = f(U \cap D) = B - f(U^c \cap D).$$

Since $U^c \cap D$ is compact, so is $f(U^c \cap D)$ by Example (5.2), and $g^{-1}(U) = B \cap W$ where $W = [f(U^c \cap D)]^c$ is open. According to Exercise 2.1 $g^{-1}(U)$ is then relatively open in B. ◆

There is another important set property besides compactness which is preserved under continuous mappings. A set H is *connected* if it is not the union of two nonempty, disjoint, relatively open subsets. That is, H is connected if whenever $H = J_1 \cup J_2$, J_1, J_2 relatively open and $J_1 \cap J_2 = \varnothing$, it follows that either $J_1 = \varnothing$ or $J_2 = \varnothing$.

The continuous image of a connected set is connected. Indeed if $f: H \to$

$\mathbf{R}^m$ is continuous and $f(H)$ is not connected,

$$f(H) = J_1 \cup J_2$$

where J_1, J_2 are relatively open in $f(H)$; $J_1 \cap J_2 = \varnothing$; and neither J_1 nor J_2 is empty. The same is true for the sets $f^{-1}(J_1)$ and $f^{-1}(J_2)$, so that the set $H = f^{-1}(J_1) \cup f^{-1}(J_2)$ cannot be connected either.

Very few additional facts about connectivity are needed for this book. With minor omissions they are:

(1)   The closed unit interval $[0, 1]$ is connected. To prove this suppose J_1 and J_2 are disjoint, relatively open sets in $[0, 1]$, and to be specific suppose $0 \in J_1$. If J_2 is not empty there is a point $c \in J_2$. In this eventuality put

(5.4) $b = \sup \{a \in J_1 : a < c\},$

and consider the two possibilities (i) $b \in J_1$ and (ii) $b \in J_2$. Each of these leads to a contradiction with (5.4). Elaborating on this, note first that since J_2 is relatively open

$$(c - \delta, c + \delta) \cap [0, 1] \subset J_2$$

for some $\delta > 0$; so $b \leq c - \delta < c$. If $b \in J_1$, $(b - \varepsilon, b + \varepsilon) \cap [0, 1] \subset J_1$ for some $\varepsilon > 0$ and b is not the supremum of the set of a's in (5.4). If $b \in J_2$, $(b - \varepsilon, b + \varepsilon) \cap [0, 1] \subset J_2$ for some $\varepsilon > 0$ and b is not even a limit point of J_1, let alone the supremum of the set of a's in (5.4).

(2)   If each pair p, q of points of H belongs to a connected subset $A_{p,q}$ of H, then H itself is connected. If H were not connected under these conditions, $H = J_1 \cup J_2$ as above with $J_1 \neq \varnothing$ and $J_2 \neq \varnothing$. Choose $p \in J_1$ and $q \in J_2$; then $A_{p,q} = (A_{p,q} \cap J_1) \cup (A_{p,q} \cap J_2)$ and these last two sets are nonempty, disjoint, and relatively open in $A_{p,q}$, violating the hypothesis that $A_{p,q}$ is connected.

A continuous map $g : [0, 1] \to H$ is called an arc in H joining $g(0)$ to $g(1)$, and a set H is called *arcwise connected* if each pair p, q of points of H can be joined by an arc in H.

(3)   An arcwise connected set H is connected because an arc $g : [0, 1] \to H$ joining p and q provides a connected subset $A_{p,q} = g([0, 1])$ satisfying the conditions of (2) above.

Exercises

5.1   In the following let $f : A \cup B \to \mathbf{R}$ and $f|_A : A \to \mathbf{R}$, $f|_B : B \to \mathbf{R}$ denote the restrictions of f to the sets A and B respectively.

(a) Show that f need not be continuous if $f|_A$ and $f|_B$ are continuous.
(b) If A and B are open and $f|_A$, $f|_B$ are continuous, show f is continuous.
(c) If A and B are closed and $f|_A$, $f|_B$ are continuous, show f is continuous.

5.2 Let $f: \mathbf{R}^2 \to \mathbf{R}$ be given by

$$f(a, b) = \frac{ab(a - b)}{(a^2 + b^2)^{3/2}} \qquad \text{if } (a, b) \neq (0, 0);$$

$$f(0, 0) = 0.$$

Let $f_a: \mathbf{R} \to \mathbf{R}$ be the map $\lambda \to f(a, \lambda)$ and $f^b: \mathbf{R} \to \mathbf{R}$ the map $\lambda \to f(\lambda, b)$. Show that for each $a, b \in \mathbf{R}$ the maps f_a and f^b are continuous but that f is not continuous. [HINT: $f(1/n, 1/n) = 0; f(1/n, -1/n) = 1/\sqrt{2}$.]

5.3 Show that if J is a connected subset of R containing a and b with $a < b$, then $J \supset [a, b]$.

5.4 (Based on Exercise 5.3.) Show that each connected subset of $\mathbf{R}$ has one of the forms (a, b), $[a, b)$, $(a, b]$, $(a, + \infty)$, $[a, + \infty)$, $(- \infty, a)$, $(- \infty, a]$, $[a, b]$, $(- \infty, + \infty) = \mathbf{R}$ where $a \leq b$.

5.5 Show that the map $f: B \to \mathbf{R}^n$ is continuous at $p \in B$ if and only if for each $\varepsilon > 0$ there is a $\delta(p) > 0$ such that $\|q - p\| < \delta(p)$, $q \in B$, implies that $\|f(q) - f(p)\| < \varepsilon$. The δ needed here depends in general on p.

Definition. A map $f: B \to \mathbf{R}^n$ is *uniformly continuous on B* if and only if for each $\varepsilon > 0$ there is a $\delta > 0$ (that does not depend on p) such that $\|q - p\| < \delta$, $q, p \in B$ implies $\|f(q) - f(p)\| < \varepsilon$.

5.6 Show by example that not every continuous function is uniformly continuous.

5.7 Prove that each continuous function f on a compact set B is uniformly continuous on B.

Recall that the diameter of the subset $A \subset \mathbf{R}^n$ is the number

$$\text{diameter } (A) = \sup \{\|p - q\|: p, q \in A\}.$$

If $\phi: B \to \mathbf{R}^n$, the *oscillation of ϕ at the point $p \in B$* is

$$\text{oscillation}_p (\phi) = \inf \{\text{diameter } [f(B \cap B_\varepsilon(p))]: \varepsilon > 0\}.$$

5.8 Show that the map $\phi: B \to \mathbf{R}^n$ is continuous at p if and only if oscillation$_p (\phi) = 0$.

5.9 Let $\phi: \mathbf{R}^n \to \mathbf{R}^n$ be described by

$$x^m \circ \phi(p) = \sum_{k=1}^{n} a_k^m x^k(p)$$

where (a_k^m) is a real $n \times n$ matrix.

(a) Show that ϕ is linear, that is, $\phi(\lambda p + \mu q) = \lambda \phi(p) + \mu \phi(q)$ whenever $p, q \in R^n$ and $\lambda, \mu \in \mathbf{R}$.

(b) Show that each linear map $\phi: \mathbf{R}^n \to \mathbf{R}^n$ has the above form for some matrix (a_m^k).

(c) Under what conditions on (a_m^k) is ϕ continuous?

(d) Under what conditions on (a_m^k) is ϕ one-one?

(e) When is ϕ an open mapping? That is, when is it true that $\phi(W)$ is open in $\mathbf{R}^n$ whenever W is open in $\mathbf{R}^n$?

CHAPTER TWO

Differentiation on $\mathbf{R}^n$

6   Differentiation

The value of a function f on $\mathbf{R}^n$ at the point $p = (a^1, \ldots, a^n)$ is usually denoted by $f(a^1, \ldots, a^n)$. Regarded as a function of a_k alone with all the a^j's except the kth being treated as constants, the derivative of f with respect to a^k is denoted by $D_k f$ or $\partial f / \partial x^k$ and called the *partial derivative of f with respect to x^k*. $x^1, \ldots, x^n$ here are the cartesian coordinate variables. Many of the arguments involving partial derivatives are most conveniently expressed in vector notation. For this purpose let $e_1 = (1, 0, \ldots, 0), \ldots, e_n = (0, 0, \ldots, 1)$, e_k being the n-tuple which has a one in the kth position and zeros elsewhere. Thus

$$(6.1) \qquad D_k f(p) = \lim_{h \to 0} \frac{f(p + h e_k) - f(p)}{h}.$$

The ordinary mean value theorem of differential calculus implies that if $D_k f(q)$ exists at every point of the line segment joining p to $p + b e_k$, that is, at every $q = p + \theta b e_k$, $0 \le \theta \le 1$, then

$$(6.2) \qquad f(p + b e_k) - f(p) = b D_k f(q)$$

where $q = p + \theta b e_k$ for some $\theta \in [0, 1]$.

(6.3) Example. Given two points p and q of $\mathbf{R}^n$, note that $q - p = h^1 e_1 + \cdots + h^n e_n$ where $h^i = x^i(q) - x^i(p)$. Let $p_0 = p$, $p_1 = p_0 + h^1 e_1, \ldots, p_k = p_{k-1} + h^k e_k, \ldots, p_n = p_{n-1} + h^n e_n = q$. Suppose f is a function defined on an open set containing the polygonal path $p_0 p_1 \cdots p_n$ made up of the line segments $\overline{p_{k-1} p_k}$ joining p_{k-1} to p_k, and that $D_k f$ exists at all points of the segment $\overline{p_{k-1} p_k}$ for each k. Then for some choice of points $q_j \in \overline{p_{j-1} p_j}$,

$$(6.4) \qquad f(q) - f(p) = \sum_{k=1}^{n} [x^k(q) - x^k(p)] (D_k f)(q_k).$$

13

The proof is based on (6.2). In fact

(6.5)
$$f(p_k) - f(p_{k-1}) = h^k D_k f(q_k)$$

for some $q_k \in \overline{p_{k-1}p_k}$, and (6.4) is obtained by summing (6.5) from $k = 1$ to $k = n$.

Formula (6.4) shows that if the first partial derivatives of f exist and are bounded in a neighborhood of the point p, then f is continuous at p. In general the mere existence of first partial derivatives in a neighborhood of p does not imply continuity at p.

(6.6) Example. The function f defined by

$$f(x, y) = \cos \frac{\pi}{2} \frac{x^2 - y^2}{x^2 + y^2} \qquad \text{when } x^2 + y^2 > 0,$$

$$f(x, y) = 0 \qquad \text{when } x^2 + y^2 = 0$$

has first partial derivatives at every point of $\mathbf{R}^2$, but it is not continuous at $(0, 0)$. In fact the sequence $p_k = (1/k, 1/k)$ converges to $(0, 0)$ while

$$0 = f(0, 0) \neq \lim_k f\left(\frac{1}{k}, \frac{1}{k}\right) = 1.$$

Contrast this with the one-dimensional case where the mere existence of a derivative at p is sufficient to insure continuity at p.

A major consequence of equation (6.4) is the chain rule for partial derivatives. The hypothesis of this theorem concerns a map $\phi: W \to U$ of an open set W of $\mathbf{R}^m$ into the open ball U of $\mathbf{R}^n$ and a function f defined on U (see Figure 2). For convenience let $x^1, \ldots, x^n$ denote cartesian coordinate functions on $\mathbf{R}^n$ and $y^1, \ldots, y^m$ cartesian coordinate functions on $\mathbf{R}^m$.

(6.7) Theorem (The chain rule). Suppose that (1) the partial derivatives $D_1 f, \ldots, D_n f$ exist on U and are continuous at $\phi(q)$; (2) the functions $x^1 \circ \phi, \ldots, x^n \circ \phi$ have partial derivatives $D_j(x^k \circ \phi)(q)$ at

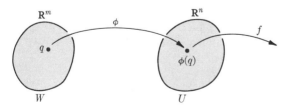

FIGURE 2

q $(j, k = 1, \ldots, m)$. Then $D_j(f \circ \phi)(q) = (\partial f \circ \phi / \partial y^j)(q)$ exists, and

(6.8) $\dfrac{\partial f \circ \phi}{\partial y^j}(q) = \displaystyle\sum_{k=1}^{n} \dfrac{\partial x^k \circ \phi}{\partial y^j}(q) \dfrac{\partial f}{\partial x^k}[\phi(q)], \quad (j = 1, 2, \ldots, m)$.

Remark. Equation (6.8) is equivalent to

$$D_j(f \circ \phi)(q) = \sum_{k=1}^{n} D_j(x^k \circ \phi) \cdot (q) D_k f[\phi(q)].$$

PROOF. Let e_j be the m-tuple with a one in the jth position and zeros elsewhere. Since

$$\lim_{h \to 0} \frac{x^k \circ \phi(q + he_j) - x^k \circ \phi(q)}{h} = \frac{\partial x^k \circ \phi}{\partial y^j}(q)$$

it follows in particular that $\lim\limits_{h \to 0} x^k \circ \phi(q + he_j) = x^k \circ \phi(q)$, so that when h is small all the points $\phi(q + he_j)$ together with the line segments connecting them belong to U, and formula (6.4) can be applied to give

(6.9)

$$\frac{f \circ \phi(q + he_j) - f \circ \phi(q)}{h} = \sum_{k=1}^{n} \frac{x^k \circ \phi(q + he_j) - x^k \circ \phi(q)}{h} \frac{\partial f}{\partial x^k}[q_k(h)],$$

where for the present argument the only fact needed about $q_k(h)$ is that $\lim\limits_{h \to 0} q_k(h) = q$ $(k = 1, 2, \ldots, n)$. Taking the limit in (6.9) as $h \to 0$ and using the continuity of $\partial f / \partial x^k$ $(k = 1, \ldots, n)$ at q gives (6.8). ◆

(6.10) Corollary. Suppose the first partial derivatives of the function f exist in a neighborhood of $q \in \mathbf{R}^n$ and are continuous at q. Then for each $p \in \mathbf{R}^n$,

(6.11) $\dfrac{d}{dt} f(q + tp) \Big|_{t=0} = \displaystyle\sum_{k=1}^{n} x^k(p) \dfrac{\partial f}{\partial x^k}(q)$.

PROOF. Apply (6.8) with ϕ equal to the map $t \to q + tp$ of $\mathbf{R}^1$ into $\mathbf{R}^n$, and the "q" of (6.8) corresponding to the point $t = 0$ of $\mathbf{R}^1$. Note that $x^k \circ \phi(t) = x^k(q + tp) = x^k(q) + tx^k(p)$; so $\partial x^k \circ \phi / \partial t = x^k(p)$. ◆

One consequence of (6.11) is a multivariate mean value theorem: If f has continuous partial derivatives in an open set V which contains the line segment joining p and q, then

(6.12) $f(p) - f(q) = \displaystyle\sum_{k=1}^{n} [x^k(p) - x^k(q)] \dfrac{\partial f}{\partial x^k}(q_0)$

where q_0 is a point on the line segment $\overline{pq}$. Equation (6.12) is obtained by applying the ordinary mean value theorem to the function $g(t) = f[q + t(p - q)]$ on the interval $t \in [0, 1]$, getting

$$g(1) - g(0) = g'(t_0)$$

for some $t_0 \in (0, 1)$, and then using (6.11) to evaluate the derivative $g'(t_0)$.

(6.13) Example. To give an application of (6.12) suppose that the map ϕ: $U \to \mathbf{R}^n$ of the open convex[1] subset U of $\mathbf{R}^n$ assigns to the point $q \in U$ the n-tuple $\phi(q) = (f^1(q), \ldots, f^n(q))$, and that for each i, j with $1 \leq i, j \leq n$

(6.14)
$$\left| \frac{\partial f^i}{\partial x^i}(q) \right| \leq M, \qquad q \in U.$$

Then

(6.15)
$$\| \phi(q) - \phi(p) \| \leq nM \| q - p \|, \qquad p, q \in U.$$

PROOF. Formula (6.15) follows from (6.12) together with (6.14).

(6.16)
$$|f^i(q) - f^i(p)| \leq M \sum_{k=1}^{n} |x^k(q) - x^k(p)|.$$

The inequality $|a^1| + \cdots + |a^n| \leq \sqrt{n}\, \{(a^1)^2 + \cdots + (a^n)^2\}^{1/2}$ then yields

(6.17)
$$|f^i(q) - f^i(p)| \leq \sqrt{n}\, M \| q - p \|$$

from which formula (6.15) follows by squaring, summing over j, and taking square roots. ◆

Exercises

6.1 Suppose $f: U \to \mathbf{R}$ is a function on the open set U of $\mathbf{R}^n$ whose first partial derivatives $\partial f / \partial x^k$ exist and are continuous on U. Suppose that at each $p \in U$ not all the derivatives $(\partial f / \partial x^k)(p)$, $k = 1, 2, \ldots, n$ are zero. Prove that the set $S = \{q \in U : f(q) = 0\}$ of zeros of f has no interior points.

6.2 Show that if the function $f: U \to \mathbf{R}$ has continuous derivatives on the open set U of $\mathbf{R}^n$ and f has a maximum at $q \in U$, then $(\partial f / \partial x^k)(q) = 0, 1 \leq k \leq n$.

6.3 Let $C(t) = (f_1(t), \ldots, f_n(t))$, $t \in [0, 1]$, be an arc in $\mathbf{R}^n$, and suppose $f_1, \ldots, f_n$ are differentiable on $(0, 1)$. If $n = 1$, the mean value theorem states that $C(1) - C(0) = C'(t_0)$ for some $t_0 \in (0, 1)$, where $C'(s) = (f_1'(s), \ldots, f_n'(s))$, $s \in [0, 1]$. For what dimensions n is this true? Give proofs or counterexamples.

6.4 Let $\phi: W \to U$ be continuous, one-one, and have a continuous inverse where W and U are open subsets of $\mathbf{R}^n$. Suppose that the functions $x^k \circ \phi$,

---

[1] A subset U of $\mathbf{R}^n$ is convex if the line segment $\overline{pq}$ joining p to q is a subset of U whenever $p, q \in U$.

$x^k \circ \phi^{-1}$, $1 \le k \le n$, have continuous first partial derivatives on their respective domains. Show that

$$\delta_k^j = \sum_{m=1}^{n} \frac{\partial x^i \circ \phi}{\partial x^m}(p) \frac{\partial x^m \circ \phi^{-1}}{\partial x^k}[\phi(p)],$$

$1 \le j, k \le n$, $p \in W$.

6.5   Generalize Theorem (6.7) to cover second-order partial derivatives of the type $(\partial^2 f \phi / \partial y^i \partial y^j)(q)$.

6.6   Verify that the function f of Example (6.6) has first-order partial derivatives at the origin.

6.7   Suppose that f is a C^1 function on the cube $D = \{(a^1, \ldots, a^n) : |a^k| < \varepsilon, 1 \le k \le n\}$ and that $\partial f / \partial x^{k+1} = 0, \ldots, \partial f / \partial x^n = 0$ on D. Show there is a function h depending only on k variables such that $f(p) = h[x^1(p), \ldots, x^k(p)]$, $p \in D$.

7   Higher-order derivatives. Taylor series expansions

The following theorem on the interchange of the order of differentiation is seldom used in its full generality, but it does simplify both the notation and computations involving higher-order partial derivatives, and it has many important consequences.

(7.1)   Theorem.   Suppose the function f is defined on the open set U of $\mathbf{R}^n$ and that $D_k f$, $D_j f$, and $D_k(D_j f)$ exist on U. Suppose further that $D_k(D_j f)$ is continuous on U. Then $D_j(D_k f)$ exists on U and

$$(7.2) \qquad D_j(D_k f)(q) = D_k(D_j f)(q), \qquad q \in U.$$

PROOF.   For any function g on U, set $\Delta_m^h g(p) = g(p + he_m) - g(p)$ when h is small enough so that $p + he_m \in U$. These difference operators satisfy two easily verified identities: (1) $\Delta_j^h \Delta_k^\varepsilon = \Delta_k^\varepsilon \Delta_j^h$ (they commute), and (2) $\Delta_j^h D_k g = D_k \Delta_j^h g$ when $D_k g$ is defined on U. Furthermore according to the mean value theorem, whenever $D_j f$ exists on U,

$$(7.3) \qquad h^{-1} \Delta_j^h f \cdot (q) = D_j f[q + h\theta(h)e_j]$$

where $0 \le \theta(h) \le 1$ and $\theta(h)$ depends only on h if q is considered fixed. Applying $\varepsilon^{-1} \Delta_k^\varepsilon$ to (7.3) and using the mean value theorem on the term $\varepsilon^{-1} \Delta_k^\varepsilon \cdot (D_j f)[q + h\theta(h)e_j]$ gives

$$(7.4) \qquad (\varepsilon^{-1} \Delta_k^\varepsilon)(h^{-1} \Delta_j^h) f \cdot (q) = D_k(D_j f) \cdot [q + h\theta(h)e_j + \varepsilon\tau(h, \varepsilon)e_k]$$

where $0 \le \tau(h, \varepsilon) \le 1$. Taking the limit as $\varepsilon \to 0$ in (7.4) and using the fact that $D_k(D_j f)$ is continuous gives

$$D_k(D_j f) \cdot [q + h\theta(h)e_j] = D_k(h^{-1}\Delta_j^h f) \cdot (q) = h^{-1}\Delta_j^h \cdot (D_k f) \cdot (q)$$

and (7.2) itself follows by then passing to the limit as $h \to 0$. ◆

Partial derivatives of higher order than the first order are denoted in the conventional manner. For example

$$D_1(D_3 f) = \frac{\partial^2 f}{\partial x^1 \, \partial x^3} ; \qquad D_1[D_1(D_3 f)] = \frac{\partial^3 f}{(\partial x^1)^2 \, \partial x^3} .$$

Many of these higher-order partial derivatives can be identified using the result of Theorem (7.1) once it is known that they are continuous on an open set. A function f is C^k on U or *continuously differentiable of class k on U* if the function f and all its partial derivatives of orders less than or equal to k are continuous on U. The function f is C^∞ on U if all its partial derivatives are continuous on U. The phrase "continuously differentiable of class k on U" or "C^k on U" is also applied to a map $\phi: U \to \mathbf{R}^m$. There it means that each of the functions $x^1 \circ \phi, \ldots, x^m \circ \phi$ is C^k on U when $x^1, \ldots, x^m$ are cartesian coordinates on $\mathbf{R}^m$.

The material in this book is not in general concerned with questions of just how differentiable a certain function or map is. Sometimes the degree of differentiability is mentioned, but where it is not the reader can assume the objects under discussion are differentiable enough to allow the computations indicated and still preserve continuity. Little is lost by assuming all functions and maps which occur to be C^∞ unless otherwise mentioned.

In several variables Taylor's theorem with remainder is a straightforward consequence of the corresponding theorem in one variable together with Corollary (6.10). If $h^{(j)}$ denotes the jth derivative of h with respect to the variable s, Taylor's theorem in one variable states that for a function h which is $(m + 1)$ times continuously differentiable on an interval including $[0, s]$,

$$(7.5) \qquad h(s) = h(0) + sh^{(1)}(0) + \frac{s^2}{2!} h^2(0) + \cdots + \frac{s^m}{m!} h^{(m)}(0) + R_m(s)$$

where the remainder term $R_m(s)$ can be expressed in various ways, one of which is

$$(7.6) \qquad R_m(s) = \int_0^1 \frac{(1 - t)^m}{m!} h^{(m+1)}(ts) \, dt.$$

Suppose now that the function f is C^{m+1} on an open set containing the line segment joining p and q. Then according to Corollary (6.10), if $h(s) = f[q + s(p - q)]$,

$$(7.7) \qquad h^{(1)}(s) = \sum_{k=1}^{n} x^k(p - q) \frac{\partial f}{\partial x^k} [q + s(p - q)], \qquad s \in [0, 1].$$

That is, the derivative of h with respect to s can be computed by applying the operator

$$D = \sum_{k=1}^{n} x^k(p - q) \frac{\partial}{\partial x^k}$$

to f and evaluating the result Df at $q + s(p - q)$. If Df is given the role of f in (7.7), the corresponding h is $Df[q + s(p - q)] = h^{(1)}$ and (7.7) becomes

$$h^{(2)}(s) = D(Df)[q + s(p - q)], \qquad s \in [0, 1].$$

This procedure can be continued as long as the functions f, Df, D^2f, $\ldots$, D^kf which substitute for f in (7.7) are continuously differentiable (on an open set containing the line segment joining p and q), because without this Corollary (6.10) cannot be used. That is,

(**7.8**) $$h^{(j)}(s) = D^j f[q + s(p - q)], \qquad j \le m + 1.$$

Equation (7.5) can be applied directly with $s = 1$ to give Taylor's theorem with remainder as quoted below.

(**7.9**) **Taylor's theorem with remainder.** If f is C^{m+1} on the ball $B_r(q)$ of radius r centered at q and D is the partial differential operator

$$D = \sum_{k=1}^{n} [x^k(p) - x^k(q)] \frac{\partial}{\partial x^k}, \qquad p \in B_r(q),$$

then

(**7.10**) $$f(p) = f(q) + Df(q) + \cdots + \frac{D^m f(q)}{m!} + R_m(p)$$

where

(**7.11**) $$R_m(p) = \int_0^1 \frac{(1 - t)^m}{m!} (D^{m+1}f)(q + t(p - q)) \, dt.$$

Remark. The remainder $R_m(p)$ can be estimated just as in the case of one variable. For example, let M_{m+1} be the supremum of the absolute value of all the $(m + 1)$st order derivatives of f on the ball $B_r(q)$. Then

(**7.12**)

$$D^{m+1}f = \sum_{\substack{j_1, \ldots, \\ j_{m+1}=1}}^{n} [x^{j_1}(p) - x^{j_1}(q)] \cdots [x^{j_{m+1}}(p) - x^{j_{m+1}}(q)] \cdot \frac{\partial^{m+1}f}{\partial x^{j_1} \cdots \partial x^{j_{m+1}}},$$

while

$$|x^{j_1}(p) - x^{j_1}(q)| \cdots |x^{j_{m+1}}(p) - x^{j_{m+1}}(q)|$$

$$\le [\max \{|x^1(p) - x^1(q)|, \ldots, |x^n(p) - x^n(q)|\}]^{m+1}$$

$$\le \|p - q\|^{m+1}.$$

There are n^{m+1} terms in the sum (7.12), each of which is less than $\|p - q\|^{m+1} M_{m+1}$, giving

$$|R_m(p)| \leq M_{m+1} \cdot \frac{n^{m+1}\|p - q\|^{m+1}}{m!} \int_0^1 (1 - t)^m \, dt$$

or

$$|R_m(p)| \leq \frac{M_{m+1}}{(m + 1)!} [n\|p - q\|]^{m+1}, \qquad p \in B_r(q).$$

Exercises

7.1 Show that the function h defined by

$$h(p) = \begin{cases} \exp [1/(1 - \|p\|^2)], & \|p\| < 1, \\ 0, & \|p\| \geq 1, \end{cases}$$

is C^∞ on $\mathbf{R}^n$.

7.2 If $\phi \colon U \to \mathbf{R}^n$ is a C^1 map of the open set U of $\mathbf{R}^m$ into $\mathbf{R}^n$, show that

$$\textbf{(7.13)} \qquad \phi(q + tp) = \phi(q) + \sum_{j=1}^m tx^j(p)P_j + o(t),$$

where $P_j = (D_j(x^1 \circ \phi)(q), \dots, D_j(x^n \circ \phi)(q)) \in \mathbf{R}^n$ and $o(t) \in \mathbf{R}^n$ and satisfies $t^{-1}o(t) \to 0$ as $t \to 0$ for fixed p and q.

7.3 If $\phi \colon U \to \mathbf{R}^n$ is a C^2 map of the open set U of $\mathbf{R}^m$ into $\mathbf{R}^n$, improve Exercise 7.2 by showing that (7.13) holds with $\|o(t)\| \leq K\|tp\|^2$ for some constant K (depending on q and ϕ).

7.4 If $f \colon U \to \mathbf{R}$ is a C^3 function on the open set U of $\mathbf{R}^n$ show that

$$\textbf{(7.14)} \qquad f(q + tp) = f(q) + t \sum_{k=1}^n x^k(p)D_k f(q)$$

$$+ \frac{t^2}{2} \sum_{i,j=1}^n x^i(p)x^j(p)D_i D_j f(q) + o(t^2)$$

where $|o(t^2)| \leq K\|tp\|^3$ for some constant K (depending on q and f).

7.5 Suppose that $f \colon U \to \mathbf{R}$ is a C^3 function on the open subset U of $\mathbf{R}^n$ with $q \in U$ and $D_k f(q) = 0$, $1 \leq k \leq n$; some $D_i D_j f(q) \neq 0$. Show that f has a local minimum at q if and only if

$$\sum_{i,j=1}^n \lambda^i \lambda^j D_i D_j f(q) \geq 0$$

for each choice of $\lambda^1, \dots, \lambda^n$. [HINT: Use (7.14).]

8 The inverse function theorem

The inverse function theorem adequately summarizes the results obtained in proving it, so that it is almost never necessary to actually use details of the proof itself. With this in mind the reader who is in a hurry can learn the content of the theorem by reading it without proof and then pass on to the following sections, where some of the many consequences of this important theorem are developed.

The proof of the inverse function theorem used here proceeds by induction, switching variables one at a time, so that the central argument focuses on the one-dimensional case. The heart of the argument is contained in the lemma below.

(8.1) Lemma. Suppose $\phi: U \to \mathbf{R}^n$ is a C^1 map of the open set U of $\mathbf{R}^n$ into $\mathbf{R}^n$ described by

$$x^1 \circ \phi = x^1,$$

$$\cdot$$
$$\cdot$$
(8.2)
$$\cdot$$

$$x^{n-1} \circ \phi = x^{n-1},$$

$$x^n \circ \phi = f,$$

where f is C^1 on U. If $(\partial f/\partial x^n)(q_0) \neq 0$ at some point $q_0 \in U$, then (i) q_0 has a neighborhood A on which ϕ is one-one, and (ii) $\phi(U)$ is a neighborhood of $\phi(q_0)$.

PROOF. To be specific suppose that $(\partial f/\partial x^n)(q_0) > 0$ and L is some positive number chosen so that $(\partial f/\partial x^n)(q_0) > L > 0$. Using the continuity of $\partial f/\partial x^n$ on U and the fact that U is open, choose $\varepsilon > 0$ so small that the closed n-cube $A(\varepsilon)$ of side 2ε centered at q_0,

$$A(\varepsilon) = \{(t^1, \ldots, t^n): |t^i - x^i(q_0)| \le \varepsilon, 1 \le i \le n\},$$

is contained in U and $(\partial f/\partial x^n)(q) \ge L, q \in A(\varepsilon)$ (see Figure 3). ϕ is one-

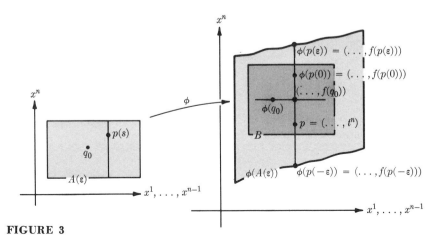

FIGURE 3

one on $A(\varepsilon)$. In fact if $\phi(q) = \phi(p)$ for two fixed points $p, q \in A(\varepsilon)$, then

$$x^k(q) = x^k \circ \phi(q) = x^k \circ \phi(p) = x^k(p), \qquad 1 \leq k \leq n - 1,$$

by (8.2) and using this in (6.12) shows that

$$0 = x^n \circ \phi(p) - x^n \circ \phi(q) = f(p) - f(q) = [x^n(p) - x^n(q)]\frac{\partial f}{\partial x^n}(q')$$

where q' is on the line segment $\overline{pq}$. Since $(\partial f / \partial x^n)(q') \geq L > 0$, it follows that $x^n(p) = x^n(q)$ too, and consequently $p = q$ and ϕ is one-one on $A(\varepsilon)$.

To prove assertion (ii) of the lemma choose $\delta > 0$ so small that (a) $|f(q) - f(q_0)| \leq \varepsilon L/2$ if $\|q - q_0\| \leq \delta\sqrt{n}$, and (b) $\delta < \varepsilon$. It suffices to show that every point in the rectangular neighborhood

$$B = \left\{(t^1, \ldots, t^n) : |t^j - x^j(q_0)| \leq \delta, 1 \leq j \leq n - 1; |t^n - f(q_0)| \leq \frac{\varepsilon L}{2}\right\}$$

of $\phi(q_0)$ belongs to $\phi[A(\varepsilon)]$. Let $p = (t^1, \ldots, t^n) \in B$. The points

$$p(s) = (t^1, \ldots, t^{n-1}, x^n(q_0) + s), \qquad s \in [-\varepsilon, \varepsilon],$$

belong to $A(\varepsilon)$ and

$$\phi(p(s)) = (t^1, \ldots, t^{n-1}, f[p(s)]),$$

so that $p \in \phi(A(\varepsilon))$ if $f[p(s)] = t^n$ for some $s \in [-\varepsilon, \varepsilon]$. By the intermediate value theorem $f[p(s)]$ takes on all values between $f[p(-\varepsilon)]$ and $f[p(\varepsilon)]$; so it suffices to show that

(8.3) $$f[p(-\varepsilon)] \leq t^n \leq f[p(\varepsilon)].$$

Note that

$$\frac{\partial f}{\partial x^n}[p(s)] = \frac{d}{ds}f[p(s)] \geq L > 0,$$

so that $f[p(-\varepsilon)] \leq f[p(\varepsilon)]$.

Inequality (8.3) can be established through the following argument: Since $p(0) = (t^1, \ldots, t^{n-1}, x^n(q_0))$,

$$\|p(0) - q_0\|^2 = \sum_{i=1}^{n-1} |t^i - x^i(q_0)|^2 \leq (n - 1)\delta^2$$

and according to the choice of δ,

(8.4) $$|f[p(0)] - f(q_0)| \leq \frac{\varepsilon L}{2}.$$

Since $p \in B$, $|t^n - f(q_0)| \leq \varepsilon L/2$, and this together with (8.4) shows that

(8.5) $$f[p(0)] - \varepsilon L \leq t^n \leq f[p(0)] + \varepsilon L.$$

The mean value theorem now shows that

$$f[p(0)] + \varepsilon L \leq f[p(0)] + \varepsilon \frac{\partial f}{\partial x^n}[p(s')] = f[p(\varepsilon)],$$

some $0 < s' < \varepsilon$;

$$f[p(0)] - \varepsilon L \geq f[p(0)] - \varepsilon \frac{\partial f}{\partial x^n}[p(s'')] = f[p(-\varepsilon)],$$

some $0 > s'' > -\varepsilon$, and these inequalities together with (8.5) establish (8.3). ◆

A special form of the inverse function theorem is proved now using Lemma (8.1).

(8.6)   Theorem.   Suppose $\phi: V \to \mathbf{R}^n$ is a C^k map ($k \geq 1$) of the open set V of $\mathbf{R}^n$ having the form (8.2). If $(\partial f/\partial x^n)(q_0) \neq 0$ at some point $q_0 \in V$, q_0 has an open neighborhood W such that (a) ϕ is one-one on W; (b) $\phi(W)$ is open; (c) the map $\phi^{-1}: \phi(W) \to W$ is C^k.

PROOF.   According to Lemma (8.1) q_0 has a compact neighborhood F on which ϕ is one-one; one can easily require also that $(\partial f/\partial x^n)(q) \neq 0$, $q \in F$. By Theorem (5.3) the map $\phi^{-1}: \phi(F) \to F$ is continuous. The second conclusion of Lemma (8.1) applied with $U = $ interior (F) and q_0 replaced by any point of interior (F) shows that ϕ [interior (F)] is open, so that the subset $W = $ interior (F) satisfies requirements (a) and (b), and in addition $\phi^{-1}: \phi(W) \to W$ is continuous. Thus it suffices to show ϕ^{-1} is C^k.

Let $p \in \phi(W)$, $e_j = (0, \ldots, 1, \ldots, 0)$ with the one in the jth position as in Section 6, and suppose throughout the argument h is so small that (i) the line segment joining p to $p + he_j$ belongs to $\phi(W)$ and (ii) the line segment joining $\phi^{-1}(p)$ to $\phi^{-1}(p + he_j)$ belongs to W (see Figure 4). Then applying (6.12) to the function $x^n \circ \phi$ yields

$$(8.7) \qquad x^n \circ \phi[\phi^{-1}(p + he_j)] - x^n \circ \phi[\phi^{-1}(p)]$$

$$= \sum_{k=1}^{n} [x^k \circ \phi^{-1}(p + he_j) - x^k \circ \phi^{-1}(p)] \frac{\partial x^n \circ \phi}{\partial x^k}[\beta(h)]$$

where $\beta(h)$ is on the line segment joining $\phi^{-1}(p)$ to $\phi^{-1}(p + he_j)$ in W. The left-hand side of (8.7) reduces to $h\delta_j^n$. If $k \leq n - 1$ it follows from (8.2) that $x^k \circ \phi^{-1} = x^k$; so

$$x^k \circ \phi^{-1}(p + he_j) - x^k \circ \phi^{-1}(p) = h\delta_j^k, \qquad k \leq n - 1,$$

and (8.7) becomes

$$h\delta_j^n = \sum_{k=1}^{n-1} h\delta_j^k \frac{\partial x^n \circ \phi}{\partial x^k}[\beta(h)] + [x^n \circ \phi^{-1}(p + he_j) - x^n \circ \phi^{-1}(p)]$$

$$\times \frac{\partial x^n \circ \phi}{\partial x^n}[\beta(h)]$$

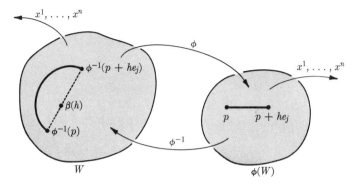

FIGURE 4

or

(8.8) $$\frac{x^n \circ \phi^{-1}(p + he_j) - x^n \circ \phi^{-1}(p)}{h}$$

$$= \left\{ \frac{\partial x^n \circ \phi}{\partial x^n} [\beta(h)] \right\}^{-1} \left\{ \delta_j^n - \sum_{k=1}^{n-1} \delta_j^k \frac{\partial x^n \circ \phi}{\partial x^k} [\phi^{-1}(p)] \right\}.$$

Equation (8.8) shows that $(\partial x^n \circ \phi^{-1}/\partial x^j)\,(p)$ exists and is equal to

(8.9)

$$\frac{\partial x^n \circ \phi^{-1}}{\partial x^j}\,(p) = \left\{ \frac{\partial x^n \circ \phi}{\partial x^n}\,(\phi^{-1}(p)) \right\}^{-1} \left\{ \delta_j^n - \sum_{k=1}^{n-1} \delta_j^k \frac{\partial x^n \circ \phi}{\partial x^k} [\phi^{-1}(p)] \right\},$$

obtained by taking the limit as $h \to 0$ in (8.8). It follows immediately from (8.9) plus the previously mentioned fact $x^k \circ \phi^{-1} = x^k$, $k \leq n - 1$, that ϕ^{-1} is C^1 on $\phi(W)$. To get higher-order differentiability for ϕ^{-1} notice that

$$\frac{\partial}{\partial x^j} \left\{ \frac{\partial x^n \circ \phi}{\partial x^k} \circ \phi^{-1} \right\}\,(p) = \sum_{i=1}^{n} \frac{\partial^2 x^n \circ \phi}{\partial x^i \, \partial x^k} [\phi^{-1}(p)] \frac{\partial x^i \circ \phi^{-1}}{\partial x^j}\,(p);$$

so using the C^1 differentiability of ϕ^{-1} the right-hand side of (8.9) can be differentiated provided ϕ is C^2 to show that ϕ^{-1} is also C^2. This procedure can be continued to give an expression for the kth-order partials of $x^n \circ \phi^{-1}$ involving the kth and lower-order partials of $x^n \circ \phi$ and partial derivatives of $x^i \circ \phi^{-1}$, $1 \leq i \leq n$, of order less than k. In this manner it can be shown that ϕ^{-1} is C^k so long as ϕ is. ◆

With the aid of Theorem (8.6) it is now possible to establish

The inverse function theorem. Suppose $\psi\colon U \to \mathbf{R}^n$ is a map of the open set U of $\mathbf{R}^n$ into $\mathbf{R}^n$ and that the functions $x^1 \circ \psi, \ldots, x^n \circ \psi$ are

C^k on U with $k \geq 1$. If $\det\left[(\partial x^i \circ \psi/\partial x^j)(q_0)\right] \neq 0$ at some point $q_0 \in U$ there is an open set W containing q_0 such that (i) the map $\psi|_W \colon W \to \psi(W)$ obtained by restricting ψ to W is one-one onto; (ii) $\psi(W)$ is open; and (iii) the functions $x^1 \circ (\psi|_W)^{-1}, \ldots, x^n \circ (\psi|_W)^{-1}$ are C^k on $\psi(W)$. That is, the map $\psi \colon W \to \psi(W)$ and its inverse $\psi^{-1} \colon \psi(W) \to W$ are both C^k.

PROOF. Let (A_i^j) be the matrix inverse of $\left[(\partial x^i \circ \psi/\partial x^j)(q_0)\right]$ and let $A \colon \mathbf{R}^n \to \mathbf{R}^n$ be the linear transformation defined by

$$x^k \circ A(p) = \sum_{j=1}^{n} A_j^k x^j(p), \qquad p \in \mathbf{R}^n.$$

Put $\phi = A \circ \psi$. ψ satisfies (i), (ii), and (iii) for W if and only if ϕ does; so it suffices to prove the theorem for ϕ. The chief advantage of switching to ϕ is that

(8.10) $$\frac{\partial x^i \circ \phi}{\partial x^j}(q_0) = \sum_{m=1}^{n} A_m^i \frac{\partial x^m \circ \psi}{\partial x^j}(q_0) = \delta_j^i.$$

Let $\phi_1, \ldots, \phi_n$ be the $\mathbf{R}^n$-valued maps defined on U by

$$\phi_1(p) = (x^1(p), \ldots, x^{n-1}(p), x^n \circ \phi(p));$$
$$\phi_2(p) = (x^1(p), \ldots, x^{n-2}(p), x^{n-1} \circ \phi(p), \quad x^n \circ \phi(p));$$

(8.11)
$$\cdot$$
$$\cdot$$
$$\cdot$$

$$\phi_n(p) = (x^1 \circ \phi(p), \ldots, x^n \circ \phi(p)) = \phi(p).$$

Since

$$x^i \circ \phi_k = \begin{cases} x^i, & i \leq n - k, \\ x^i \circ \phi, & i > n - k, \end{cases}$$

it follows immediately from (8.10) that

(8.12) $$\frac{\partial x^i \circ \phi_k}{\partial x^j}(q_0) = \delta_j^i, \qquad 1 \leq i, j \leq n.$$

Let S_k stand for the statement: "There is an open set W_k containing q_0 such that (i) the map $\phi_k|_{W_k} \colon W_k \to \phi_k(W_k)$ obtained by restricting ϕ_k to W_k is one-one onto; (ii) $\phi_k(W_k)$ is open; and (iii) the map $(\phi_k|_{W_k})^{-1} \colon \phi_k(W_k) \to W_k$ is C^k."

S_n is the desired conclusion for ϕ; so it suffices to establish these statements by induction. S_1 follows from Theorem (8.6) because ϕ_1 has the form (8.2) of the ϕ in Theorem (8.6) and $(\partial x^n \circ \phi_1/\partial x^n)(q_0) = 1 \neq 0$. Suppose now that S_k has been established. It is evident from (8.11) that the map $\phi_{k+1} \circ \phi_k^{-1} \colon \phi_k(W_k) \to \mathbf{R}^n$ has the form (8.2) of the ϕ in Theorem (8.6) if $n - k$ and n are interchanged in (8.2), and with this interchange $\phi_{k+1} \circ \phi_k^{-1}$

will satisfy the hypothesis of Theorem (8.6) at $\phi_k(q_0)$ provided

$$(8.13) \qquad \frac{\partial x^{n-k} \circ \phi_{k+1} \circ \phi_k^{-1}}{\partial x^{n-k}} [\phi_k(q_0)] \neq 0.$$

Several computations are necessary to establish (8.13). First

$$\delta_i^j = \frac{\partial x^j}{\partial x^i}(q_0) = \sum_{m=1}^n \frac{\partial x^j \circ \phi_k^{-1}}{\partial x^m} [\phi_k(q_0)] \frac{\partial x^m \circ \phi_k}{\partial x^i}(q_0)$$

$$= \sum_{m=1}^n \frac{\partial x^j \circ \phi_k^{-1}}{\partial x^m} [\phi_k(q_0)] \, \delta_i^m, \qquad \text{by (8.12)},$$

and accordingly

$$(8.14) \qquad \delta_i^j = \frac{\partial x^j \circ \phi_k^{-1}}{\partial x^i} [\phi_k(q_0)].$$

Next

$$\frac{\partial x^{n-k} \circ \phi_{k+1} \circ \phi_k^{-1}}{\partial x^{n-k}} [\phi_k(q_0)] = \sum_{j=1}^n \frac{\partial x^{n-k} \circ \phi_{k+1}}{\partial x^j}(q_0) \frac{\partial x^j \circ \phi_k^{-1}}{\partial x^{n-k}} [\phi_k(q_0)]$$

$$= \sum_{j=1}^n \delta_j^{n-k} \, \delta_{n-k}^j = 1,$$

which proves (8.13).

Theorem (8.6) applied to $\phi_{k+1} \circ \phi_k^{-1}$ shows that there is an open set $U_{k+1} \subset \phi_k(W_k)$ containing $\phi_k(q_0)$ such that (i) $\phi_{k+1} \circ \phi_k^{-1}$ is one-one on U_{k+1}; (ii) $\phi_{k+1} \circ \phi_k^{-1}(U_k)$ is open; and (iii) $(\phi_{k+1} \circ \phi_k^{-1}|_{U_{k+1}})^{-1}$ is C^k. S_{k+1} is then true with $W_{k+1} = \phi_k^{-1}(U_k)$, and the proof of the inverse function theorem is completed by finite induction to show that S_n is true. ◆

Exercises

8.1 Let $\phi \colon \mathbf{R} \to \mathbf{R}$ be the map described in terms of the cartesian coordinate x by $x \circ \phi = x^3$. Show ϕ is one-one and $\phi(U)$ is open whenever U is open, but ϕ does not satisfy the hypothesis of the inverse function theorem and ϕ^{-1} is not differentiable.

8.2 Let $\phi \colon U \to \mathbf{R}^m$ and suppose $\phi(U)$ is open in $\mathbf{R}^m$. If ϕ is one-one and ϕ^{-1} is differentiable (at least C^1) show that $\det [(\partial x^k \circ \phi/\partial x^i)(p)] \neq 0$, $p \in U$.

9 Change of variables in multiple integrals

This section uses some integration theory not developed in this book and can be skipped by the reader. It is designed to show how the proof of the inverse function theorem given above lends itself to establishing the well-known formula for changing variables in multiple integrals, which can be formulated as follows:

(9.1)   Theorem.   Suppose that U is an open subset of $\mathbf{R}^n$ and that $\psi: U \to \mathbf{R}^n$ is a C^1 map whose Jacobian

$$J(\psi)(q) = \det\left[\frac{\partial x^i \circ \psi}{\partial x^j}(q)\right] \neq 0, \qquad q \in U.$$

Then

(9.2) $\displaystyle\int_U \cdots \int h \, dx^1 \cdots dx^n = \int_{\psi(U)} \cdots \int h \circ \psi^{-1} |J(\psi^{-1})| \, dx^1 \cdots dx^n$

for every integrable function h on U.

PROOF.   The proof is divided into two sections—first a section recalling some properties of the integral and then a series of steps belonging to the proof proper.

The essential facts needed from integration theory are:

(a) It suffices to prove (9.2) for h's which vanish outside of a compact subset D of U. This comes from the fact that if $D_1 \subset D_2 \subset \cdots \subset D_k \subset D_{k+1} \subset \cdots$ is an increasing sequence of compact subsets of U whose union is U itself, $\bigcup_{k=1}^{\infty} D_k = U$, and I_{D_k} is the characteristic function of D_k, $I_{D_k}(p) = 1$ if $p \in D_k$ and $I_{D_k}(p) = 0$ if $p \notin D_k$; then

(9.3) $\displaystyle\lim_{k \to \infty} \int_U \cdots \int h I_{D_k} \, dx^1 \cdots dx^n = \int_U \cdots \int h \, dx^1 \cdots dx^n,$

together with the fact that $\psi(D_k)$ forms a similar sequence for $\psi(U)$ and $(h I_{D_k}) \circ \psi^{-1} = (h \circ \psi^{-1}) I_{\psi(D_k)}$. If (9.2) is valid with h replaced by $h I_{D_k}$, passing to the limit on both sides as $k \to \infty$ and using (9.3) gives (9.2).

(b) The formula for changing variables in one dimension:

(9.4) $\displaystyle\int_{f(W)} g(s) \, ds = \int_W g \circ f(t) |f'(t)| \, dt$

in which f is a one-one C^1 function with nonvanishing derivative on W.

(c) Fubini's theorem in the form which relates the n-fold integral over U to an iterated integral, a one-dimensional integral followed by an integral over the projection of U onto the $(n - 1)$-dimensional subspace $\{p : x^n(p) = 0\}$ in $\mathbf{R}^n$.

(9.5)

$$\int_U \cdots \int h(s^1, \ldots, s^n) \, ds^1 \cdots ds^n$$

$$= \int_{\mathbf{R}^{n-1}} \cdots \int \left[\int_{\{s^n : (s^1, \ldots, s^n) \in U\}} h(s^1, \ldots, s^n) \, ds^n\right] ds^1 \cdots ds^{n-1}.$$

Note that the function of $(s^1, \ldots, s^{n-1})$ in brackets on the right-hand side of (9.5) vanishes whenever $(s^1, \ldots, s^{n-1}, 0)$ is not in the projection of U on the set $\{p : x^n(p) = 0\}$.

The remainder of the proof breaks into a sequence of steps:

1°. If $\psi_1 : U \to \psi_1(U)$ and $\psi_2 : \psi_1(U) \to \psi_2 \circ \psi_1(U)$ satisfy the hypothesis of the theorem on their respective domains and the theorem is true for the maps ψ_1 and ψ_2, then it is valid for the map $\psi_2 \circ \psi_1$. The details of this argument involve just two facts other than the validity of (9.2) for ψ_2 and ψ_1—namely, the chain rule for partial derivatives and the product rule for determinants [see Example (16.18)], which are used to show that

$$J(\psi_1^{-1} \circ \psi_2^{-1})(q) = \det \left\{ \frac{\partial x^i \circ \psi_1^{-1} \circ \psi_2^{-1}}{\partial x^j}(q) \right\}$$

$$= \det \left\{ \sum_{k=1}^{n} \frac{\partial x^i \circ \psi_1^{-1}}{\partial x^k} [\psi_2^{-1}(q)] \frac{\partial x^k \circ \psi_2^{-1}}{\partial x^j}(q) \right\}$$

$$= J(\psi_1^{-1})[\psi_2^{-1}(q)] J(\psi_2^{-1})(q),$$

so that

$$\int_U \cdots \int h \, dx^1 \cdots dx^n = \int_{\psi_1(U)} \cdots \int h \circ \psi_1^{-1} |J(\psi_1^{-1})| \, dx^1 \cdots dx^n$$

$$= \int_{\psi_2 \circ \psi_1(U)} \cdots \int h \circ \psi_1^{-1} \circ \psi_2^{-1} |J(\psi_1^{-1}) \circ \psi_2^{-1}| \, |J(\psi_2^{-1})| \, dx^1 \cdots dx^n$$

$$= \int_{(\psi_2 \circ \psi_1)(U)} \cdots \int h \circ (\psi_2 \circ \psi_1)^{-1} |J[(\psi_2 \circ \psi_1)^{-1}]| \, dx^1 \cdots dx^n.$$

2°. It suffices to show that each point $p \in U$ has an open neighborhood U_p on which the theorem is true. The argument for this is topological. Assume the open sets U_p exist and, following (a), that there is a compact set $D \subset U$ with the property that $h \circ \psi(p) = 0$ if $p \notin D$. The class $\{U_p : p \in D\}$ forms an open covering of D, and (see Exercise 4.8) there is a number $\varepsilon > 0$ such that whenever diameter $(B) \leq \varepsilon$, $B \subset D$, the set B belongs entirely to one of the sets U_p in the covering. Then it is easy to see that $h = h_1 + \cdots + h_m$, where h_k vanishes except on a set of diameter less than ε—just chop D up using a small enough rectangular mesh and suitably apportion the resulting rectangles together with their faces. By assumption the theorem will be true for the h_k's and hence for h itself.

3°. Because of step 2° there is no loss of generality in assuming that U is so small that the maps $\phi_1, \ldots, \phi_n = A \circ \psi$ of (8.11) are one-one on U with C^1 inverses,

$$\psi = A^{-1} \circ (\phi_n \circ \phi_{n-1}^{-1}) \cdots (\phi_2 \circ \phi_1^{-1}) \circ \phi_1,$$

and step 1° now shows that it suffices to prove the theorem for the maps

$\phi_1, \phi_k \circ \phi_{k-1}^{-1}, 1 < k \leq n$, and A^{-1}. Except for a renumbering of coordinates the maps $\phi_1, \phi_k \circ \phi_{k-1}^{-1}, 1 < k \leq n$, all have the form $\phi: V \to \mathbf{R}^n$ with

$$x^1 \circ \phi = x^1,$$

(9.6)

$$\cdot$$
$$\cdot$$
$$\cdot$$

$$x^{n-1} \circ \phi = x^{n-1},$$
$$x^n \circ \phi = f,$$

where f is C^1 and $(\partial f/\partial x^n)(q_0) \neq 0$ on V. As a nonsingular linear transformation A^{-1} can also be written as a product of transformations of the type (9.6) mixed with transformations which permute two variables of the type

(9.7)
$$x^m \circ \phi = x^m, \qquad \text{if } m \neq j, k;$$
$$x^j \circ \phi = x^k, \qquad x^k \circ \phi = x^j.$$

This last remark is nothing other than the statement that A^{-1} is a product of elementary row divisors (see the appendix to this section).

4°. It remains to show that (9.2) holds when ψ has either of the types (9.6) or (9.7). The trivial verification when ψ has type (9.7) is left to the reader. When ψ has type (9.6), so does $\phi = \psi^{-1}: \psi(V) \to V$ and

$$\int_V \cdots \int h \circ \phi |J(\phi)| \, dx^1 \cdots dx^n$$

$$= \int_{R^{n-1}} \cdots \int \left[\int_{\{s^n:(s^1,\ldots,s^n)\varepsilon V\}} h(s^1, \ldots, s^{n-1}, f(s^1, \ldots, s^n)) \right.$$

$$\left. \times \left| \frac{\partial f}{\partial x^n}(s^1, \ldots, s^n) \right| ds^n \right] ds^1 \cdots ds^{n-1}.$$

Using (9.4), we obtain

$$\int_{R^{n-1}} \cdots \int \left[\int_{\{t^n:(s^1,\ldots,s^{n-1},t^n)\varepsilon\phi(V)\}} h(s^1, \ldots, s^{n-1}, t^n) \, dt^n \right] ds^1 \cdots ds^{n-1},$$

which equals

$$\int_{\phi(V)} \cdots \int h \, dt^1 \cdots dt^n$$

and yields (9.2) on making the substitutions $\phi = \psi^{-1}$, $V = \psi(U)$, and $\phi(V) = U$. $\blacklozenge$

Exercises

9.1   Let $\phi: \mathbf{R}^n \to \mathbf{R}^n$ be the linear transformation

(9.8)
$$\phi(q) = x^1(q)p_1 + \cdots + x^n(q)p_n$$

where $p_1, \ldots, p_n \in \mathbf{R}^n$. That is, $x^k \circ \phi = \Sigma_j x^k(p_j)x^j$, x^j cartesian coordinates. Show that the Jacobian $J(\phi) = \det [x^k(p_j)]$.

9.2 (Based on Exercise 9.1.) If $\square(q_1, \ldots, q_n)$ denotes the generalized parallelogram

$$\square(q_1, \ldots, q_n) = t^1 q_1 + \cdots + t^n q_n, \qquad 0 < t^i < 1, 1 \leq i \leq n,$$

in $\mathbf{R}^n$, then $\phi(\square(e_1, \ldots, e_n)) = \square(p_1, \ldots, p_n)$ for the ϕ of (9.8) where e_j is the n-tuple with a one in the jth position and zeros elsewhere. Use (9.2) to show that

$$n\text{-volume }[\square(p_1, \ldots, p_n)] = |\det [x^k(p_j)]|$$

where $n\text{-volume } (U) = \displaystyle\int \cdots \int_U dx^1 \cdots dx^n$ for each open set $U \subset \mathbf{R}^n$.

Section 9 appendix

The remainder of this section is an extract from linear algebra devoted to showing how the nonsingular linear transformation A^{-1} can be represented as a product of transformations of type (9.6) or (9.7) as required in the proof of Theorem (9.1). To begin with, a linear transformation B on $\mathbf{R}^n$ is described by an $n \times n$ matrix (B_i^j), where B_i^j is the element in the jth row and ith column of (B_i^j), through the equations

$$x^k \circ B = \sum_{j=1}^{n} B_j^k x^j, \qquad 1 \leq k \leq n.$$

In the following B is also used to denote the matrix, $B = (B_i^j)$.

Exercise 1. Show that $A \circ B$ is represented by the matrix product AB whose jth row, ith column element is $\Sigma_{k=1}^n A_k^j B_i^k$.

Because of Exercise 1 it suffices to show that, as matrices, $A^{-1} = E_1 E_2 \cdots E_J$, where the matrices $E_1, \ldots, E_J$ correspond to linear transformations of type (9.6) or (9.7). The E_k's can be restricted to three types.

Elementary permutations. The matrix of the elementary permutation $P(j, k)$, $1 \leq j < k \leq n$, is the same as the $n \times n$ identity matrix except that the jth and kth rows are interchanged.

Exercise 2. Show that $P(j, k)$ has type (9.7).
Exercise 3. Show that the matrix of $P(j, k) \circ B$ is the same as the matrix of B except that the jth and kth rows of B have been interchanged.
Exercise 4. Describe $B \circ P(j, k)$ after the manner of Exercise 3.

Multiplications. The matrix of a multiplication $M(\lambda, j)$, $\lambda \neq 0$ and $1 \leq j \leq n$, is the same as the $n \times n$ identity matrix except that the jth row is multiplied by λ.

Exercise 5. Show that $M(\lambda, j)$ has type (9.6).

Exercise 6. Show that the matrix of $M(\lambda, j) \circ B$ is the same as the matrix of B except that the jth row has been multiplied by λ.

Exercise 7. Describe the matrix of $B \circ M(\lambda, j)$.

Shears. The matrix of the shear $S(i, \lambda, k)$, $\lambda \in R$ and $i \neq k$, is the same as the $n \times n$ identity matrix except that λ times the kth row has been added to the ith row.

Exercise 8. Show that $S(i, \lambda, k)$ has type (9.6).

Exercise 9. Show that the matrix of $S(i, \lambda, k) \circ B$ is the same as the matrix of B except that λ times the kth row of B has been added to the ith to get the ith row of $S(i, \lambda, k)B$.

Exercise 10. Describe the matrix of $B \circ S(i, \lambda, k)$.

Exercise 11. Show that $S(i, \lambda, k) = M(\lambda^{-1}, k)S(i, 1, k)M(\lambda, k)$ if $\lambda \neq 0$. What is $S(i, 0, k)$?

Exercise 12. Show that $M(\lambda, k) = P(k, n)M(\lambda, n)P(k, n)$.

Exercise 13. Show that det $\{P(i, j)\}$ = det $\{S(i, \lambda, k)\}$ = 1 and det $\{M(\lambda, j)\}$ = λ.

Exercise 14. Show that every shear, multiplication, and elementary permutation is a product of transformations of the form $P(i, i + 1)$, $1 \le i < n$; $M(\lambda, n)$, $\lambda \neq 0$; and $S(1, n, 1)$. Use the results of Exercises 11 and 12.

According to the above definitions and exercises, in order to show that $A^{-1} = E_1E_2 \cdots E_J$ where the E_k's correspond to transformations of type (9.6) and (9.7), it suffices to show that $E_1E_2 \cdots E_JA = I$, the $n \times n$ identity matrix, where the E_k's are shears, multiplications, or elementary permutations. Exercises 3, 6, and 9 show how the matrix EB differs from that of B when E has one of these forms, so that in operational language it suffices to show that the matrix A can be reduced to the identity matrix by a sequence of permutations of two rows, multiplications of a row by a nonzero scalar, and operations which add a multiple of one row to another. An effective procedure is outlined below.

Step 1. Since det $(A) \neq 0$, not all elements in the first column of A are zero. Use a permutation if necessary to be sure the element in the first column first row is not zero.

Step 2. Using a sequence of shears of type $S(k, \lambda, 1)$, reduce all other elements in the first column to zero.

Step 3. Again, since det $(A) \neq 0$, not all elements in the second column rows 2 through n are zero. Using a permutation if necessary, make sure that the element in the second-row second-column position is not zero.

Step 4. Using shears $S(k, \lambda, 2)$, reduce all other elements in the second column to zeros.

Continue this procedure until all the off-diagonal elements are zero. No diagonal element can be zero, since so far the determinant of the matrix has not been changed.

Last step. Using multiplications, reduce all diagonal elements to 1's.

(9.9) Example. The procedure outlined above is illustrated below in a manner which demonstrates how it can be used effectively to compute the inverse of a matrix A.

$$A = \begin{bmatrix} 1 & 3 & 5 \\ -1 & 4 & 2 \\ 1 & -1 & 2 \end{bmatrix}; \qquad I = \begin{bmatrix} 1 & 0 & 0 \\ 0 & 1 & 0 \\ 0 & 0 & 1 \end{bmatrix}.$$

Multiply both on the left by $S(2, 1, 1)$ and then by $S(3, -1, 1)$ to get

$$\begin{bmatrix} 1 & 3 & 5 \\ 0 & 7 & 7 \\ 0 & -4 & -3 \end{bmatrix} \text{ and } \begin{bmatrix} 1 & 0 & 0 \\ 1 & 1 & 0 \\ -1 & 0 & 1 \end{bmatrix} \qquad \text{respectively.}$$

Multiply these on the left by $M(\frac{1}{7}, 2)$ to get

$$\begin{bmatrix} 1 & 3 & 5 \\ 0 & 1 & 1 \\ 0 & -4 & -3 \end{bmatrix} \text{ and } \begin{bmatrix} 1 & 0 & 0 \\ \frac{1}{7} & \frac{1}{7} & 0 \\ -1 & 0 & 1 \end{bmatrix}.$$

Now apply $S(1, -3, 2)$ and $S(3, 4, 2)$ on the left to get

$$\begin{bmatrix} 1 & 0 & 2 \\ 0 & 1 & 1 \\ 0 & 0 & 1 \end{bmatrix} \text{ and } \begin{bmatrix} \frac{4}{7} & -\frac{3}{7} & 0 \\ \frac{1}{7} & \frac{1}{7} & 0 \\ -\frac{3}{7} & \frac{4}{7} & 1 \end{bmatrix}.$$

As a final step apply $S(1, -2, 3)$ and $S(2, -1, 3)$ to get

$$I = \begin{bmatrix} 1 & 0 & 0 \\ 0 & 1 & 0 \\ 0 & 0 & 1 \end{bmatrix} \text{ and } A^{-1} = \begin{bmatrix} \frac{10}{7} & -\frac{11}{7} & -2 \\ \frac{4}{7} & -\frac{3}{7} & -1 \\ -\frac{3}{7} & \frac{4}{7} & 1 \end{bmatrix}.$$

Recording the above steps in order gives

$$A^{-1} = S(2, -1, 3)S(1, -2, 3)S(3, 4, 2)S(1, -3, 2)M(\tfrac{1}{7}, 2)S(3, -1, 1)S(2, 1, 1).$$

Exercise 15. Find the inverse of the matrix

$$A = \begin{bmatrix} 0 & -1 & 4 \\ 1 & 1 & 2 \\ 0 & -1 & 5 \end{bmatrix}$$

using row operations as above.

Exercise 16. Using the results of Exercises 4, 7, and 10, describe a method of calculating A^{-1} using column operations and use this method to calculate the inverse of the matrix A in Exercise 15.

10   The implicit function theorem

This theorem gives one answer to the question: When can the equation $F(x, y) = 0$ be solved for y in terms of x or, more generally, when can the system of m equations

$$F^1(x^1, \ldots , x^n; y^1, \ldots , y^m) = 0,$$

(10.1)

$$F^m(x^1, \ldots , x^n; y^1, \ldots , y^m) = 0$$

be solved for the y^j's in terms of $x^1, \ldots , x^n$? Just as the inverse function theorem establishes the existence of a local inverse without ever exhibiting it, the implicit function theorem will establish that under suitable conditions the y^j's can be expressed in terms of the x^i's in (10.1) without showing how to effect this solution. The two theorems are almost different versions of the same theorem, each being easily established from the other.

In order to match the formulation (10.1) the letters $y^1, \ldots , y^m$ are used in this section as other names for the cartesian coordinate variables $x^{n+1}, \ldots , x^{n+m}$ on $\mathbf{R}^{n+m}$.

(10.2)   Theorem (The implicit function theorem).   Suppose the m functions $F^1, \ldots , F^m$ are C^k ($k \geq 1$) on the open set $U \subset \mathbf{R}^{n+m}$ and vanish at the point $q \in U$ where

(10.3)
$$\det \begin{bmatrix} \dfrac{\partial F^1}{\partial y^1}(q) & \cdots & \dfrac{\partial F^1}{\partial y^m}(q) \\ \vdots & & \vdots \\ \dfrac{\partial F^m}{\partial y^1}(q) & \cdots & \dfrac{\partial F^m}{\partial y^m}(q) \end{bmatrix} \neq 0.$$

Then the equations (10.1) can be solved uniquely for the y^j's in terms of the x^k's at q. More precisely, the point $(x^1(q), \ldots , x^n(q)) \in \mathbf{R}^n$ has a neighborhood V on which there are m functions $f^1, \ldots , f^m$ such that

$$y^j(q) = f^j[x^1(q), \ldots , x^n(q)], \qquad 1 \leq j \leq m;$$

(10.4) $F^i(x^1(p), \ldots , x^n(p);$

$f^1[x^1(p), \ldots , x^n(p)], \ldots , f^m[x^1(p), \ldots , x^n(p)]) = 0, \quad 1 \leq i \leq m, \, p \in V.$

The functions $f^1, \ldots , f^m$ are C^k on V and uniquely determined by the conditions (10.4).

PROOF.   This theorem will appear as a by-product of other results later on [cf. Example (11.5f)]. To prove it let ϕ be the map of $U \to \mathbf{R}^{n+m}$

defined by

$$\phi(p) = (x^1(p), \ldots, x^n(p), F^1(p), \ldots, F^m(p)), \qquad p \in U.$$

$$\det\left\{\frac{\partial x^i \circ \phi}{\partial x^j}(q)\right\} = \det \begin{bmatrix} 1 & \cdots & 0 & 0 & \cdots & & 0 \\ & & & & & & \\ & & & & & & \\ 0 & \cdots & 1 & 0 & \cdots & & 0 \\ * & \cdots & * & \dfrac{\partial F^1}{\partial y^1}(q) & \cdots & & \dfrac{\partial F^1}{\partial y^m}(q) \\ & & & & & & \\ & & & & & & \\ * & \cdots & * & \dfrac{\partial F^m}{\partial y^1}(q) & \cdots & & \dfrac{\partial F^m}{\partial y^m}(q) \end{bmatrix} \neq 0,$$

so that according to the inverse function theorem there is an open set W, $q \in W \subset U$, such that $\phi: W \to \phi(W)$ and $\phi^{-1}: \phi(W) \to W$ are both C^k maps. For V take any connected open subset of

$$B = \{(a^1, \ldots, a^n) : (a^1, \ldots, a^n, 0, \ldots, 0) \in \phi(W)\}$$

containing $(x^1(q), \ldots, x^n(q))$ and put

$$f^j(a^1, \ldots, a^n) = y^j \circ \phi^{-1}(a^1, \ldots, a^n, 0, \ldots, 0),$$

$$(a^1, \ldots, a^n) \in V, 1 \leq j \leq m.$$

(10.5)

$$f^j[x^1(q), \ldots, x^n(q)] = y^j \circ \phi^{-1}[x^1(q), \ldots, x^n(q), F^1(q), \ldots, F^m(q)]$$

$$= y^j \circ \phi^{-1} \circ \phi(q) = y^j(q),$$

$$F^i[x^1(p), \ldots, x^n(p); f^1(x^1(p), \ldots, x^n(p)), \ldots, f^m(x^1(p), \ldots)]$$

$$= x^{n+i} \circ \phi \circ \phi^{-1}(p) = x^{n+i}(p) = 0, \qquad p \in V,$$

so that the functions $f^1, \ldots, f^m$ on V satisfy (10.4). Equations (10.5) show they are C^k on V. To establish uniqueness let $g^1, \ldots, g^m$ be another set of continuous maps which satisfy (10.4) and put

(10.6)
$$G(p) = (x^1(p), \ldots, x^n(p), g^1(p), \ldots, g^m(p)), \qquad p \in V;$$
$$F(p) = (x^1(p), \ldots, x^n(p), f^1(p), \ldots, f^m(p)), \qquad p \in V.$$

Observe that if $G(p) \in W$, then

$$\phi(G(p)) = \phi(F(p)) = (x^1(p), \ldots, x^n(p), 0, \ldots, 0)$$

and since ϕ is one-one it follows that $G(p) = F(p)$. As a consequence the sets

$$\{p \in V : G(p) = F(p)\} = \{p \in V : G(p) \in W\}$$

and

$$\{p \in V : G(p) \neq F(p)\}$$

are both open. They are disjoint and cover V, so that one of them must be empty because V is connected. By (10.4) $G(x^1(q), \ldots, x^n(q)) = F(x^1(q), \ldots, x^n(q))$. Thus the second set is empty, $G(p) = F(p)$, $p \in V$, and uniqueness has been established as asserted.   ◆

Exercises

10.1   Under what conditions can the system

$$a_1^1 x^1 + a_2^1 x^2 + b_1^1 y^1 + b_2^1 y^2 = 0,$$
$$a_1^2 x^1 + a_2^2 x^2 + b_1^2 y^1 + b_2^2 y^2 = 0$$

be solved for the y's in terms of the x's? How is this related to Cramer's rule?

10.2   Use the implicit function theorem to prove the inverse function theorem.

11 Local coordinates

The inverse function theorem has many applications, among the most useful of which is the freedom it pe mits in choosing a suitable system of local coordinates.

(11.1)   Definition.   A family $z^1, \ldots, z^n$ of C^k differentiable functions on the open set U in $\mathbf{R}^n$ forms a (C^k) *local coordinate system* for U if
   (i) The map $z: p \rightarrow (z^1(p), \ldots, z^n(p))$ of $U \rightarrow \mathbf{R}^n$ is one-one.
   (ii)

$$\det \begin{bmatrix} D_1 z^1(q) & \cdots & D_1 z^n(q) \\ \cdot & & \cdot \\ \cdot & & \cdot \\ \cdot & & \cdot \\ D_n z^1(q) & \cdots & D_n z^n(q) \end{bmatrix} \neq 0, \qquad q \in U.$$

Several consequences of this definition are immediate: (a) From (ii) and the inverse function theorem it follows that $z(U)$ is a neighborhood of $z(q)$ for each $q \in U$ and hence that $z(U)$ is open in $\mathbf{R}^n$. (The map z plays the role of the map ϕ in the inverse function theorem. Note $x^i \circ \phi = z^i$.) (b) The map $z^{-1}: z(U) \rightarrow U$ is C^k. Because of (a) and (b) whenever h is a continuously differentiable function on U, $h \circ z^{-1}$ is a continuously differentiable function on $z(U)$ and it is customary to use the notation (see Figure 5)

(11.2) $\dfrac{\partial h}{\partial z^k}(p)$ to mean $D_k(h \circ z^{-1})[z(p)]$.

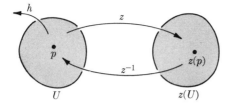

FIGURE 5

In words, the $\partial h/\partial z^k$ corresponds precisely to the derivative of h as a function of $z^1, \ldots, z^n$ with the variables $z^j, j \neq k$, being treated as constants. If $x^1, \ldots, x^n$ are cartesian coordinates, $(\partial h/\partial x^k)(p) = D_k h(p)$ with its usual meaning.

The chain rule for local coordinates: Suppose that $y^1, \ldots, y^n$ is another local coordinate system for U with associated map $u: U \rightarrow y(U)$. The chain rule [Theorem (6.7)] applied to the maps

$$y(U) \xrightarrow{\ z^k \circ y^{-1}\ } z(U) \xrightarrow{\ h \circ z^{-1}\ } \mathbf{R};$$
$$y(p) \xrightarrow{\hspace{2cm}} z(p) \xrightarrow{\hspace{2cm}} h(p)$$

yields

$$\frac{\partial h}{\partial y^m}(p) = D_m(h \circ y^{-1}) \cdot [y(p)]$$

$$= D_m(h \circ z^{-1} \circ z \circ y^{-1})[y(p)]$$

$$= \sum_{k=1}^n D_k(h \circ z^{-1})[z(p)] D_m(z^k \circ y^{-1})[y(p)]$$

$$= \sum_{k=1}^n \frac{\partial h}{\partial z^k}(p) \frac{\partial z^k}{\partial y^m}(p),$$

a formula referred to as the *chain rule for partial derivatives*.

(11.3) **Theorem.** If $y^1, \ldots, y^n$ is a system of local coordinates for the open neighborhood U of p and $z^1, \ldots, z^n$ are continuously differentiable functions on U such that determinant $[(\partial z^i/\partial y^j)(p)] \neq 0$, then $z^1, \ldots, z^n$ is a system of local coordinates for some open neighborhood V of p.

PROOF. Because of the inverse function theorem it suffices to show that determinant $[D_k z^i(p)] \neq 0$. According to the chain rule

$$D_k z^i(p) = \sum_{j=1}^n \frac{\partial z^i}{\partial y^j}(p) D_k y^j(p),$$

and hence

(11.4) $$\det [D_k z^i(p)] = \det \left[\frac{\partial z^i}{\partial y^j}(p)\right] \det [D_k y^j(p)],$$

which is not zero since neither of the factors on the right-hand side of (11.4) is zero. ◆

(11.5) **Example.** Consider the set $S = \{p \in \mathbf{R}^n : F^1(p) = 0, \ldots, F^m(p) = 0\}$ of simultaneous zeros of the m functions $F^1, \ldots, F^m$, and suppose that at the point $q \in S$ the $m \times n$ matrix

(11.6)

$$\begin{bmatrix} \dfrac{\partial F^1}{\partial x^1}(q) & \cdots & \dfrac{\partial F^1}{\partial x^n}(q) \\ \cdot & & \cdot \\ \cdot & & \cdot \\ \cdot & & \cdot \\ \dfrac{\partial F^m}{\partial x^1}(q) & \cdots & \dfrac{\partial F^m}{\partial x^n}(q) \end{bmatrix}$$

has rank m. (If this last condition is not fulfilled S can be quite complicated at q.) Without loss of generality one can as well assume that the $m \times m$ submatrix consisting of the last m columns of (11.6) has a nonzero determinant. Then it is easily checked that the functions $z^1 = x^1, \ldots, \; z^{n-m} = x^{n-m}, \; z^{n-m+1} = F^1, \ldots, z^n = F^m$ form a local coordinate system in some open neighborhood U of q and

(11.7) $U \cap S = \{q \in U : z^{n-m+1}(q) = 0, \ldots, z^n(q) = 0\}.$

If, as usual, $z : U \to \mathbf{R}^n$ is the map $p \to (z^1(p), \ldots, z^n(p))$, $z(U \cap S)$ is just the slice cut from $z(U)$ by the linear subspace of points whose last m coordinates are zero.

These arguments lie very close to the implicit function theorem. Since $x^k(p) = z^k(p)$ if $1 \leq k \leq n - m$,

$$x^i(p) = x^i \circ z^{-1}(z^1(p), \ldots, z^n(p))$$
$$= x^i \circ z^{-1}(x^1(p), \ldots, x^{n-m}(p), z^{n-m+1}(p), \ldots, z^n(p)), \qquad p \in U,$$

which becomes

$$x^i(p) = x^i \circ z^{-1}(x^1(p), \ldots, x^{n-m}(p), 0, \ldots, 0), \qquad p \in U \cap S,$$

and solves $F^i(x^1, \ldots, x^n) = 0, 1 \leq i \leq m$, for $x^{n-m+1}, \ldots, x^n$ in terms of $x^1, \ldots, x^{n-m}$.

We turn now to specific examples of local coordinate systems. Four examples are given (besides cartesian coordinates themselves)—namely, polar coordinates, cylindrical coordinates, spherical coordinates, and a special set of coordinates adapted for problems with toroidal symmetry. These serve to illustrate the possibilities and furnish a base on which later examples can be built. Each of these examples except for polar coordinates arises in the same manner as an inverse of a map $h : \mathbf{R}^3 \to \mathbf{R}^3$ restricted to an open subset U of $\mathbf{R}^3$ on which h is one-one. To fit the usual notation it is convenient to take two copies of $\mathbf{R}^3$, namely $\mathbf{R}_a^3$ and $\mathbf{R}_b^3$, and to regard h as a map $h : \mathbf{R}_a^3 \to \mathbf{R}_b^3$. x^1, x^2, x^3 denote cartesian coordinates on $\mathbf{R}_b^3$, while the letters used to designate cartesian coordinates on $\mathbf{R}_a^3$ vary with the example. In the case of polar coordinates $h: R_a^2 \to R_b^2$ but other details are similar.

(11.8) Example (Polar coordinates). Let r, θ be cartesian coordinates for $\mathbf{R}_a^2$ and let $h: \mathbf{R}_a^2 \to \mathbf{R}_b^2$ be the map defined by

$$x^1 \circ h = r \cos \theta; \qquad x^2 \circ h = r \sin \theta.$$

h is one-one on the subset $U = \{q \in \mathbf{R}_a^2 : 0 < r(q), -\pi < \theta(q) < \pi\}$ and the functions $r \circ h^{-1}$, $\theta \circ h^{-1}$ defined on $h(U) = \{p \in \mathbf{R}_b^2 : 0 < x^1(p) \text{ or } x^2(p) \neq 0\}$ are known as polar coordinates on $\mathbf{R}^2$.

(11.9) Example (Cylindrical coordinates). Let r, θ, z be cartesian coordinates for $\mathbf{R}_a^3$ and let $h: \mathbf{R}_a^3 \to \mathbf{R}_b^3$ be the map defined by

$$x^1 \circ h = r \cos \theta; \qquad x^2 \circ h = r \sin \theta; \qquad x^3 \circ h = z.$$

h is one-one on the subset $U = \{q \in \mathbf{R}_a^3 : 0 < r(q), -\pi < \theta(q) < \pi\}$ and the functions $r \circ h^{-1}$, $\theta \circ h^{-1}$, $z \circ h^{-1}$ defined on $h(U)$ are known as cylindrical coordinates on $\mathbf{R}^3$.

(11.10) Example (Spherical coordinates). Let ρ, θ, ϕ be cartesian coordinates for $\mathbf{R}_a^3$ and let $h: \mathbf{R}_a^3 \to \mathbf{R}_b^3$ be the map defined by

$$x^1 \circ h = \rho \cos \theta \sin \phi;$$
$$x^2 \circ h = \rho \sin \theta \sin \phi;$$
$$x^3 \circ h = \rho \cos \phi.$$

h is one-one on the subset $U = \{q \in \mathbf{R}_a^3 : 0 < \rho(q), -\pi < \theta(q) < \pi, 0 < \phi(q) < \pi\}$ and the functions $\rho \circ h^{-1}$, $\theta \circ h^{-1}$, $\phi \circ h^{-1}$ defined on $h(U)$ are known as spherical coordinates on $\mathbf{R}^3$.

(11.11) Example. Let w, θ, β be cartesian coordinates for $\mathbf{R}_a^3$ and let $h: \mathbf{R}_a^3 \to \mathbf{R}_b^3$ be the map defined by $(b > 0)$

$$x^1 \circ h = (b + w \cos \beta) \cos \theta;$$

$$x^2 \circ h = (b + w \cos \beta) \sin \theta;$$

$$x^3 \circ h = w \sin \beta.$$

h is one-one on the subset $U = \{q \in \mathbf{R}_a^3 : 0 < w(q) < b, -\pi < \theta(q) < \pi, -\pi < \beta(q) < \pi\}$ and the functions $w \circ h^{-1}$, $\theta \circ h^{-1}$, $\beta \circ h^{-1}$ form a set of coordinates for $h(U)$ particularly suited for studying the tori generated by rotating circles in the x^1,x^3-plane centered at $x^1 = b$, $x^3 = 0$ about the x^3-axis. In fact θ is the variable θ of cylindrical or spherical coordinates; w is the distance from the circle about which these tori center; and β is the angle of elevation or depression above the x^1,x^2-plane measured looking outward from the nearest point on this central circle.

The h of Example (11.11) is also one-one on the subset $\pi = \{q \in \mathbf{R}_a^3 : 0 < w(q), -\pi < \theta(q) < \pi, -\pi/2 < \beta(q) < \pi/2\}$ and the functions $w \circ h^{-1}$, $\theta \circ h^{-1}$, $\beta \circ h^{-1}$ form a set of coordinates for $h(V)$ which is the exterior of the circular cylinder of radius b whose axis of symmetry is the x^3-axis. In particular if $b = 0$, then wh^{-1}, θh^{-1}, $h^{-1} + (\pi/2)$ are just the ordinary spherical coordinates for $\mathbf{R}^3$.

Exercises

11.1   Suppose that u and v are C^1 functions on the open subset U of $\mathbf{R}^2$ which satisfy

$$\frac{\partial u}{\partial x^1} = \frac{\partial v}{\partial x^2}; \qquad \frac{\partial u}{\partial x^2} = -\frac{\partial v}{\partial x^1}.$$

Show that whenever one of the above first partial derivatives is not zero each point $p \in U$ has an open neighborhood on which u, v form a local coordinate system.

11.2   Let f be C^1 on U and suppose p belongs to the surface described by $f = 0$ in U. Show that the functions $z^1 = f$, $z^k = x^k$, $1 < k \leq n$ form a local coordinate system in some neighborhood of p if and only if $(\partial f/\partial x^1)(p) \neq 0$. What is the equation of the surface $f = 0$ in the coordinate system $z^1, \ldots, z^n$?

11.3   Show that a map $\phi: U \to \mathbf{R}^n$ is C^k if and only if for each $q \in \phi(U)$ there is a C^k local coordinate system $z^1, \ldots, z^n$ on an open neighborhood V of q in $\mathbf{R}^n$ such that the functions $z^1 \circ \phi, \ldots, z^n \circ \phi$ are C^k on $\phi^{-1}(V) \subset U$.

12 Maps of **R**ⁿ into **R**^m

At the heart of any study of continuously differentiable maps ϕ of the open set U of $\mathbf{R}^n$ into $\mathbf{R}^m$ is the whole concept of rank. There is a good reason for this: In the small any map ϕ behaves at q very much like the associated affine transformation,

$$x^k \circ \phi(p) = x^k \circ \phi(q) + \sum_{j=1}^{n} \frac{\partial x^k \circ \phi}{\partial x^j}(q)[x^k(p) - x^k(q)] + \text{small terms},$$

so that it is quite reasonable to expect that the local properties of ϕ will reflect those of this affine transformation. The reader will notice that the rank of ϕ at q is by definition just the rank of this affine transformation.

(12.1)   Definition.   Suppose that $y^1, \ldots, y^n$ is a local coordinate system for the open set V and that $z^1, \ldots, z^m$ is a local coordinate system for some open neighborhood of $\phi(p)$. Then the *rank of ϕ at p* is the rank of the $(n \times m)$ matrix

$$(12.2) \quad \begin{bmatrix} \dfrac{\partial z^1 \circ \phi}{\partial y^1}(p) & \dfrac{\partial z^2 \circ \phi}{\partial y^1}(p) & \cdots & \dfrac{\partial z^m \circ \phi}{\partial y^1}(p) \\[2mm] \dfrac{\partial z^1 \circ \phi}{\partial y^2}(p) & \dfrac{\partial z^2 \circ \phi}{\partial y^2}(p) & \cdots & \dfrac{\partial z^m \circ \phi}{\partial y^2}(p) \\[2mm] \cdot & \cdot & & \cdot \\ \cdot & \cdot & & \cdot \\ \cdot & \cdot & & \cdot \\[2mm] \dfrac{\partial z^1 \circ \phi}{\partial y^n}(p) & \dfrac{\partial z^2 \circ \phi}{\partial y^n}(p) & \cdots & \dfrac{\partial z^m \circ \phi}{\partial y^n}(p) \end{bmatrix}$$

It is the maximum number of linearly independent columns (or equivalently of linearly independent rows) in the matrix (12.2). More specifically, the rank of ϕ at p is k if there is a $(k \times k)$ submatrix

$$\begin{bmatrix} \dfrac{\partial z^{i_1} \circ \phi}{\partial y^{j_1}}(p) & \dfrac{\partial z^{i_2} \circ \phi}{\partial y^{j_1}}(p) & \cdots & \dfrac{\partial z^{i_k} \circ \phi}{\partial y^{j_1}}(p) \\[2mm] \cdot & \cdot & & \cdot \\ \cdot & \cdot & & \cdot \\ \cdot & \cdot & & \cdot \\[2mm] \dfrac{\partial z^{i_1} \circ \phi}{\partial y^{j_k}}(p) & \dfrac{\partial z^{i_2} \circ \phi}{\partial y^{j_k}}(p) & \cdots & \dfrac{\partial z^{i_k} \circ \phi}{\partial y^{j_k}}(p) \end{bmatrix}$$

with nonzero determinant and the determinant of every $(k + 1) \times (k + 1)$ submatrix formed in this manner is zero. In particular the rank of ϕ cannot be greater than m or n.

(12.3)   Theorem. Suppose $f^1, \ldots, f^k$ $(k \leq n)$ are C^N functions on the open subset U of $\mathbf{R}^n$ and the map $q \to (f^1(q), \ldots, f^k(q))$ of $U \to \mathbf{R}^k$ has rank k at the point $p \in U$. Then the set of functions $f^1, \ldots, f^k$ can be enlarged to a set $f^1, \ldots, f^k, f^{k+1}, \ldots, f^n$, which is a C^N local coordinate system for some open neighborhood of p.

PROOF.   Let $x^1, \ldots, x^n$ be a local coordinate system for an open set V which contains p and is contained in U. By renumbering the x^j's it can be assumed without loss of generality that

$$\det \begin{bmatrix} \dfrac{\partial f^1}{\partial x^1}(p) & \cdots & \dfrac{\partial f^k}{\partial x^1}(p) \\[2mm] \cdot & \cdot & \cdot \\ \cdot & & \cdot \\ \cdot & \cdot & \cdot \\[2mm] \dfrac{\partial f^1}{\partial x^k}(p) & \cdots & \dfrac{\partial f^k}{\partial x^k}(p) \end{bmatrix} \neq 0.$$

If one then puts $f^{k+1} = x^{k+1}, \ldots, f^n = x^n$,

(12.4)

$$\det\left[\frac{\partial f^i}{\partial x^j}(p)\right] = \det \begin{bmatrix} \frac{\partial f^1}{\partial x^1}(p) & \cdots & \frac{\partial f^k}{\partial x^1}(p) & 0, & \cdots, & 0 \\ \vdots & & \vdots & \vdots & & \vdots \\ \frac{\partial f^1}{\partial x^k}(p) & \cdots & \frac{\partial f^k}{\partial x^k}(p) & 0, & \cdots, & 0 \\ \hline & & & 1, & 0, & \cdots, & 0 \\ & & & \vdots \\ \frac{\partial f^1}{\partial x^n}(p) & \cdots & \frac{\partial f^k}{\partial x^n}(p) & 0, & \cdots, & 1 \end{bmatrix}$$

$$= \det \begin{bmatrix} \frac{\partial f^1}{\partial x^1}(p) & \cdots & \frac{\partial f^k}{\partial x^1}(p) \\ \vdots & & \vdots \\ \frac{\partial f^1}{\partial x^k}(p) & \cdots & \frac{\partial f^k}{\partial x^k}(p) \end{bmatrix} \neq 0$$

where the $(n - k) \times (n - k)$ block in the lower right-hand section of (12.4) is just the $(n - k) \times (n - k)$ identity matrix. With this observation Theorem (12.3) follows directly from Theorem (11.3). ◆

(12.5) Theorem. Let $\phi: U \to \mathbf{R}^n$ be a C^N map of the open set U of $\mathbf{R}^k$ into $\mathbf{R}^n$ and suppose that

(i) ϕ is one-one on U.
(ii) The rank of ϕ at p is k for each $p \in U$.

If $h: V \to \mathbf{R}^n$ is a C^N map of the open set V of $\mathbf{R}^m$ into $\mathbf{R}^n$ and $h(V) \subset \phi(U)$, then $\phi^{-1} \circ h: V \to U$ is a C^N map of V into $\mathbf{R}^k$ (see Figure 6).

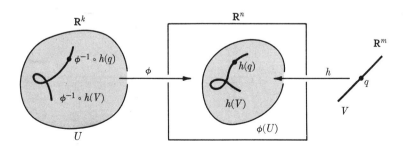

FIGURE 6

PROOF. According to Exercise 11.3 it suffices to show that for each $q \in V$ one can find a local coordinate system $y^1, \ldots, y^k$ for some open neighborhood W of $\phi^{-1} \circ h(q) \in U$ such that the functions $y^1 \circ \phi^{-1} \circ h$, $\ldots, y^k \circ \phi^{-1} \circ h$ are C^N in a neighborhood of q. This can be done as follows: Let $z^1, \ldots, z^n$ be a local coordinate system valid in some open neighborhood of $h(q)$. By renumbering the z^j's if necessary, one can assume without loss of generality that the map $p \to (z^1 \circ \phi(p), \ldots, z^k \circ \phi(p))$ has rank k at $\phi^{-1} \circ h(q)$ and thus [by Theorem (12.3)] that $y^1 = z^1 \circ \phi$, $\ldots, y^k = z^k \circ \phi$ is a local coordinate system for some neighborhood of $\phi^{-1} \circ h(q)$. But with this choice $y^j \circ \phi^{-1} \circ h = z^j \circ \phi \circ \phi^{-1} \circ h = z^j \circ h$ is C^N at q because the map $h: V \to \mathbf{R}^n$ is C^N by hypothesis. ◆

(12.6) Definition. A subset $M \subset \mathbf{R}^n$ is called a *regular k-dimensional C^N submanifold of $\mathbf{R}^n$* if each point $q \in M$ has a neighborhood U together with a map ϕ, such that

   (i) $\phi: V \to \mathbf{R}^n$ is a C^N map of an open subset V of $\mathbf{R}^k$ into $\mathbf{R}^n$.
   (ii) ϕ is one-one.
   (iii) $\phi(V) = M \cap U$.
   (iv) ϕ has rank k at each point of V.

It is important to observe that if ϕ_1, V_1 and ϕ_2, V_2 are two pairs satisfying conditions (i)–(iv) above and if $\phi_1(V_1) \cap \phi_2(V_2) \neq \varnothing$, then the map ϕ_2 restricted to the subset $W = \phi_2^{-1}[\phi_1(V_1) \cap \phi_2(V_2)]$ of V_2 is C^N while ϕ_1 both is C^N and has rank k at each point of V_1 (see Figure 7). This means according to Theorem (12.5) that the map

(12.7) $$\phi_1^{-1} \circ \phi_2: W \to V_1$$

is C^N. The concept of a differentiable manifold is based upon axiomatization of this property, but it is not pursued further here. In a descriptive sense the map ϕ provides a parametrization of the set $M \cap U$. Two different local parametrizations ϕ_1 and ϕ_2 with overlapping ranges are tied together by the condition that the map $\phi_1^{-1} \circ \phi_2$ is C^N where it is defined. For practical purposes a regular submanifold of $\mathbf{R}^n$ is usually described in one of two ways: (1) by giving an explicit parametrization for M or (2) as the set of zeros of a finite set of C^N functions $F^1, \ldots, F^m$. To be more explicit there is an alternative definition for a regular k-dimensional C^N submanifold of $\mathbf{R}^n$ given below as Theorem (12.8).

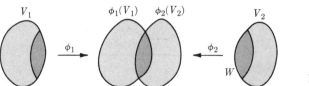

FIGURE 7

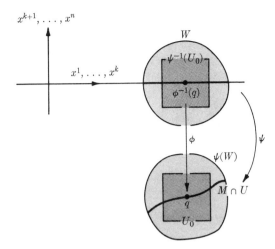

FIGURE 8

(12.8)   Theorem. M is a regular k-dimensional C^N submanifold of $\mathbf{R}^n$ if and only if each point $q \in M$ has an open neighborhood U with a C^N local coordinate system $z^1, \ldots, z^n$ such that

(12.9) $M \cap U = \{p \in U : z^{k+1}(p) = 0, \ldots, z^n(p) = 0\}.$

PROOF.   Suppose $z^1, \ldots, z^n$ and U exist at q as stated in the theorem and as usual let $z: U \to \mathbf{R}^n$ be the map $p \to (z^1(p), \ldots, z^n(p))$. Let

$$V = \{(a^1, \ldots, a^k) \in \mathbf{R}^k : (a^1, \ldots, a^k, 0, \ldots, 0) \in z(U)\}$$

and define the map $\phi: V \to \mathbf{R}^n$ by

$$\phi(a^1, \ldots, a^k) = z^{-1}(a^1, \ldots, a^k, 0, \ldots, 0).$$

$z \circ \phi(a^1, \ldots, a^k) = (a^1, \ldots, a^k, 0, \ldots, 0)$; so $\phi(V) \subset M \cap U$ and conversely if $p \in M \cap U$, $p = z^{-1}(z^1(p), \ldots, z^k(p), 0, \ldots, 0) = \phi[z^1(p), \ldots, z^k(p)] \in \phi(V)$. Thus $\phi(V) = M \cap U$. The other conditions of Definition (12.6) are easily checked, showing that M is a regular k-dimensional C^N submanifold of $\mathbf{R}^n$.

Suppose now that M is a regular k-dimensional C^N submanifold of $\mathbf{R}^n$ and let q, ϕ, V, and U be as in Definition (12.6). In outlining the argument to be used here, V is considered as a subset of $\mathbf{R}^n$ and the map ϕ extended from V to a map ψ of an open subset W of $\mathbf{R}^n$ into U (see Figure 8). The extended map ψ has rank n at $\phi^{-1}(q)$ and the z^j's can then be defined by $z^j = x^j \circ \psi^{-1}$ in some neighborhood of q. In detail, since ϕ has rank k at $\phi^{-1}(q)$, by renumbering coordinates in $\mathbf{R}^n$ if necessary it can be assumed that the map $p \to (x^1 \circ \phi(p), \ldots, x^k \circ \phi(p))$ of $V \to \mathbf{R}^k$ has rank k at $\phi^{-1}(q)$. In this case let

$$\psi(p) = \phi(x^1(p), \ldots, x^k(p)) + (0, \ldots, 0, x^{k+1}(p), \ldots, x^n(p)),$$

when $(x^1(p), \ldots, x^k(p)) \in V$, $p \in \mathbf{R}^n$, and put

$$W = \{q \in \mathbf{R}^n : (x^1(p), \ldots, x^k(p)) \in V, \psi(p) \in U\}.$$

A check shows that the $n \times n$ matrix

$$\begin{bmatrix} \dfrac{\partial x^1 \circ \psi}{\partial x^1} & \cdots & \dfrac{\partial x^1 \circ \psi}{\partial x^k} & \dfrac{\partial x^1 \circ \psi}{\partial x^{k+1}} & \cdots & \dfrac{\partial x^1 \circ \psi}{\partial x^n} \\[2mm] \vdots & & \vdots & \vdots & & \vdots \\[2mm] \dfrac{\partial x^k \circ \psi}{\partial x^1} & \cdots & \dfrac{\partial x^k \circ \psi}{\partial x^k} & \dfrac{\partial x^k \circ \psi}{\partial x^{k+1}} & \cdots & \dfrac{\partial x^k \circ \psi}{\partial x^n} \\[2mm] \hline & & & \dfrac{\partial x^{k+1} \circ \psi}{\partial x^{k+1}} & \cdots & \dfrac{\partial x^{k+1} \circ \psi}{\partial x^{k+1}} \\[2mm] & & & \vdots & & \vdots \\[2mm] & & & \dfrac{\partial x^n \circ \psi}{\partial x^{k+1}} & \cdots & \dfrac{\partial x^n \circ \psi}{\partial x^n} \end{bmatrix}$$

reduces to

$$\begin{bmatrix} \dfrac{\partial x^1 \circ \phi}{\partial x^1} & \cdots & \dfrac{\partial x^1 \circ \phi}{\partial x^k} & 0 & \cdots & 0 \\[2mm] \vdots & & \vdots & \vdots & & \vdots \\[2mm] \dfrac{\partial x^k \circ \phi}{\partial x^1} & \cdots & \dfrac{\partial x^k \circ \phi}{\partial x^k} & 0 & & 0 \\[2mm] \hline & & & 1 & \cdots & 0 \\[2mm] & & & \vdots & & \vdots \\[2mm] & & & 0 & \cdots & 1 \end{bmatrix}$$

and has rank n at the point $\phi^{-1}(q)$ because the upper left $k \times k$ matrix has rank k there. If U_0 is a neighborhood of q on which ψ^{-1} is one-one and has rank n, then the local coordinates $z^1 = x^1 \circ \psi^{-1}, \ldots, z^n = x^n \circ \psi^{-1}$ on U_0 satisfy (12.9). In fact if $p \in U_0$ and $z^{k+j}(p) = 0$, $1 \le j \le n - k$, then $x^{k+j} \circ \psi^{-1}(p) = 0$, $1 \le j \le n - k$, and

$$\psi^{-1}(p) = (a^1, \ldots, a^k, 0, \ldots, 0)$$

where $(a^1, \ldots, a^k) \in V$. That is, $p = \psi(a^1, \ldots, a^k, 0, \ldots, 0)$ $= \phi(a^1, \ldots, a^k) \in \phi(V)$. Hence $p \in \phi(V) \cap U_0 = M \cap U_0$. On the other hand if $p \in M \cap U_0$, $p = \phi(a^1, \ldots, a^k) = \psi(a^1, \ldots, a^k, 0, \ldots, 0)$ for some $(a^1, \ldots, a^k, 0, \ldots, 0) \in W$ and

$$z^{k+j}(p) = 0, \qquad 1 \le j \le n - k. \quad \blacklozenge$$

(12.10)   Example.   If $F^1, \ldots, F^m$ are C^N functions, the subset M of points $q \in \mathbf{R}^n$, where $F^1(q) = 0, \ldots, F^m(q) = 0$ and the matrix

$$
\begin{bmatrix}
\dfrac{\partial F^1}{\partial x^1}(q) & \cdots & \dfrac{\partial F^1}{\partial x^n}(q) \\
\vdots & & \vdots \\
\dfrac{\partial F^m}{\partial x^1}(q) & \cdots & \dfrac{\partial F^m}{\partial x^n}(q)
\end{bmatrix}
$$

has rank m, form a regular $(n - m)$-dimensional C^N submanifold of $\mathbf{R}^n$. In fact at each point $q \in M$ the map $q \to (F^1(q), \ldots, F^m(q))$ of $\mathbf{R}^n \to \mathbf{R}^m$ has rank m, and by Theorem (12.3) the set $F^1, \ldots, F^m$ can be enlarged to a set $z^1, \ldots, z^{n-m}, z^{n-m+1} = F^1, \ldots, z^n = F^m$, which is a C^N local coordinate system for some open neighborhood U of q. Theorem (12.8) then shows that M is a submanifold of $\mathbf{R}^n$ as stated.

In euclidean three-space, for example, an equation of the form $F = 0$ describes a regular two-dimensional submanifold or surface, $S = \{p : F(p) = 0\}$, if the derivatives $\partial F/\partial x^1$, $\partial F/\partial x^2$, $\partial F/\partial x^3$ are not all zero at some point of S. This condition can be restated in the usual vector terminology as grad $F(q) \neq 0$, $q \in S$.

Two equations $F = 0$, $G = 0$ describe a regular one-dimensional submanifold or a curve if the matrix

$$
\begin{bmatrix}
\dfrac{\partial F}{\partial x^1} & \dfrac{\partial F}{\partial x^2} & \dfrac{\partial F}{\partial x^3} \\
\dfrac{\partial G}{\partial x^1} & \dfrac{\partial G}{\partial x^2} & \dfrac{\partial G}{\partial x^3}
\end{bmatrix}
$$

has rank 2 at each point of $C = \{p : F(p) = 0, G(p) = 0\}$. Using vector notation this can be rephrased as grad $F(p) \times$ grad $G(p) \neq 0$, $p \in C$.

Exercises

The first three exercises below illustrate some of the behavior that can be expected when the matrix (11.6) does not have maximum rank. Describe S and check the rank of (11.6).

12.1 $F = (x^1)^2 + (x^2)^2 - (x^3)^2$ on $\mathbf{R}^3$; $q = (0, 0, 0)$.

12.2 $F^1 = (x^1 - 1)^2 + (x^2)^2 + (x^3)^2 - 1$; $F^2 = (x^1 - 2)^2 + (x^2)^2 + (x^3)^2 - 4$; $q = (0, 0, 0)$.

12.3 $F(p) = \exp[1/(1 - \|p\|^2)]$ if $\|p\| < 1$, $F(p) = 0$ if $\|p\| \geq 1$. This function is actually C^∞ on $\mathbf{R}^3$. Its set of zeros is the exterior of the open unit ball centered at the origin.

12.4   Describe the set $\{(e^t \cos(t), e^t \sin(t)) : t \in \mathbf{R}\}$. Is this set a regular one-dimensional submanifold of $\mathbf{R}^2$?

12.5   Describe the set $\{(t, \sin(1/t)) : t > 0\} \cup \{(0, t) : t \in \mathbf{R}\}$. Is this set a regular one-dimensional submanifold of $\mathbf{R}^2$?

12.6   If M is any subset of $\mathbf{R}^n$ and k any nonnegative integer, show that the set M_k of points $q \in M$ which have a neighborhood U and a map ϕ satisfying (i)–(iv) of Definition (12.6) for some fixed $N \geq 1$ is a regular k-dimensional C^N submanifold of **R**^{n}.

12.7 Show that if M_1 and M_2 are regular k-dimensional submanifolds of **R**^{n} and closure $(M_1) \cap$ closure $(M_2) = \varnothing$, then $M_1 \cup M_2$ is a regular k-dimensional submanifold of **R**^{n}.

12.8 Let M be a regular k-dimensional C^N submanifold of **R**^{n} ($N \geq 1$). Definition: A function $f \colon M \to \mathbf{R}$ is differentiable of class C^N if and only if for each triple U, ϕ, V satisfying conditions (i)–(iv) of Definition (12.6) the function $f \circ \phi \colon V \to \mathbf{R}$ is C^N on V. Show in this case that each $q \in M$ has a neighborhood W with a C^N function $F \colon W \to \mathbf{R}$ such that $F(p) = f(p)$, $p \in W \cap M$.

12.9 Suppose that U is an open subset of **R**^{n} and that the map $\phi \colon U \to \mathbf{R}^n$ has rank n at every point $q \in U$. Show that $\phi(U)$ is open in **R**^{n}.

12.10 Suppose that U is an open subset of **R**^{k} and that the map $\phi \colon U \to \mathbf{R}^n$ has rank k at each point $q \in U$.

(a) Show that each point $p \in U$ has an open neighborhood U_p such that $\phi(U_p)$ is a regular k-dimensional submanifold of **R**^{n}.

(b) Show that $\phi(U)$ is a countable union of regular k-dimensional submanifolds of **R**^{n}. [HINT: See Exercise 2.16.]

(c) (This part is more difficult than the usual exercise.) Show that if $n > k$, $\phi(U)$ does not have any interior points. [HINT: A subset E or **R**^{n} is called nowhere dense if closure (E) does not have any interior points. A regular k-dimensional ($k < n$) submanifold M is nowhere dense. Show that an open subset of **R**^{n} cannot be the union of a countable number of nowhere dense sets by imitating the argument outlined in Exercise 3.10 with $\{p_1, \ldots, p_k\}$ there replaced by the union $N_1 \cup N_2 \cup \cdots \cup N_k$ of the first k nowhere dense sets. To complete the proof of (c) use part (b) above.]

CHAPTER THREE

Vectors and Covectors

13 Vectors

A *vector at* p is an operator X_p of the form

$$(13.0) \qquad X_p = b^1 \frac{\partial}{\partial x^1}\Big|_p + \cdots + b^n \frac{\partial}{\partial x^n}\Big|_p$$

($|_p$ indicates evaluation at p) whose domain is the set of all functions f which are C^1 at p.

$$X_p f = b^1 \frac{\partial f}{\partial x^1}(p) + \cdots + b^n \frac{\partial f}{\partial x^n}(p).$$

If $x^1, \ldots, x^n$ are the coordinate functions used in (13.0), the preceding equation shows that $X_p x^j = b^j$, so that

$$X_p f = (X_p x^1) \frac{\partial f}{\partial x^1}(p) + \cdots + (X_p x^n) \frac{\partial f}{\partial x^n}(p).$$

X_p satisfies the two relations

$$(13.1) \qquad X_p(af + bg) = a X_p f + b X_p g, \qquad a, b \text{ constants},$$

and

$$(13.2) \qquad X_p(fg) = (X_p f)g(p) + f(p)(X_p g).$$

It is an automatic consequence of (13.1) and (13.2) above that if C is a constant, $C X_p C = X_p C^2 = C X_p C + (X_p C)C = 2C \cdot X_p C$; so $X_p C = 0$. More can be said: If J_p is any operator on those functions which are C^{k+1} ($k \geq 0$) at p satisfying

$$J_p(af + bg) = a J_p f + b J_p g$$

and

$$J_p(fg) = (J_p f)g(p) + f(p)(J_p g),$$

there is a unique vector X_p at p such that $J_p f = X_p f$ whenever f is C^{k+2} at p. Thus equations (13.1) and (13.2) are almost characteristic of vectors at p. The argument for this last assertion is based on the observation that

$$\textbf{(13.3)} \qquad f(q) = f(p) + \sum_{k=1}^{n} [x^k(q) - x^k(p)] \left[\frac{\partial f}{\partial x^k}(p) + R_k(q) \right]$$

where

$$R_k(q) = \int_0^1 \left\{ \frac{\partial f}{\partial x^k} [p + t(q - p)] - \frac{\partial f}{\partial x^k}(p) \right\} dt$$

whenever f is C^1 on $B_r(p)$ and $q \in B_r(p)$. If J_p is now applied to both sides of (13.3) and it is observed (i) that

$$J_p[f(p)] = J_p[x^k(p)] = J_p \left[\frac{\partial f}{\partial x^k}(p) \right] = 0$$

because J_p applied to a constant function is zero, and (ii) that R_k is C^{k+1} on $B_r(q)$ when f is C^{k+2} there, the result obtained is

$$J_p f = \sum_{k=1}^{n} (J_p x^k) \left[\frac{\partial f}{\partial x^k}(p) + R_k(p) \right] + \sum_{k=1}^{n} [x^k(p) - x^k(p)][J_p R_k]$$

$$= \sum_{k=1}^{n} (J_p x^k) \frac{\partial f}{\partial x^k}(p).$$

Thus

$$X_p = (J_p x^1) \frac{\partial}{\partial x^1}\bigg|_p + \cdots + (J_p x^n) \frac{\partial}{\partial x^n}\bigg|_p$$

is the only vector for which $X_p f = J_p f$ whenever f is C^{k+2} at p.

The sum $X_p + Y_p$ of two vectors at p is a vector at p, $(X_p + Y_p)f = X_p f + Y_p f$, and a scalar multiple aX_p of a vector at p is a vector at p, $(aX_p)f = a(X_p f)$. With this addition and scalar multiplication the vectors at p form an n-dimensional vector space naturally isomorphic with the space of n-tuples $(b^1, \ldots, b^n)$ through the association (13.0), usually called the tangent space to $\mathbf{R}^n$ at p and denoted by $T_p(\mathbf{R}^n)$.

(13.4) Example. If the curve $C: (-1, 1) \to \mathbf{R}^n$ is C^1 at 0, the vector $C'(0)$ defined by

$$C'(0)f = \frac{df \circ C}{dt}\bigg|_{t=0} = \sum_{k=1}^{n} \frac{dx^k \circ C}{dt}(0) \frac{\partial f}{\partial x^k}[C(0)]$$

is called the *tangent vector* to the curve C at 0.

$$C'(0) = \sum_{k=1}^{n} \frac{dx^k \circ C}{dt}(0) \frac{\partial}{\partial x^k}\bigg|_{C(0)}.$$

In particular if $C(t)$ has the coordinate representation $x^i \circ C(t) = x^i(p) + tb^i$, then it is easy to compute that

$$C'(0) = b^1 \frac{\partial}{\partial x^1}\Big|_p + \cdots + b^n \frac{\partial}{\partial x^n}\Big|_p$$

and consequently every vector in $T_p(\mathbf{R}^n)$ can be realized as the tangent vector $C'(0)$ to some curve C at 0. If $C(t) = p + t(q - p)$, the tangent vector

$$C'(0) = \sum_{k=1}^{n} [x^k(q) - x^k(p)] \frac{\partial}{\partial x^k}\Big|_p$$

is often represented graphically by an arrow from p to q.

Suppose $C: (-1, 1) \to U$ is a curve in U and $\phi: U \to \mathbf{R}^n$ is a C^1 map of the open set U of $\mathbf{R}^n$ into $\mathbf{R}^m$. Then $\phi \circ C$ is a curve in $\mathbf{R}^m$ whose tangent vector at 0 operates on a differentiable function g in $\mathbf{R}^m$ according to the prescription

$$(\phi \circ C)'(0)g = \frac{d}{dt} g \circ \phi \circ C \Big|_{t=0} = C'(0)(g \circ \phi).$$

Taking this observation, let X_p be a vector at $p \in U$. The *image of X_p under ϕ* is a vector at $\phi(p)$ denoted by $\phi_*(X_p)$ and defined by

(13.5) $$\phi_*(X_p)g = X_p \cdot g \circ \phi$$

whenever g is C^1 at $\phi(p)$. If the curve C has tangent vector X_p at 0, then $\phi_*(X_p)$ is just the tangent vector to the curve $\phi \circ C$ at 0.

(13.6) **Example.** Suppose $y^1, \ldots, y^m$ is a system of coordinates for the open set $U \subset \mathbf{R}^m$; $x^1, \ldots, x^n$ is a system of coordinates for the open set $V \subset \mathbf{R}^n$; $\phi: U \to V$ is C^1; and X_p is a vector at $p \in U$. Then according to the chain rule if g is differentiable on V,

$$\phi_*(X_p)g = X_p(g \circ \phi) = \sum_{j=1}^{n} (X_p y^j) \frac{\partial g \circ \phi}{\partial y^j}(p)$$

$$= \sum_{j=1}^{n} \sum_{k=1}^{n} (X_p y^j) \frac{\partial x^k \circ \phi}{\partial y^j}(p) \frac{\partial g}{\partial x^k}[\phi(p)].$$

In operator notation

(13.7) $$\phi_*(X_p) = \sum_{j=1}^{n} \sum_{k=1}^{n} (X_p y^j) \frac{\partial x^k \circ \phi}{\partial y^j}(p) \frac{\partial}{\partial x^k}\Big|_{\phi(p)}.$$

(13.8) **Example.** A particularly simple example of (13.7) has already been exhibited. If $\partial/\partial t|_0$ denotes the vector at 0 in $\mathbf{R}^1$ defined by

$$\frac{\partial}{\partial t}\Big|_0 f = \frac{df}{dt}(0)$$

where t is the cartesian coordinate variable for $\mathbf{R}^1$, and $C: (-1, 1) \to \mathbf{R}^n$ is C^1; then the tangent vector to the curve C at 0 is just

$$C_*\left(\frac{\partial}{\partial t}\Big|_0\right) = C'(0).$$

The euclidean *length* of the vector X_p at $p \in U$ is the number $|X_p|$ defined by

(13.9)
$$|X_p| = \{(X_p x^1)^2 + \cdots + (X_p x^n)^2\}^{1/2}$$

where $x^1, \ldots, x^n$ are cartesian coordinates for U. Closely associated with the notion of length is the euclidean *scalar product* (or dot product) of two vectors X_p and Y_p. This scalar product (X_p, Y_p) is defined by

(13.10)
$$(X_p, Y_p) = \sum_{j=1}^{n} (X_p x^j)(Y_p x^j)$$

where, as in (13.9), it is essential that $x^1, \ldots, x^n$ are cartesian coordinates. The relation between the scalar product and length is

$$|X_p|^2 = (X_p, X_p).$$

The angle θ between two vectors X_p and Y_p at p is defined by the two conditions:

(13.11)
    (1) $0 \leq \theta \leq \pi$;

    (2) $(X_p, Y_p) = |X_p| |Y_p| \cos \theta.$

Exercises

13.1 The vector X_p is said to be *tangent* to the level surface $S = \{q : f(q) = f(p), p \text{ fixed}\}$ of the function f at p if $X_p f = 0$.

(a) Find all vectors tangent to the sphere $(x^1)^2 + (x^2)^2 + (x^3)^2 = 1$ at the point $(1, 0, 0)$.

(b) Find all vectors tangent to the paraboloid $x^3 = (x^1)^2 + (x^2)^2$ at the point $(1, 2, 5)$.

13.2 Suppose $x^1, \ldots, x^n$ are cartesian coordinates for $\mathbf{R}^n$ and the curve $C: (0, \infty) \to \mathbf{R}^n$ is described by $x^1 \circ C(t) = t$, $x^2 \circ C(t) = (t)^2, \ldots, x^n \circ C(t) = (t)^n$. Find tangent vector $X_{C(t_0)} = C_*(\partial/\partial t |_{t_0})$ to C at $C(t_0)$ in terms of $\partial/\partial x^1 |_{C(t_0)}, \ldots, \partial/\partial x^n |_{C(t_0)}$. Calculate $|X_{C(t_0)}|$ and find the cosine of the angle between $X_{C(t_0)}$ and $\partial/\partial x^3 |_{C(t_0)}$.

13.3 Let x^1, x^2, x^3 be a coordinate system for $\mathbf{R}^3$ and y^1, y^2 a coordinate system for $\mathbf{R}^2$. Let the map $\phi : \mathbf{R}^3 \to \mathbf{R}^2$ be given by

$$y^1 \circ \phi = x^1 x^3; \qquad y^2 \circ \phi = (x^1)^2 + x^2 x^3.$$

(a) Find the vector $Z = \phi_* (\partial/\partial x^1 |_{(1,2,-1)})$ and evaluate Zf where $f = y^1 \sin y^2$.

(b) Find all vectors $X = a (\partial/\partial x^1) + b (\partial/\partial x^2) + c (\partial/\partial x^3)$ at $(0, 1, 0)$ such that $\phi_*(X) = 0$.

13.4 Show that $(\partial/\partial x^i |_p, X_p) = X_p x^i$ when $x^1, \ldots, x^n$ are cartesian coordinates.

13.5 Suppose x^1, x^2, x^3 are cartesian coordinates in $\mathbf{R}^3$ and $z^1 = x^1 + x^2$, $z^2 = x^1 - x^2$, $z^3 = x^1 + x^2 + x^3$, so that the z's form a coordinate system too. Find vectors Y_1, Y_2, and Y_3 such that $(\partial/\partial z^i, Y_j) = \delta_{ij}$.

13.6   Prove that the scalar product satisfies

(i) $(X_p + Y_p, Z_p) = (X_p, Z_p) + (Y_p, Z_p)$.
(ii) $(aX_p, Z_p) = a(X_p, Z_p)$.
(iii) $(X_p, Z_p) = (Z_p, X_p)$.
(iv) $(X_p, X_p) > 0$ unless $X_p = 0$.

13.7   If $u^1, \ldots, u^n$ is a coordinate system for $\mathbf{R}^n$ and $Y_1, \ldots, Y_n$ are vectors (at p) satisfying $(\partial/\partial u^i, Y_j) = \delta_{ij}$, show that

$$X = \sum_{m=1}^{n} (X, Y_m) \frac{\partial}{\partial u^m}$$

for each vector X at p.

13.8   Under the hypothesis of Exercise 13.7 note that

$$Y_m = \sum_{k=1}^{n} (Y_m, Y_k) \frac{\partial}{\partial u^k}$$

and use this to show that

$$\sum_{k=1}^{n} (Y_m, Y_k) \left(\frac{\partial}{\partial u^k}, \frac{\partial}{\partial u^j} \right) = \delta_{mj}.$$

That is, the matrices $[(Y_m, Y_k)]$ and $[(\partial/\partial u^k, \partial/\partial u^i)]$ are inverses of each other.

13.9   Show that if $u^1, \ldots, u^n$ is a coordinate system for $\mathbf{R}^n$ then det $[(\partial/\partial u^i, \partial/\partial u^i)] \neq 0$ at p, and use this to show that there exist vectors $Y_1, \ldots, Y^n$ at p such that $(\partial/\partial u^i, Y_j) = \delta_{ij}$. [HINT: Define Y_k as suggested by the results of Exercise 13.8.]

13.10   If $\phi: U \to V$ and $\psi: V \to W$ show that $(\psi \circ \phi)_*(X_p) = \psi_*[\phi_*(X_p)]$ for each $X_p \in T_p(\mathbf{R}^n)$, $p \in U$. In particular if $C: (-1, 1) \to U$ is a curve in U and $\phi: U \to V$, show that the tangent vector $(\phi \circ C)'(t)$ to the curve $\phi \circ C$ at t is just $\phi_*\{C'(t)\}$.

13.11   (The Gram-Schmidt orthonormalization process.) If $X_1, \ldots, X_k$ are linearly independent vectors at p define the vectors $Y_1, \ldots, Y_k$ recursively as follows:

$$Y_1 = \|X_1\|^{-1}X_1; \qquad Y_{j+1} = \|Z_{j+1}\|^{-1}Z_{j+1},$$

where

$$Z_{j+1} = X_{j+1} - \sum_{i=1}^{j} (X_{j+1}, Y_i) Y_i.$$

(a) Show that the vectors $Y_1, \ldots, Y_k$ are orthonormal. That is, show that $(Y_i, Y_j) = \delta_{ij}, 1 \leq i, j \leq k$.

(b) Show that $X_j = \sum_{i=1}^{j} (X_j, Y_i) Y_i, 1 \leq j \leq k$, so that $Y_1, \ldots, Y_j$ span the same subspace of $T_p(R^n)$ as $X_1, \ldots, X_j$.

(c) If

$$X_1 = \frac{\partial}{\partial x^1} - \frac{\partial}{\partial x^2} + 3\frac{\partial}{\partial x^3},$$

$$X^2 = \frac{\partial}{\partial x^1} + \frac{\partial}{\partial x^2} + \frac{\partial}{\partial x^3},$$

$$X^3 = \frac{\partial}{\partial x^2} + \frac{\partial}{\partial x^3},$$

with evaluation at p being understood, find Y_1, Y_2, and Y_3.

14 Vector fields

A *vector field* X *on the open set* $U \subset \mathbf{R}^n$ is a map $p \to X_p$ which assigns to each point $p \in U$ a vector X_p at p. If $x^1, \ldots, x^n$, denote cartesian coordinate functions for $\mathbf{R}^n$,

$$X_p = b^1(p) \left. \frac{\partial}{\partial x^1} \right|_p + \cdots + b^n(p) \left. \frac{\partial}{\partial x^n} \right|_p, \qquad p \in U.$$

The vector field $p \to X_p$ is a C^k *vector field on* U if all the functions $b^1, \ldots, b^n$ are C^k on U.

The sum $X + Y$ of two vector fields and the product fX of a vector field by a function on the left are again vector fields defined in the natural manner. The notation Xf is reserved to denote the function $(Xf)(q) = X_q f$ defined whenever f is C^1 on U.

Exercises

In the first two exercises below x^1, x^2, x^3 are cartesian coodinates for R^3 and U is the set

$$U = \{p \in \mathbf{R}^3 \colon x^1(p) > 0 \text{ or } x^2(p) \neq 0\}.$$

14.1 (Cylindrical coordinates.) The three functions, r, θ, z defined on U by $x^1 = r \cos \theta$; $x^2 = r \sin \theta$; $x^3 = z$; $-\pi < \theta < \pi$; and $r > 0$ form a coordinate system for U. Show that $(\partial/\partial r, \partial/\partial r) = 1$; $(\partial/\partial r, \partial/\partial \theta) = 0$; $(\partial/\partial r, \partial/\partial z) = 0$; $(\partial/\partial \theta, \partial/\partial \theta) = r^2$; $(\partial/\partial \theta, \partial/\partial z) = 0$; $(\partial/\partial z, \partial/\partial z) = 1$ on U.

14.2 (Spherical coordinates.) The three functions ρ, θ, ϕ defined on U by $x^1 = \rho \cos \theta \sin \phi$; $x^2 = \rho \sin \theta \sin \phi$; $x^3 = \rho \cos \phi$; $-\pi < \theta < \pi$; $\rho > 0$; and $0 < \phi < \pi$ form a coordinate system for U. Show that $(\partial/\partial \rho, \partial/\partial \rho) = \rho^2 \sin^2 \phi$, $(\partial/\partial \phi, \partial/\partial \phi) = \rho^2$, and the other scalar products are zero.

14.3 (a) If X and Y are C^1 vector fields on the open set U in $\mathbf{R}^n$ and Z_p is the operator $f \to Z_p f = X_p(Yf) - Y_p(Xf)$, show that Z_p satisfies (13.1) and (13.2) whenever f and g are C^2 on U, and hence that Z_p determines a unique vector at p. The vector field Z determined at each $p \in U$ in this manner is denoted by $Z = [X, Y]$. It is a C^0 vector field.

(b) If

$$X = \sum_{j=1}^n (Xx^j) \frac{\partial}{\partial x^j} \quad \text{and} \quad Y = \sum_{i=1}^n (Yx^i) \frac{\partial}{\partial x^i},$$

find the components of $Z = [X, Y]$ in terms of the Xx^j and the Yx^i.

(c) If

$$X = \sin x^1 \frac{\partial}{\partial x^1} - \cos x^2 \frac{\partial}{\partial x^2}$$

and

$$Y = e^{x^1} \frac{\partial}{\partial x^1} + x^1 \frac{\partial}{\partial x^2},$$

find $[X, Y]$.

15 Covectors

A *covector* ω_p *at* p is a linear map $X_p \rightarrow \omega_p(X_p)$ whose domain is the space $T_p(\mathbf{R}^n)$ of vectors at p and whose values are real numbers. The linearity means

(**15.1**) $$\omega_p(aX_p + bY_p) = a\omega_p(X_p) + b\omega_p(Y_p).$$

The simplest example of a covector is the covector $(df)_p$ called the *gradient* of f at p and sometimes written $(\text{grad } f)_p$, and defined whenever f is C^1 at p by the equation

(**15.2**) $$(df)_p(X_p) = X_p f.$$

The sum of two covectors α_p and ω_p at p and the scalar multiple $a\omega_p$ of ω_p by the constant a are defined in the natural manner by

$$(\omega_p + \alpha_p)(X_p) = \omega_p(X_p) + \alpha_p(X_p)$$

and

$$(a\omega_p)(X_p) = a\omega_p(X_p).$$

With this addition and scalar multiplication the covectors at p form a vector space $T_p^*(\mathbf{R}^n)$. If ω_p is applied to the equation

(**15.3**) $$X_p = (X_p x^1) \frac{\partial}{\partial x^1}\Big|_p + \cdots + (X_p x^n) \frac{\partial}{\partial x^n}\Big|_p$$

and (15.2) is used to change $X_p x^k$ to $(dx^k)_p(X_p)$, (15.3) becomes

(**15.4**) $$\omega_p(X_p) = \omega_p\left(\frac{\partial}{\partial x^1}\Big|_p\right)(dx^1)_p(X_p) + \cdots + \omega_p\left(\frac{\partial}{\partial x^n}\Big|_p\right)(dx^n)_p(X_p).$$

Since (15.4) holds for every vector X_p at p, it can be restated as

(**15.5**) $$\omega_p = \omega_p\left(\frac{\partial}{\partial x^1}\Big|_p\right)(dx^1)_p + \cdots + \omega_p\left(\frac{\partial}{\partial x^n}\Big|_p\right)(dx^n)_p,$$

showing that $(dx^1)_p, \ldots, (dx^n)_p$ span the linear space $T_p^*(\mathbf{R}^n)$. It is worth noting at the present time that according to (15.5)

$$(df)_p = \sum_{m=1}^{n} (df)_p\left(\frac{\partial}{\partial x^m}\Big|_p\right)(dx^m)_p$$

or, since $(df)_p(\partial/\partial x^m |_p) = (\partial f/\partial x^m)(p)$,

(**15.6**) $$(df)_p = \sum_{m=1}^{n} \frac{\partial f}{\partial x^m}(p)(dx^m)_p,$$

which certainly has a familiar ring.

If $\phi: U \rightarrow \mathbf{R}^n$ is a C^1 map of the open set U of $\mathbf{R}^n$ into $\mathbf{R}^n$ and $\omega_{\phi(p)}$ is a covector at $\phi(p)$, $p \in U$, then $\phi^*\{\omega_{\phi(p)}\}$ is the covector at p defined by

$$\phi_*\{\omega_{\phi(p)}\}(X_p) = \omega_{\phi(p)}(\phi_*[X_p]).$$

In particular,

(15.7) $\qquad \phi^*([df]_{\phi(p)})(X_p) = (df)_{\phi(p)}\phi_*(X_p) = \phi_*(X_p)f = X_p(f \circ \phi)$

$$= [d(f \circ \phi)]_p(X_p),$$

which, if ϕ^*f is defined by $\phi^*f(p) = f \circ \phi(p)$, can be abbreviated $\phi^*d = d\phi^*$. Note that ϕ^* and ϕ_* carry objects in opposite directions.

(15.8) **Example.** Suppose $y^1, \ldots, y^m$ is a system of coordinates for the open set $U \subset \mathbf{R}^m$; $x^1, \ldots, x^n$ is a system of coordinates for the open set $V \subset \mathbf{R}^n$; $\phi: U \to V$ is C^1; and $\omega_p = C_1(dx^1)_p + \cdots + C_n(dx^n)_p$ is a covector at $q = \phi(p)$. Then

(15.9) $\qquad \phi^*(\omega_q) = \displaystyle\sum_{k=1}^{n} C_k \phi^*(dx^k)_p = \sum_{k=1}^{n} C_k[d(x^k \circ \phi)]_p$

$$= \sum_{k=1}^{n} C_k \sum_{j=1}^{m} \frac{\partial x^k \circ \phi}{\partial y_j}(dy^i)_p.$$

(15.10) **Example.** There is an important manner in which covectors can be obtained from vectors. If Y_p is a vector at p, the map

(15.11) $\qquad\qquad X_p \to (X_p, Y_p), \qquad X_p \in T_p(\mathbf{R}^n)$

is a covector at p. Moreover every covector at p can be obtained in this way.

(15.12) **Theorem.** For each covector $\omega_p \in T^*(\mathbf{R}^n)$ there is a unique vector Y_p such that

(15.13) $\qquad\qquad (X_p, Y_p) = \omega_p(X_p), \qquad X_p \in T_p(\mathbf{R}^n),$

and conversely for fixed $Y_p \in T_p$ the left side of (15.13) defines a unique covector ω_p. The correspondence $Y_p \leftrightarrow \omega_p$ is a linear isomorphism between $T_p(\mathbf{R}^n)$ and $T_p^*(\mathbf{R}^n)$ and this relationship is denoted in the future by $Y_p = \omega_p^{\#}$ or $\omega_p = Y_p^{\#}$.

PROOF. The theorem is proved by the two formulas

$$Y_p = \omega_p^{\#} = \sum_{j=1}^{n} \omega_p\left(\frac{\partial}{\partial x^j}\bigg|_p\right)\frac{\partial}{\partial x^j}\bigg|_p;$$

(15.14)

$$\omega_p = Y_p^{\#} = \sum_{k=1}^{n}\left(\frac{\partial}{\partial x^j}\bigg|_p, Y_p\right)(dx^j)_p,$$

in which $x^1, \ldots, x^n$ are cartesian coordinates. To check the first, if

Y_p is given by (15.14),

$$(X_p, Y_p) = \left(X_p, \sum_{j=1}^{n} \omega_p \left(\frac{\partial}{\partial x^j}\Big|_p\right) \frac{\partial}{\partial x^j}\Big|_p\right)$$

$$= \sum_{j=1}^{n} \omega_p \left(\frac{\partial}{\partial x^j}\Big|_p\right) \left(X_p, \frac{\partial}{\partial x^j}\Big|_p\right)$$

$$= \sum_{j=1}^{n} \omega_p \left(\frac{\partial}{\partial x^j}\Big|_p\right) X_p x^j = \omega_p(X_p).$$

If Y'_p were another vector satisfying (15.13) then

$$|Y_p - Y'_p|^2 = (Y_p - Y'_p, Y_p) - (Y_p - Y'_p, Y'_p)$$
$$= \omega_p(Y_p - Y'_p) - \omega_p(Y_p - Y'_p) = 0;$$

so $Y_p = Y'_p$, establishing the uniqueness. The converse is proved similarly. ◆

The results of Theorem (15.12) can be exploited to define a scalar product for covectors, using one of the three equalities

(**15.15**) $$(\omega_p, \alpha_p) = (\omega_p^\#, \alpha_p^\#)$$

$$= \omega_p(\alpha_p^\#)$$

$$= \alpha_p(\omega_p^\#).$$

All three of these possibilities yield the same value for (ω_p, α_p). If x^1, $\ldots$, x^n are cartesian coordinates, since $(dx^j)^\# = \partial/\partial x^j|_p$ it follows that

(**15.16**) $$([dx^i]_p, [dx^j]_p) = \delta^{ij}.$$

The vector-space isomorphism $\#\colon T_p(\mathbf{R}^n) \to T_p^*(\mathbf{R}^n)$ and its inverse (which is also denoted by $\#$) is sometimes used to eliminate the concept of covector. If this choice is made, the gradient of the function f is the vector field $(df)^\#$ rather than the covector field df, and all other covector concepts are changed accordingly. Although conceptually sound, this procedure has difficulties of the following sort: If $\phi\colon U \to V$ is a differentiable map of U into V and f is a function on V, then it is reasonable to consider f on V and $f \circ \phi$ on U as corresponding objects and by extension the vector field $d(f \circ \phi)^\#$, representing the gradient of $f \circ C$, should transform into $(df)^\#$ under the map ϕ_* used to transform vectors at p into vectors at $\phi(p)$. In general this does not happen, as the following example shows.

(**15.17**) **Example.** Suppose $\phi\colon (-1, 1) \to (0, 6)$ is given by $x \circ \phi = 3x + 3$. Then if $f(p) = x(p)$, $p \in (0, 6)$, $f \circ \phi = 3x + 3$ on $(-1, 1)$. Calculations show that $d(f \circ \phi) = 3\,dx$; $[d(f \circ \phi)]^\# = 3\,\partial/\partial x$. ($x$ is a cartesian coordinate variable.)

Now the vector $\partial/\partial x \,|_t$ is transformed by ϕ_* into the vector

$$\phi_* \left(\frac{\partial}{\partial x}\Big|_t \right) = \frac{\partial}{\partial x} (3x + 3) \frac{\partial}{\partial x}\Big|_{3t+3} = 3 \frac{\partial}{\partial x}\Big|_{3t+3}.$$

Consequently, $\phi_* \{ [d(f \circ \phi)]^{\#} \} = 9 \, \partial/\partial x$ on $(0, 6)$. On the other hand $(df)^{\#} = (dx)^{\#} = \partial/\partial x$ on $(0, 6)$.

To handle this situation one must realize that (1) either one must give up the correspondence between $d(f \circ \phi)^{\#}$ and $(df)^{\#}$ or (2) one must recognize two kinds of vectors, those transforming like $\partial/\partial x$ (contravariant) and those transforming like $(dg)^{\#}$ (covariant). In the second approach it is forbidden to add two vectors of different types so that the transformation rules will remain manageable.

In this book the first approach is taken, and the quantities which are alternatively treated as covariant vectors are treated here as covectors transforming according to ϕ^*. The gradient is a covector and $d(f \circ \phi) = \phi^* \, df$, so that $d(f \circ \phi)$ and df do indeed correspond under the right transformation rules.

Exercises

15.1   If $f = e^{x^1} \sin x^2$ and $X_p = 3 \, \partial/\partial x^1 \,|_p + \partial/\partial x^2 \,|_p$, compute $(df)_p(X_p)$ when $x^1(p) = 3$, $x^2(p) = \pi/3$.

15.2   Suppose z^1, z^2, z^3 are coordinates for $\mathbf{R}^3$ and x^1, x^2 for $\mathbf{R}^2$. Let $\phi : \mathbf{R}^3 \to \mathbf{R}^2$ be the map described by $x^1 \circ \phi = z^1 z^2 + z^3$; $x^2 \circ \phi = (z^1)^2 z^3$. Compute $\phi^*(dx^1 + 3dx^2)$ at the point p when $z^1(p) = 1$, $z^2(p) = 0$, $z^3(p) = -2$.

15.3   (a) Suppose

$$X_1 = 3 \frac{\partial}{\partial x^1} - \frac{\partial}{\partial x^2} \; ; \quad X_2 = \frac{\partial}{\partial x^2} + \frac{\partial}{\partial x^3} \; ; \quad X_3 = \frac{\partial}{\partial x^1} + \frac{\partial}{\partial x^3} \cdot$$

Find covectors ω^1, ω^2, ω^3 such that $\omega^i(x_j) = \delta^i_j$. (Evaluation at p is understood here but left out of the notation because the answer does not depend on p in this case.)

(b) Using these ω's, show that $Y = \omega^1(Y)X_1 + \omega^2(Y)X_2 + \omega^3(Y)X_3$ for any vector Y at p.

15.4   Show $[d(fg)]_p = f(p)(dg)_p + g(p)(df)_p$ in two ways, first using (15.6) and then using (13.2) and (15.2).

15.5   If $\phi : U \to V$ and $\psi : V \to W$, show that $(\psi \circ \phi)\omega_q = \phi^*[\psi^*(\omega_q)]$ for each $\omega_q \in T_q^*(\mathbf{R}^n)$, $q \in W$. This can be done using (15.9) or using the equation that precedes (15.7) and Exercise 13.10.

15.6   Suppose f is C^1 on U and $(df)_p \neq 0$. The vector X_p is *tangent* to the hypersurface $\{q : f(q) = f(p)\}$ at p if $(df)_p(X_p) = 0$, that is, if $X_p f = 0$. Show that the set M_p of vectors tangent to the hypersurface with equation $f = f(p)$ at p is an $(n-1)$-dimensional subspace of $T_p(\mathbf{R}^n)$.

15.7   (a) Suppose that $X_1, \ldots, X_n$ span $T_p(\mathbf{R}^n)$. Show that there are covectors $\omega^1, \ldots, \omega^n$ in $T_p^*(\mathbf{R}^n)$ such that $\omega^i(x_j) = \delta_j^i$ and that

$$Y = \sum_{m=1}^{n} \omega^m(Y)X_m$$

for each $Y \in T_p(\mathbf{R}^n)$.

(b) Show that $\omega^1, \ldots, \omega^n$ are linearly independent and hence form a basis for the n-dimensional space $T_p^*(\mathbf{R}^n)$.

15.8 The vector X_p is normal to the level surface of h at p if $(X_p, Y_p) = 0$ for each Y_p which is tangent to the hypersurface $\{q : h(q) = h(p)\}$ at p. Show that $(dh_p)^\#$ is normal to the level surface of h at p.

15.9 Show that $(dx^1)_p, \ldots, (dx^n)_p$ are linearly independent if $x^1, \ldots, x^n$ is a coordinate system in some neighborhood of p.

15.10 Show that if $y^1, \ldots, y^n$ is a coordinate system for $U \subset \mathbf{R}^3$ then any vector field X on U can be written as

$$X = \sum_{k=1}^{n} (X^\#, dy^k) \frac{\partial}{\partial y^k}.$$

15.11 If $y^1, \ldots, y^n$ is a coordinate system for $U \subset \mathbf{R}^3$ show that the $n \times n$ matrices $a_{ij} = (\partial/\partial y^i, \partial/\partial y^j)$ and $b_{ij} = (dy^i, dy^j)$ are inverses of each other at every point of U.

15.12 Using Exercise 15.11, show that if ρ, σ, ϕ are spherical coordinates for $\mathbf{R}^3$, then $(d\rho, d\rho) = 1$; $(d\theta, d\theta) = \{\rho \sin \phi\}^{-2}$; $(d\phi, d\phi) = \rho^{-2}$, and that all other scalar products between two of the covectors $d\rho, d\theta, d\phi$ are zero.

CHAPTER FOUR

Elements of Multilinear Algebra

16 Introduction

This chapter is primarily algebraic in nature, treating the exterior algebra of a finite-dimensional vector space V together with its dual space V^*.

If V is an n-dimensional vector space over the field of real numbers the space V^* of linear maps of V into $\mathbf{R}$ is called the dual of V. The sum $w^* + v^*$ of two elements of V^* and multiplication of v^* by the scalar $a \in \mathbf{R}$ are defined in the natural manner as maps by

(16.1)
$$(w^* + v^*)(v) = w^*(v) + v^*(v), \qquad v \in V;$$
$$(av^*)(v) = a[v^*(v)], \qquad v \in V.$$

With this addition and scalar multiplication V^* is a linear space (vector space), and in keeping with the applications intended for this section the elements of V will be called *vectors* and those of V^* *covectors*.

If $e_1, \ldots, e_n$ is a basis for V, each $v \in V$ is uniquely expressible as a linear combination of the e_j's,

(16.2)
$$v = a^1 e_1 + \cdots + a^n e_n, \qquad a^k \in \mathbf{R} \text{ all } k,$$

and if $f_1, \ldots, f_n$ are elements of another linear space W there is precisely one linear map $\phi: V \to W$ for which $\phi(e_k) = f_k$, $k = 1, 2, \ldots, n$. If v is given by (16.2),

$$\phi(v) = a^1 f_1 + \cdots + a^n f_n.$$

As an application of this result, suppose k is fixed and $W = \mathbf{R}$. Let e^k be the linear map of $V \to \mathbf{R}$ determined by $e^k(e_j) = \delta_j^k$. $e^k \in V^*$ and the set $\{e^1, \ldots, e^n\}$ constitutes a basis for V^* called the *dual basis* to $e_1, \ldots, e_n$. The proof is deferred until Theorem (16.11).

(16.3) **Example.** The covectors $(dx^1), \ldots, (dx^n)_p$ are a basis for $T_p^*(\mathbf{R}^n)$, which is dual to the basis $\partial/\partial x^1 \big|_p, \ldots, \partial/\partial x^n \big|_p$ of $T_p(\mathbf{R}^n)$.

A *k-covector* is a map

$$(v_1, \ldots, v_k) \to \omega(v_1, \ldots, v_k)$$

of (ordered) k-tuples of vectors into **R** which satisfies two relations:
(1) It is multilinear in the sense that for each m the map

(16.4) $$v_m \to (v_1, \ldots, v_{m-1}, v_m, v_{m+1}, \ldots, v_k)$$

is linear when $v_1, \ldots, v_{m-1}, v_{m+1}, \ldots, v_k$ are fixed vectors in V.
(2) It is alternating or skew-symmetric, which means

(16.5) $$\omega(v_1, \ldots, v_i, \ldots, v_j, \ldots, v_k)$$

$$= -\omega(v_1, \ldots, v_j, \ldots, v_i, \ldots, v_k),$$

so that ω changes sign when two arguments are interchanged.

It is worthwhile recalling at this point some properties of permutations of integers. Denote by S_k the set of permutations σ of the integers 1, 2, ..., k. Each $\sigma \in S_k$ is a one-one map of the set $\{1, 2, \ldots, k\}$ onto itself and is completely described by the ordered k-tuple $(\sigma(1), \sigma(2), \ldots, \sigma(k))$. S_k has $k!$ elements corresponding to the $k!$ such k-tuples. In a finite sequence of the type $\sigma(1), \sigma(2), \ldots, \sigma(k)$, each time that a larger integer precedes a smaller, $\sigma(i) > \sigma(j)$ when $i < j$, an inversion occurs in the natural order $1, 2, \ldots, k$. For example, the sequence 4 1 3 2 has four inversions and the sequence 1 3 4 2 two. A permutation σ is called *odd* or *even* according to whether the number of inversions in the sequence $\sigma(1), \ldots, \sigma(k)$ is odd or even, and the sign of a permutation, sign (σ), is $+1$ if σ is even and -1 if σ is odd.

An important consequence of (16.5) is that

(16.6) $$\omega(v_1, \ldots, v_k) = \text{sign } (\sigma)\omega(v_{\sigma(1)}, \ldots, v_{\sigma(k)}), \qquad \sigma \in S_k.$$

Before indicating why (16.6) is valid, consider as an illustration for the permutation 4 1 3 2,

$$\omega(v_1, v_2, v_3, v_4) = -\omega(v_1, v_2, v_4, v_3)$$

$$= \omega(v_1, v_4, v_2, v_3)$$

$$= -\omega(v_4, v_1, v_2, v_3)$$

$$= \omega(v_4, v_1, v_3, v_2)$$

where each term is obtained from the term which precedes it by applying (16.5) to interchange vectors in adjacent positions. In general (16.6) can be derived in the same manner by first moving $v_{\sigma(1)}$ to the first position by a sequence of adjacent interchanges each of which creates one inversion, then moving $v_{\sigma(2)}$ to the second position in the same manner, and continuing this until the expression sign $(\sigma)\omega(v_{\sigma(1)}, \ldots, v_{\sigma(k)})$ has been built up. Each adjacent interchange creates an inversion in the preceding order; so the number of steps needed to achieve this is just the number of inversions in $\sigma(1), \ldots, \sigma(k)$.

With the natural addition and scalar multiplication the k-covectors form a linear space denoted by $\wedge^k V^*$; the remainder of this section is devoted to finding a basis for this space. Among the observations which will prove useful is the following:

(16.7) Theorem. Suppose $e_1, \ldots, e_n$ is a basis for V. If ω_1 and ω_2 are both k-covectors and

(16.8) $\qquad \omega_1(e_{i_1}, \ldots, e_{i_k}) = \omega_2(e_{i_1}, \ldots, e_{i_k})$

$$\text{whenever } 1 \le i_1 < \cdots < i_k \le n,$$

then $\omega_1 = \omega_2$.

PROOF. First note that $\omega_1(e_{j_1}, \ldots, e_{j_k}) = \omega_2(e_{j_1}, \ldots, e_{j_k})$ for any $j_1, \ldots, j_k, 1 \le j_m \le n$. The reason is that both sides are zero if two of the j_m's are equal, and if no two are equal there is a permutation σ of the integers $1, \ldots, k$ such that $1 \le j_{\sigma(1)} < j_{\sigma(2)} < \cdots < j_{\sigma(k)} \le n$. Then (16.6) and (16.8) imply

(16.9) $\qquad \omega_1(e_{j_1}, \ldots, e_{j_k}) = \text{sign } (\sigma)\omega_1(e_{j_{\sigma(1)}}, \ldots, e_{j_{\sigma(k)}})$

$$= \text{sign } (\sigma)\omega_2(e_{j_{\sigma(1)}}, \ldots, e_{j_{\sigma(k)}})$$

$$= \omega_2(e_{j_1}, \ldots, e_{j_k}).$$

Next if

$$v_i = \sum_{m_i = 1}^{n} a_i^{m_i} e_{m_i},$$

then by the multilinearity and (16.9),

$$\omega_1(v_1, \ldots, v_k) = \sum_{m_1 = 1}^{n} \sum_{m_2 = 1}^{n} \cdots \sum_{m_k = 1}^{n} a_1^{m_1} \cdots a_k^{m_k} \omega_1(e_{m_1}, \ldots, e_{m_k})$$

$$= \sum_{m_1 = 1}^{n} \cdots \sum_{m_k = 1}^{n} a_1^{m_1} \cdots a_k^{m_k} \omega_2(e_{m_1}, \ldots, e_{m_k})$$

$$= \omega_2(v_1, \ldots, v_k),$$

concluding the proof. ◆

If $\alpha^1, \ldots, \alpha^k \in V^*$ the map

(16.10) $\qquad (v_1, \ldots, v_k) \to \dfrac{1}{k!} \det \begin{bmatrix} \alpha^1(v_1) & \cdots & \alpha^1(v_k) \\ \cdot & & \cdot \\ \cdot & & \cdot \\ \cdot & & \cdot \\ \alpha^k(v_1) & \cdots & \alpha^k(v_k) \end{bmatrix}$

is a k-covector which, anticipating later definitions, is denoted by

$$(\alpha^1 \wedge \cdots \wedge \alpha^k)(v_1, \ldots, v_k) = \frac{1}{k!} \det \{(\alpha^j(v_i))\}.$$

(16.11) Theorem. $e^1, \ldots, e^n$ is a basis for V^* dual to $e_1, \ldots, e_n$; the

$$\binom{n}{k} = \frac{n!}{k!(n-k)!}$$

k-covectors $(e^{i_1} \wedge \cdots \wedge e^{i_k})$, $1 \leq i_1 < \cdots < i_k \leq n$, form a basis for $\wedge^k V^*$. If ω is any k-covector,

(16.12) $$\omega = \sum_{i_1 < \cdots < i_k} k! \omega(e_{i_1}, \ldots, e_{i_k})(e^{i_1} \wedge \cdots \wedge e^{i_k}).$$

PROOF. If $1 \leq j_1 < \cdots < j_k \leq n$,

$$(e^{i_1} \wedge \cdots \wedge e^{i_k})(e_{j_1}, \ldots, e_{j_k}) = \frac{1}{k!} \det \begin{bmatrix} e^{i_1}(e_{j_1}) & \cdots & e^{i_k}(e_{j_k}) \\ \cdot & & \cdot \\ \cdot & & \cdot \\ \cdot & & \cdot \\ e^{i_k}(e_{j_1}) & \cdots & e^{i_k}(e_{j_k}) \end{bmatrix}$$

$$= \frac{1}{k!} \det \begin{bmatrix} \delta^{i_1}_{j_1} & \cdots & \delta^{i_1}_{j_k} \\ \cdot & & \cdot \\ \cdot & & \cdot \\ \cdot & & \cdot \\ \delta^{i_k}_{j_1} & \cdots & \delta^{i_k}_{j_k} \end{bmatrix}.$$

If $i_1 < j_1$, then $i_1 < j_1 < j_2 \cdots < j_k$ and the entire first row of this determinant consists of zeros. Similarly for $j_1 < i_1$. In that case the first column is a column of zeros. Consequently, expanding by minors when $i_1 = j_1$,

$$(e^{i_1} \wedge \cdots \wedge e^{i_k})(e_{j_1}, \ldots, e_{j_k}) = \frac{1}{k!} \delta^{i_1}_{j_1} \det \begin{bmatrix} \delta^{i_2}_{j_2} & \cdots & \delta^{i_2}_{j_k} \\ \cdot & & \cdot \\ \cdot & & \cdot \\ \cdot & & \cdot \\ \delta^{i_k}_{j_2} & \cdots & \delta^{i_k}_{j_k} \end{bmatrix}.$$

A continuation of the above reasoning yields

(16.13) $$(e^{i_1} \cdots e^{i_k})(e_{j_1}, \ldots, e_{j_k}) = \frac{1}{k!} \delta^{i_1}_{j_1} \delta^{i_2}_{j_2} \cdots \delta^{i_k}_{j_k}$$

when $1 \leq i_1 < \cdots < i_k \leq n$ and $1 \leq j_1 < \cdots < j_k \leq n$, and this is the key to the proof.

The $(e^{i_1} \wedge \cdots \wedge e^{i_k})$ are linearly independent, because if

$$\sum_{i_1 < \cdots < i_k} b_{i_1 \cdots i_k}(e^{i_1} \wedge \cdots \wedge e^{i_k}) = 0,$$

then according to (16.13)

$$b_{j_1 \cdots j_k} = k! \sum_{i_1 < \cdots < i_k} b_{i_1 \cdots i_k}(e^{i_1} \wedge \cdots \wedge e^{i_k})(e_{j_1}, \ldots, e_{j_k}) = 0$$

where $1 \leq j_1 < \cdots < j_k \leq n$. Equation (16-12) shows that the $(e^{i_1} \wedge \cdots \wedge e^{i_k})$'s span $\wedge^k V^*$; it suffices to establish (16.12). Since both sides of (16.12) are k-covectors, Theorem (16.7) shows that (16.12) is valid if it holds when both sides are evaluated on k-tuples of the form $(e_{j_1}, \ldots, e_{j_k})$, $1 \leq j_1 < \cdots < j_k \leq n$, and that this is so follows easily from (16.13). ◆

(16.14) Example. Let $V = \mathbf{R}^n$ be the vector space of n-tuples of real numbers represented as row vectors $v = (a_1, \ldots, a^n)$. V^* can then be thought of as the space of n-tuples of real numbers represented as column vectors, and the action of the covector v^* on v is just the number obtained by multiplying the $1 \times n$ matrix v by the $n \times 1$ matrix v^*. Namely, $v^*(v) = vv^*$. With this understanding, if $f_1, \ldots, f_n$ constitute a basis for V,

$$f_1 = (a_{11}, a_{12}, \ldots, a_{1n}),$$

$$f_2 = (a_{21}, a_{22}, \ldots, a_{2n}), \ldots,$$

$$f_n = (a_{n1}, a_{n2}, \ldots, a_{nn}),$$

the dual basis

$$f_1^* = \begin{bmatrix} b_{11} \\ b_{21} \\ \cdot \\ \cdot \\ \cdot \\ b_{n1} \end{bmatrix}, \quad f_2^* = \begin{bmatrix} b_{12} \\ b_{22} \\ \cdot \\ \cdot \\ \cdot \\ b_{n2} \end{bmatrix}, \quad \ldots, \quad f_n^* = \begin{bmatrix} b_{1n} \\ b_{2n} \\ \cdot \\ \cdot \\ \cdot \\ b_{nn} \end{bmatrix}$$

can be computed from the fact that the matrix product

$$\begin{bmatrix} a_{11} & a_{12} & \cdots & a_{1n} \\ a_{21} & a_{22} & & a_{2n} \\ \cdot & \cdot & & \cdot \\ \cdot & \cdot & & \cdot \\ \cdot & \cdot & & \cdot \\ a_{n1} & a_{n2} & \cdots & a_{nn} \end{bmatrix} \begin{bmatrix} b_{11} & b_{12} & \cdots & b_{1n} \\ b_{21} & b_{22} & & b_{2n} \\ \cdot & \cdot & & \cdot \\ \cdot & \cdot & & \cdot \\ \cdot & \cdot & & \cdot \\ b_{n1} & b_{n2} & \cdots & b_{nn} \end{bmatrix} = \begin{bmatrix} 1 & 0 & \cdots & 0 \\ 0 & 1 & \cdots & 0 \\ \cdot & \cdot & & \cdot \\ \cdot & \cdot & & \cdot \\ 0 & 0 & \cdots & 1 \end{bmatrix}$$

of the a_{ij}'s and the b_{jk}'s yields the matrix $f_k^*(f_i) = \delta_{ik}$, the $n \times n$ identity matrix.

(16.15) Example. In the notation of Example (16.14) if $h_1 = (a_{11}, a_{12}, \ldots, a_{1n})$, $h_2 = (a_{21}, a_{22}, \ldots, a_{2n})$, $\ldots$, $h_k = (a_{k1}, a_{k2}, \ldots, a_{kn})$ and

$$v_1^* = \begin{bmatrix} b_{11} \\ b_{21} \\ \cdot \\ \cdot \\ \cdot \\ b_{n2} \end{bmatrix}, \quad v_2^* = \begin{bmatrix} b_{12} \\ b_{22} \\ \cdot \\ \cdot \\ \cdot \\ b_{n2} \end{bmatrix}, \quad \ldots, \quad v_k^* = \begin{bmatrix} b_{1k} \\ b_{2k} \\ \cdot \\ \cdot \\ \cdot \\ b_{nk} \end{bmatrix},$$

then

$$k!(v_1^* \wedge v_2^* \wedge \cdots \wedge v_k^*)(h_1, \ldots, h_k) = \det \begin{bmatrix} v_1^*(h_1) & \cdots & v_k^*(h_k) \\ \cdot & & \cdot \\ \cdot & & \cdot \\ \cdot & & \cdot \\ v_1^*(h_k) & \cdots & v_k^*(h_k) \end{bmatrix}$$

$$= \det \begin{bmatrix} a_{11} & a_{12} & \cdots & a_{1n} \\ a_{21} & a_{22} & \cdots & a_{2n} \\ \cdot & \cdot & & \cdot \\ \cdot & \cdot & & \cdot \\ \cdot & \cdot & & \cdot \\ a_{k1} & a_{k2} & \cdots & a_{kn} \end{bmatrix} \begin{bmatrix} b_{11} & b_{12} & \cdots & b_{1k} \\ b_{21} & b_{22} & \cdots & b_{2k} \\ \cdot & \cdot & & \cdot \\ \cdot & \cdot & & \cdot \\ \cdot & \cdot & & \cdot \\ b_{n1} & b_{n2} & \cdots & b_{nk} \end{bmatrix}.$$

That is, $k!(v_1^* \wedge \cdots \wedge v_k^*)(h_1, \ldots, h_k)$ is the determinant of the $k \times k$ matrix obtained by matrix multiplying the $k \times n$ matrix associated with the h's times the $n \times k$ matrix associated with the v^*'s.

The defining equation for the k-covector $\alpha^1 \wedge \cdots \wedge \alpha^k$,

$$k!(\alpha^1 \wedge \cdots \wedge \alpha^k)(v_1, \ldots, v_k) = \det \begin{bmatrix} \alpha^1(v_1) & \cdots & \alpha^1(v_k) \\ \cdot & & \cdot \\ \cdot & & \cdot \\ \cdot & & \cdot \\ \alpha^k(v_1) & \cdots & \alpha^k(v_k) \end{bmatrix},$$

leads to many identities which are immediate consequences of corresponding identities for determinants. For example,

$$\alpha^1 \wedge \cdots \wedge \alpha^i \wedge \cdots \wedge \alpha^j \wedge \cdots \wedge \alpha^k$$
$$= -\alpha^1 \wedge \cdots \wedge \alpha^j \wedge \cdots \wedge \alpha^i \wedge \cdots \wedge \alpha^k$$

corresponds to the fact that a determinant changes sign when two rows are interchanged. More generally,

$$\alpha^{\sigma(1)} \wedge \cdots \wedge \alpha^{\sigma(k)} = \text{sign}\,(\sigma)\alpha^1 \wedge \cdots \wedge \alpha^k$$

whenever σ is a permutation of the integers $1, \ldots, k$. Similarly,

$$(\lambda\alpha^1 + \mu\beta^1) \wedge \alpha^2 \wedge \cdots \wedge \alpha^k$$
$$= \lambda(\alpha^1 \wedge \alpha^2 \wedge \cdots \wedge \alpha^k) + \mu(\beta^1 \wedge \alpha^2 \wedge \cdots \wedge \alpha^k)$$

with corresponding relations describing linearity in the other $k - 1$ positions.

(16.16) Example. Suppose that the k 1-covectors $\alpha^1, \ldots, \alpha^k$ are linearly related to the k 1-covectors $e^1, \ldots, e^k$, so that

$$\alpha^1 = c_1^1 e^1 + \cdots + c_k^1 e^k,$$
$$\alpha^2 = c_1^2 e^1 + \cdots + c_k^2 e^k,$$
$$\cdot$$
$$\cdot$$
$$\cdot$$
$$\alpha^k = c_1^k e^1 + \cdots + c_k^k e^k,$$

for some choice of the constants c_i^j. Using linearity in each position,

$$\alpha^1 \wedge \cdots \wedge \alpha^k = \left(\sum_{j_1} c_{j_1}^1 e^{j_1}\right) \wedge \cdots \wedge \left(\sum_{j_k} c_{j_k}^k e^{j_k}\right)$$
$$= \sum_{j_1, \ldots, j_k} c_{j_1}^1 c_{j_2}^2 \cdots c_{j_k}^k e^{j_1} \wedge \cdots \wedge e^{j_k}.$$

Since $e^{j_1} \wedge \cdots \wedge e^{j_k} = 0$ if two of the j_i's are identical, this sum reduces to

$$\sum_{\sigma} c_{\sigma(1)}^1 c_{\sigma(2)}^2 \cdots c_{\sigma(k)}^k e^{\sigma(1)} \wedge \cdots \wedge e^{\sigma(k)}$$
$$= \left[\sum_{\sigma} c_{\sigma(1)}^1 \cdots c_{\sigma(k)}^l \text{ sign } (\sigma)\right] e^1 \wedge \cdots \wedge e^k$$
$$= \det (c_i^j) e^1 \wedge \cdots \wedge e^k$$

where σ ranges over all permutations of $1, \ldots, k$ in the summations above. That is,

(16.17) $$\alpha^1 \wedge \cdots \wedge \alpha^k = \det (C) e^1 \wedge \cdots \wedge e^k$$

where C is the $k \times k$ matrix (c_i^j).

(16.18) Example (The multiplication rule for determinants.) Let $C = (c_i^j)$ and $B = (b_i^j)$ be $k \times k$ matrices, and suppose that the covectors $e^1, \ldots, e^k$ are linearly independent so that $e^1 \wedge \cdots \wedge e^k \neq 0$. Define

$$\alpha^j = \sum_i c_i^j e^i, \quad \beta^j = \sum_m b_m^j \alpha^m, \quad 1 \leq j \leq k,$$

and note that as a consequence

$$\beta^j = \sum_i \left(\sum_m b_m^j c_i^m\right) e^i.$$

So the $k \times k$ matrix of coefficients of the β's in terms of the e's is just the matrix product BC. It follows from (16.17) that

$$\alpha^1 \wedge \cdots \wedge \alpha^k = \det (C) e^1 \wedge \cdots \wedge e^k;$$
$$\beta^1 \wedge \cdots \wedge \beta^k = \det (B) \alpha^1 \wedge \cdots \wedge \alpha^k;$$
$$\beta^1 \wedge \cdots \wedge \beta^k = \det (BC) e^1 \wedge \cdots \wedge e^k;$$

yielding

$$\det (BC)e^1 \wedge \cdots \wedge e^k = \det (B) \det (C)e^1 \wedge \cdots \wedge e^k$$

or, since $e^1 \wedge \cdots \wedge e^k \neq 0$,

(16.19) $\det (BC) = \det (B) \det (C).$

Exercises

16.1   In the notation of Example 16.14 if $f_1 = (3, 7, 2)$, $f_2 = (-1, 1, -1)$, and $f_3 = (1, 0, 1)$, find the basis f_1^*, f_2^*, f_3^* dual to f_1, f_2, f_3.

16.2   If $h_1 = (1, 1, 0, 1)$, $h_2 = (-1, 1, 2, 0)$,

$$v_1^* = \begin{bmatrix} 1 \\ -1 \\ 3 \\ 2 \end{bmatrix}, \qquad v_2^* = \begin{bmatrix} -1 \\ 1 \\ 1 \\ 1 \end{bmatrix},$$

find $(v_1^* \wedge v_2^*)(h_1, h_2)$.

16.3   Show that if $k > n = \dim V$ and ω is a k-covector, then $\omega = 0$.

16.4   Let $V = T_p(\mathbf{R}^n)$ and $X_1, \ldots, X_n$ form an orthonormal basis for $T_p(\mathbf{R}^n)$ with dual basis $\alpha^1, \ldots, \alpha^n$ of $T_p^*(\mathbf{R}^n)$. Show that $(\alpha^i)^\# = X_i$ and deduce from this that $\alpha^1, \ldots, \alpha^n$ are orthonormal in $T_p^*(\mathbf{R}^n)$.

16.5   Let $Y_1, \ldots, Y_k$ be a basis for $T_p(\mathbf{R}^k)$ with dual basis $\omega^1, \ldots, \omega^k$ for $T_p^*(\mathbf{R}^k)$ and let $\phi \colon U \to \mathbf{R}^n$ be a differentiable map of the neighborhood U of p into $\mathbf{R}^n$. Put $X_1 = \phi_*(Y_1), \ldots, X_k = \phi_*(Y_k)$ and let $\alpha_j = X_j^\#$ $(1 \leq j \leq k)$; so $\alpha_j(Z) = (Z, X_j)$ for each $Z \in T_{\phi(p)}(\mathbf{R}^n)$. Show that

$$\phi^*(\alpha_j) = \sum_{m=1}^{k} (X_m, X_j)\omega^m.$$

16.6   Show that every basis $\omega^1, \ldots, \omega^n$ for V^* is the dual basis for a unique basis $w_1, \ldots, w_n$ of V.

16.7   Show that $\alpha^1 \wedge \cdots \wedge \alpha^k = 0$ if and only if the α^i's are dependent, i.e., not independent.

16.8   Show, from (16.6) and the fact that nonzero k-covectors exist, that if $\sigma, \rho \in S_k$, then

$$\operatorname{sign} (\rho\sigma) = \operatorname{sign} (\rho) \operatorname{sign} (\sigma).$$

16.9   Show that

$$\operatorname{sign} (\sigma) = \prod_{1 \leq i < j \leq k} \frac{\sigma(j) - \sigma(i)}{j - i}, \qquad \sigma \in S_k.$$

16.10   Show that

$$\operatorname{sign} (\sigma) = \prod_{1 \leq i < j \leq k} \frac{\sigma\rho(j) - \sigma\rho(i)}{\rho(j) - \rho(i)}, \qquad \rho, \sigma \in S_k,$$

and use this to establish that $\operatorname{sign} (\rho\sigma) = \operatorname{sign} (\sigma) \operatorname{sign} (\rho)$.

17 Multilinear maps and the antisymmetrization operator

An a-multilinear map α is a map

$$(v_1, \ldots, v_a) \to \alpha(v_1, \ldots, v_a)$$

of a-tuples of vectors into R which is linear in each variable v_i. The natural sum of two a-multilinear maps is an a-multilinear map and the tensor product $\alpha \otimes \beta$ of an a-multilinear map α and a b-multilinear map β is the $(a + b)$-multilinear map $\alpha \otimes \beta$ defined by

$$(\textbf{17.1}) \qquad (\alpha \otimes \beta)(v_1, \ldots, v_{a+b}) = \alpha(v_1, \ldots, v_a)\beta(v_{a+1}, \ldots, v_{a+b}).$$

Note that in general $\alpha \otimes \beta \neq \beta \otimes \alpha$.

If α is an a-multilinear map its antisymmetrization As (α) is the a-multilinear map

$$(\textbf{17.2}) \qquad \text{As } (\alpha) \cdot (v_1, \ldots, v_a) = \frac{1}{a!} \sum_{\sigma \in S_a} \text{sign } (\sigma)\alpha(v_{\sigma(1)}, \ldots, v_{\sigma(a)})$$

where S_a is the set of the $a!$ permutations of the integers $\{1, \ldots, a\}$ and sign (σ) is the sign of the permutation σ [sign $(\sigma) = -1$ if σ is odd and sign $(\sigma) = 1$ if σ is even]. If $\rho \in S_a$,

$$\text{sign } (\rho) \text{ As } (\alpha) \cdot (v_{\rho(1)}, \ldots, v_{\rho(a)})$$

$$(\textbf{17.3}) \qquad \begin{aligned} &= \frac{1}{a!} \sum_{\sigma \in S_a} \text{sign } (\rho) \text{ sign } (\sigma)\alpha(v_{\rho\sigma(1)}, \ldots, v_{\rho\sigma(a)}) \\[2mm] &= \frac{1}{a!} \sum_{\sigma \in S_a} \text{sign } (\rho\sigma)\alpha(v_{\rho\sigma(1)}, \ldots, v_{\rho\sigma(a)}) \\[2mm] &= \text{As } (\alpha) \end{aligned}$$

because $\rho\sigma$ ranges over S_a as σ ranges over S_a. Equation (17.3) shows that As (α) is alternating and is consequently an a-covector. Furthermore, if α itself is an a-covector all the terms on the right-hand side of (17.2) are equal to $\alpha(v_1, \ldots, v_a)$ by (16.6) and As $(\alpha) = \alpha$. To summarize:

   (i) As (α) is an a-covector.
   (ii) As $(\omega) = \omega$ if ω is an a-covector.
   (iii) As $(\text{As } [\alpha]) = \text{As } (\alpha)$.

(17.4) Lemma. The antisymmetrization operator satisfies the identities:

   (iv) As $(\alpha^1 + \alpha^2) = \text{As } (\alpha^1) + \text{As } (\alpha^2)$, α_1 and α_2 a-multilinear.

$(\textbf{17.5})$ (v) As $(\alpha \otimes \beta) = (-1)^{ab} \text{As } (\beta \otimes \alpha)$, α a-multilinear, β b-multilinear.

   (vi) As $[\alpha \otimes \text{As } (\beta)] = \text{As } [\text{As } (\alpha) \otimes \beta] = \text{As } (\alpha \otimes \beta)$.

PROOF. (iv) is immediate from the definition (17.2). (v) can be established by letting $\tau \in S_{a+b}$ be the permutation

$$(\tau[1], \ldots, \tau[a+b]) = (a+1, a+2, \ldots, a+b, 1, 2, \ldots, a).$$

sign $(\tau) = (-1)^{ab}$. Now

$$\text{As } (\beta \otimes \alpha) \cdot (v_1, \ldots, v_{a+b})$$

(17.6)

$$= (-1)^{ab} \text{ As } (\beta \otimes \alpha)(v_{\tau(1)}, \ldots, v_{\tau(a+b)})$$

$$= \frac{(-1)^{ab}}{(a+b)!} \sum_{\sigma \in S_{a+b}} \text{sign } (\sigma)\beta(v_{\tau\sigma(1)}, \ldots)\alpha(v_{\tau\sigma(b+1)}, \ldots),$$

which can be altered by letting $\sigma = \tau^{-1}\rho\tau$, so that sign $(\sigma) = $ sign (ρ) and ρ ranges over S_{a+b} as σ does. Equation (17.6) then becomes

$$\frac{(-1)^{ab}}{(a+b)!} \sum_{\rho \in S_{a+b}} \text{sign } (\rho)\beta(v_{\rho\tau(1)}, \ldots)\alpha(v_{\rho\tau(b+1)}, \ldots)$$

$$= \frac{(-1)^{ab}}{(a+b)!} \sum_{\rho \in S_{a+b}} \text{sign } (\rho)\beta(v_{\rho(a+1)}, \ldots)\alpha(v_{\rho(1)}, \ldots)$$

$$= (-1)^{ab} \text{ As } (\alpha \otimes \beta) \cdot (v_1, \ldots, v_{a+b}).$$

(vi) is established by making use of (i), (16.6), and a change of the order of summation.

(17.7) $\quad$ As $(\alpha \otimes \beta) \cdot (v_1, \ldots, v_{a+b})$

$$= \frac{1}{a!} \sum_{\sigma \in S_a} \text{sign } (\sigma) \text{ As } (\alpha \otimes \beta) \cdot (v_{\sigma(1)}, \ldots, v_{\sigma(a)}, v_{a+1}, \ldots, v_{a+b})$$

$$= \frac{1}{a!} \sum_{\sigma \in S_a} \text{sign } (\sigma) \frac{1}{(a+b)!} \sum_{\tau \in S_{a+b}} \text{sign } (\tau)\alpha(v_{\tau\sigma(1)}, \ldots)\beta(v_{\tau(a+1)}, \ldots)$$

$$= \frac{1}{(a+b)!} \sum_{\tau \in S_{a+b}} \text{sign } (\tau) \text{ As } (\alpha)(v_{\tau(1)}, \ldots, v_{\tau(a)})\beta(v_{\tau(a+1)}, \ldots, v_{\tau(a+b)})$$

$$= \text{As } (\text{As } (\alpha) \otimes \beta) \cdot (v_1, \ldots, v_{a+b}).$$

The other equality in (vi) is obtained either by a similar computation or by using (17.7) and (v). ◆

Exercises

17.1 Show that if α and β are 1-multilinear (covectors) then

$$\text{As } (\alpha \otimes \beta) = \tfrac{1}{2}\{\alpha \otimes \beta - \beta \otimes \alpha\}.$$

17.2 Show that $(\alpha \otimes \beta) \otimes \gamma = \alpha \otimes (\beta \otimes \gamma)$ and hence that no ambiguity arises if the parentheses are omitted and both of these denoted by $\alpha \otimes \beta \otimes \gamma$.

17.3 If α^1, α^2, and α^3 are covectors, show that

$$\text{As } (\alpha^1 \otimes \alpha^2 \otimes \alpha^3) = \tfrac{1}{6}\{\alpha^1 \otimes \alpha^2 \otimes \alpha^3 + \alpha^2 \otimes \alpha^3 \otimes \alpha^1 + \alpha^3 \otimes \alpha^1 \otimes \alpha^2$$
$$- \alpha^2 \otimes \alpha^1 \otimes \alpha^3 - \alpha^1 \otimes \alpha^3 \otimes \alpha^2 - \alpha^3 \otimes \alpha^2 \otimes \alpha^1\}.$$

17.4 Using the result of Exercise 17.3, show that if α^1, α^2, and α^3 are 1-multilinear, i.e., covectors, then

$$\text{As } (\alpha^1 \otimes \alpha^2 \otimes \alpha^3) = (\alpha^1 \wedge \alpha^2 \wedge \alpha^3).$$

18 The exterior product

The *exterior product* of an a-covector α and a b-covector β is the $(a + b)$-covector

(18.1)
$$\alpha \wedge \beta = \text{As } (\alpha \otimes \beta).$$

It satisfies the relations:

(18.2)
$$(i) \ \alpha \wedge (\beta_1 + \beta_2) = \alpha \wedge \beta_1 + \alpha \wedge \beta_2, \qquad \deg \beta_1 = \deg \beta_2.\text{*}$$
$$(ii) \ \alpha \wedge (\lambda\beta) = \lambda(\alpha \wedge \beta), \qquad\qquad\qquad \lambda \in R.$$
$$(iii) \ \alpha \wedge \beta = (-1)^{ab}\beta \wedge \alpha.$$
$$(iv) \ \alpha \wedge (\beta \wedge \gamma) = (\alpha \wedge \beta) \wedge \gamma.$$

For the most part these are immediate consequences of the identities (i)–(vi) satisfied by the antisymmetrization operator As and are left as exercises for the reader, with the exception of (iv), which is established by the identities

$$\alpha \wedge (\beta \wedge \gamma) = \text{As } [\alpha \otimes \text{As } (\beta \otimes \gamma)] = \text{As } (\alpha \otimes \beta \otimes \gamma)$$
$$= \text{As } [\text{As } (\alpha \otimes \beta) \otimes \gamma] = (\alpha \wedge \beta) \wedge \gamma.$$

The associativity (iv) of the exterior product makes it possible to leave off the inner parentheses in products, so that, for example, $\alpha \wedge \beta \wedge \gamma$ is used to represent either $\alpha \wedge (\beta \wedge \gamma)$ or $(\alpha \wedge \beta) \wedge \gamma$.

(18.3) Example. Suppose that α^j is an a^j-covector, $j = 1, 2, \ldots, k$; then by repeated use of (17.4)(vi) one computes that

$$\alpha^1 \wedge \alpha^2 \wedge \cdots \wedge \alpha^k = \alpha^1 \wedge [\alpha^2 \wedge (\cdots \wedge \alpha^k) \cdots]$$
$$= \text{As } (\alpha^1 \otimes [\text{As } \{\alpha^2 \cdots\}])$$
$$= \text{As } (\alpha^1 \otimes \alpha^2 \otimes \cdots \otimes \alpha^k).$$

---

*The degree of the b-covector β is the integer b, conveniently abbreviated by $\deg \beta = b$.

In particular, if $\alpha^1, \ldots, \alpha^k$ are covectors ($a_j = 1$ all j), then

$$(\alpha^1 \wedge \cdots \wedge \alpha^k)(v_1, \ldots, v_k) = \text{As}(\alpha^1 \otimes \cdots \otimes \alpha^k) \cdot (v_1, \ldots, v_k)$$

$$= \frac{1}{k!} \text{ determinant } [\alpha^i(v_i)]$$

agreeing with the notation introduced in Section 16.

Exercises

18.1   Prove (18.2)(i), (ii), and (iii).

18.2   Expand $(3e^1 + 2e^2 + e^3) \wedge (e^1 - e^2 - e^3)$ in the basis $e^1 \wedge e^2$, $e^2 \wedge e^3$, $e^1 \wedge e^3$ of (16.12) using (18.2).

18.3   If

$$\alpha^j = \sum_{i=1}^{n} a_i^j \omega^i, \qquad j = 1, 2, \ldots, n$$

where the α's and ω's are 1-covectors, show that

$$\alpha^1 \wedge \alpha^2 \wedge \cdots \wedge \alpha^n = \text{determinant } (a_j^i)\omega^1 \wedge \cdots \wedge \omega^n.$$

[HINT: Apply both sides to the n-tuple $(e_1, \ldots, e_n)$.]

Definition.   If ω is a k-covector, the *subspace determined by* ω is the subspace $E(\omega) = \{\alpha \in V^* : \alpha \wedge \omega = 0\}$ of V^*.

18.4   If e^1, e^2, e^3, e^4 are linearly independent, show that

$$E(e^1 \wedge e^2 + e^3 \wedge e^4) = \{0\}.$$

18.5   If $\alpha^1, \ldots, \alpha^k$ are linearly independent covectors, then show that $E(\alpha^1 \wedge \cdots \wedge \alpha^k)$ is the subspace spanned by $\alpha^1, \ldots, \alpha^k$ in V^*. In particular, if $\alpha^1 \wedge \cdots \wedge \alpha^k = \beta^1 \wedge \cdots \wedge \beta^k \neq 0$, show that the α's and β's span the same subspace of V^* and consequently that the β's can be expressed as linear combinations of the α's.

18.6   If λ is a k-covector with $E(\lambda) = \{0\}$, show that $k > 1$.

18.7   If ω is a k-covector, show that $\omega = e^1 \wedge \cdots \wedge e^j \wedge \lambda$ where $e^1, \ldots, e^j$ are 1-covectors forming a basis for $E(\omega)$ and λ is a $(k - j)$-covector with the property that $E(\lambda) = \{0\}$.

18.8   (Based on Exercises 18.6 and 18.7.) If ω is a k-covector, show that dimension $E(\omega) \neq k - 1$.

18.9   (Based on Exercise 18.6.) A covector ω is *decomposable* if

$$\omega = \alpha^1 \wedge \cdots \wedge \alpha^k$$

where the α's are 1-covectors. Show that ω is decomposable if and only if the dimension of $E(\omega)$ is k.

The subspace W^* of V^* *generates* the k-covector ω if ω can be expressed as a linear combination of exterior products of elements chosen from W^*.

18.10 If the subspaces W_1 and W_2 generate the k-covector ω, show that $W_1 \cap W_2$ generates ω. [HINT: Let $e^1, \ldots, e^n$ be a basis for V^* such that $e^1, \ldots, e^{j_1}$ is a basis for $W_1 \cap W_2$; $e^1, \ldots, e^{j_2}$ $(j_2 \geq j_1)$ is a basis for W_1; and $e^1, \ldots, e^{j_1}, e^{j_2+1}, \ldots, e^{j_3}$ $(j_3 \geq j_2)$ is a basis for W_2. Express ω in terms of the associated basis for $\wedge^k V^*$.]

18.11 (Based on Exercise 18.10.) Show that there is a minimal subspace $M(\omega)$ which generates the k-covector ω. The dimension of $M(\omega)$ is called the rank of ω. Show that ω is decomposable if and only if the rank of ω is k. (See Exercise 18.9 for the definition of decomposable.)

19 k-Vectors

If the words "vector" and "covector" are interchanged and subscripts changed to superscripts and vice versa in Sections 16 through 18, the result is an exposition of k-vectors and the exterior product of k-vectors. Specifically, a k-vector F is a map

$$(v^1, \ldots, v^k) \to F(v^1, \ldots, v^k)$$

of k-tuples of covectors into **R** which is both multilinear and alternating. The exterior product of the k-vector F and the m-vector H is the $(m + k)$-vector

$$(F \wedge H)(v^1, \ldots, v^{m+k})$$
$$= \frac{1}{(m + k)!} \sum_{\sigma \in S_{m+k}} \text{sign } (\sigma) F(v^{\sigma(1)}, \ldots, v^{\sigma(k)}) H(v^{\sigma(k+1)}, \ldots, v^{\sigma(m+k)}),$$

and this product satisfies the relations (14.2) (i)–(iv). 1-vectors and vectors are usually identified (cf. Exercise 19.3) and the linear space of k-vectors is appropriately denoted by $\wedge^k V$.

(19.1) **Theorem.** There is a unique map $(F, \omega) \to \langle F, \omega \rangle$ which associates a real number $\langle F, \omega \rangle$ with each pair (F, ω) consisting of a k-vector F and a k-covector and satisfies:

(1) The map $\omega \to \langle F, \omega \rangle$ is linear on $\wedge^k V^*$ for each F.
(2) The map $F \to \langle F, \omega \rangle$ is linear on $\wedge^k V$ for each ω.
(3) $\langle v_1 \wedge \cdots \wedge v_k, \alpha^1 \wedge \cdots \wedge \alpha^k \rangle = \det \{\alpha^j(v_i)\}$ when the α^i's are covectors and the v_i's vectors.

PROOF. If $e_1, \ldots, e_n$ is a basis for V and $e^1, \ldots, e^n$ the corresponding dual basis for V^*, then, according to Theorem (16.11) and its *k*-vector version, F and ω can be uniquely represented in the forms

(19.2)
$$F = \sum_{i_1 < \cdots < i_k} a^{i_1 \cdots i_k} e_{i_1} \wedge \cdots \wedge e_{i_k};$$

$$\omega = \sum_{j_1 < \cdots < j_k} b_{j_1 \cdots j_k} e^{j_1} \wedge \cdots \wedge e^{j_k}.$$

Suppose $(F, \omega) \to \langle F, \omega \rangle$ is a pairing with properties (1), (2), and (3). The calculation

(19.3) $\langle e_{i_1} \wedge \cdots \wedge e_{i_k}, e^{j_1} \wedge \cdots \wedge e^{j_k} \rangle = \det \{ \delta_{i_a}^{j_m} \} = \delta_{i_1}^{j_1} \cdots \delta_{i_k}^{j_k}$

which was made in Section 16, implies together with (1) and (2) that

(19.4) $\langle F, \omega \rangle = \sum_{i_1 < \cdots < i_k} a^{i_1 \cdots i_k} b_{i_1 \cdots i_k};$

so if it exists the pairing is certainly unique. On the other hand, if (19.4) is taken as the definition of $\langle F, \omega \rangle$ the resulting map is easily seen to satisfy (1) and (2), and the proof of Theorem (19.1) will be complete once it is shown that the map (19.4) also satisfies condition (3). With (19.4) as the definition of $\langle \ , \ \rangle$, note that properties (1) and (2) of Theorem (19.1) are sufficient to show that the maps

$$(v_1, \ldots, v_k) \to k!(e^{i_1} \wedge \cdots \wedge e^{i_k})(v_1, \ldots, v_k) = \det \{ e^{j_m}(v_i) \};$$

$$(v_1, \ldots, v_k) \to \langle v_1 \wedge \cdots \wedge v_k, e^{i_1} \wedge \cdots \wedge e^{i_k} \rangle$$

are both *k*-covectors which agree on *k*-tuples of the form $(e_{i_1}, \ldots, e_{i_k})$, $1 \le i_1 < \cdots < i_k \le n$. By Theorem (16.7) they then agree on all *k*-tuples $(v_1, \ldots, v_k)$. Turning about, for fixed $v_1, \ldots, v_k$ the maps

$$(\alpha^1, \ldots, \alpha^k) \to k!(\alpha^1 \wedge \cdots \wedge \alpha^k)(v_1, \ldots, v_k) = \det \{ \alpha^j(v_i) \};$$

$$(\alpha^1, \ldots, \alpha^k) \to \langle v_1 \wedge \cdots \wedge v_k, \alpha^1 \wedge \cdots \wedge \alpha^k \rangle$$

are both *k*-vectors which (as has just been shown) agree on *k*-tuples of the form $(e^{j_1}, \ldots, e^{j_k})$, $1 \le j_1 < \cdots < j_k \le n$. By the *k*-vector version of Theorem (12.7) they then agree on all *k*-tuples $(\alpha^1, \ldots, \alpha^k)$ and condition (3) holds. ◆

It is worth noting that the $\langle \ , \ \rangle$ notation of this section can be compared with the earlier notation for *k*-covectors ω by the relation

(19.5) $\langle v_1 \wedge \cdots \wedge v_k, \omega \rangle = k! \omega(v_1, \ldots, v_k).$

whose proof is left as an exercise.

It is usual to regard the real numbers **R** as both the space of 0-*vectors* and the space of 0-*covectors* and to extend the multiplication rules to include them. For example, if $\lambda \in \mathbf{R}$, then $\lambda \wedge \omega$ is just another notation for $\lambda \omega$ and if $\lambda, \mu \in \mathbf{R}$, $\langle \lambda, \mu \rangle = \lambda \mu$. In this notation $\wedge^{(0)} V = \wedge^{(0)} V^* = \mathbf{R}$.

Exercises

19.1 Verify (19.5).

19.2 If $w = 3e_1 \wedge e_3 - e_2 \wedge e_3$ and $\alpha = e^1 \wedge e^3 + e^2 \wedge e^3 + e^1 \wedge e^2$, evaluate $\langle w, \alpha \rangle$ (the e_i's are dual to the e^i's).

19.3 If for each $v \in V$, F_v is the 1-covector $F_v(\alpha) = \langle v, \alpha \rangle$, show that the map $v \to F_v$ is a linear isomorphism of the space V of vectors onto the space $\wedge^1 V$ of 1-vectors. (This is just the usual isomorphism of V onto V^{**}.)

20 The inner product

If F is a k-vector and ω an m-covector, the *inner product* $F \lrcorner \omega$ is the $(m - k)$-covector defined when $m \geq k$ by

(20.1) $$\langle H, F \lrcorner \omega \rangle = \langle F \wedge H, \omega \rangle, \qquad H \in \wedge^{(m-k)} V.$$

It satisfies the relations:

(i) $F \to F \lrcorner \omega$ is a linear map of $\wedge^{(k)} V \to \wedge^{(m-k)} V^*$.
(ii) $\omega \to F \lrcorner \omega$ is a linear map of $\wedge^{(m)} V^* \to \wedge^{(m-k)} V^*$.
(iii) $F \lrcorner \omega = \langle F, \omega \rangle$ if $m = k$.
(iv) $v \lrcorner (\alpha \wedge \beta) = (v \lrcorner \alpha) \wedge \beta + (-1)^{\deg \alpha} \alpha \wedge (v \lrcorner \beta)$ if $v \in V = \wedge^{(1)} V$.

Relations (i)–(iii) follow easily from (20.1) and are left as exercises. Relation (iv) can be established with the aid of the identity

(20.2) $v \lrcorner (\alpha^1 \wedge \cdots \wedge \alpha^k)$

$$= \sum_{j=1}^{k} (-1)^{j-1} \alpha^j(v) \alpha^1 \wedge \cdots \wedge \alpha^{j-1} \wedge \alpha^{j+1} \wedge \cdots \wedge \alpha^k$$

when $\alpha^1, \ldots, \alpha^k$ are covectors, or equivalently

$\langle v \wedge v_2 \wedge \cdots \wedge v_k, \alpha^1 \wedge \cdots \wedge \alpha^k \rangle$

$$= \sum_{j=1}^{k} (-1)^{j-1} \alpha^j(v) \langle v_2 \wedge \cdots \wedge v_k, \alpha^1 \wedge \cdots \wedge \alpha^{j-1} \wedge \alpha^{j+1} \wedge \cdots \wedge \alpha^k \rangle$$

$v^i \in V$, $\alpha^j \in V^*$, which amounts to expanding

$$\det \begin{bmatrix} \alpha^1(v) & \alpha^2(v) & \cdots & \alpha^k(v) \\ \alpha^1(v_2) & \alpha^2(v_2) & \cdots & \alpha^k(v_2) \\ \cdot & \cdot & & \cdot \\ \cdot & \cdot & & \cdot \\ \cdot & \cdot & & \cdot \\ \alpha^1(v_k) & \alpha^2(v_k) & \cdots & \alpha^k(v_k) \end{bmatrix}$$

by minors along the first row. In the special case that $\alpha = \alpha^1 \wedge \cdots \wedge \alpha^m$, $\beta = \alpha^{m+1} \wedge \cdots \wedge \alpha^k$, (20.2) yields

$$v \ \lrcorner \ (\alpha \wedge \beta) = (\sum_{j=1}^{m} (-1)^{j-1}\alpha^j(v)\alpha^1 \wedge \cdots \wedge \alpha^{j-1} \wedge \alpha^{j+1} \cdots \wedge \alpha^m)$$

$$\wedge \ \alpha^{m+1} \wedge \cdots \wedge \alpha^k + \alpha^1 \wedge \cdots \wedge \alpha^m$$

(20.3)
$$\wedge (\sum_{i=1}^{k-m} (-1)^m(-1)^{i-1}\alpha^{m+i}(v)\alpha^{m+1} \wedge \cdots \wedge \alpha^{m+i-1} \wedge \alpha^{m+i+1} \wedge \cdots \wedge \alpha^k)$$

$$= (v \ \lrcorner \ \alpha) \wedge \beta + (-1)^m \alpha \wedge (v \ \lrcorner \ \beta).$$

Relation (iv) follows in the general case because both sides are linear in α and β and each α, β in (iv) is a linear sum of α's and β's of the type used in (20.3).

Exercises

20.1 Establish the relations (i), (ii), and (iii) which follow (20.1).

20.2 If $v = 3e_1 + 2e_2$ and $\alpha = e^1 \wedge e^3 + e^2 \wedge e^3$, evaluate $v \ \lrcorner \ \alpha$.

20.3 If $v = 3e_1 - 2e_4 - e_5$ and $\alpha = e^1 \wedge e^3 \wedge e^5$, evaluate $v \ \lrcorner \ \alpha$.

20.4 If $F = e_2 \wedge e_3$ and $\alpha = e^1 \wedge e^2 \wedge e^3 \wedge e^4$, evaluate $F \ \lrcorner \ \alpha$.

20.5 Suppose $\omega \in \wedge^k V^*$ is a nonzero k-covector. Show that $\alpha \wedge \omega = 0$ and $v \ \lrcorner \ \omega = 0$ for some $\alpha \in V^*$, $v \in V$ implies that $\langle v, \alpha \rangle = 0$.

Definitions. For each k-vector $\omega \neq 0$ let $E(\omega) = \{\alpha \in V^* : \alpha \wedge \omega = 0\}$ as before; $F(\omega) = \{v \in V : v \ \lrcorner \ \omega = 0\}$; and for each subset $S \subset V^*$ [or $S' \subset V$] put $S^\perp = \{v \in V : \langle v, S \rangle = 0\}$ [or $S'^\perp = \{\alpha \in V^* : \langle S', \alpha \rangle = 0\}$] where $\langle v, S \rangle = 0$ means $\langle v, s \rangle = 0$ for each $s \in S$.

20.6 Show that $F(\omega) \subset E(\omega)^\perp$

20.7 If e^1, e^2, e^3, e^4 are a basis for V^* and $\omega = e^1 \wedge e^2 + e^3 \wedge e^4$, show that $E(\omega) = \{0\}$, $E(\omega)^\perp = V$, and $F(\omega) = 0$.

20.8 If ω is a decomposable k-covector in the sense that $\omega = \alpha^1 \wedge \cdots \wedge \alpha^k$ where the α's are 1-covectors, show that $F(\omega) = E(\omega)^\perp$.

20.9 Suppose ω is a nonzero k-covector and $e^1, \ldots, e^n$ is a basis for V^* with the property that $e^1, \ldots, e^j$ is a basis for $E(\omega)$. Then (cf. Exercise 18.7) $\omega = e^1 \wedge \cdots \wedge e^j \wedge \lambda$ where λ is a $(k - j)$-covector which is (i) a sum of exterior products of $e^{j+1}, \ldots, e^n$ and (ii) $E(\lambda) = \{0\}$. Show that $F(\omega) = E(\omega)^\perp \cap F(\lambda)$ and use this to show ω is decomposable if and only if $F(\omega) = E(\omega)^\perp$.

CHAPTER FIVE

Differential Forms

21 Differential forms

A *differential form* ω of degree k on the open set U or a *k-form* is a map $p \to \omega_p$ which assigns to each point $p \in U$ a k-covector $\omega_p \in \wedge^k T_p^*(\mathbf{R}^n)$. If $x^1, \ldots, x^n$ is a coordinate system valid throughout U, then according to Theorem (16.11) and Example (16.3)

$$(21.1) \qquad \omega_p = \sum_{i_1 < \cdots < i_k} f_{i_1 \cdots i_k}(p)(dx^{i_1})_p \wedge \cdots \wedge (dx^{i_k})_p, \qquad p \in U$$

where

$$(21.2) \qquad f_{i_1 \cdots i_k}(p) = k! \omega_p \left(\frac{\partial}{\partial x^{i_1}} \bigg|_p, \ \ldots, \ \frac{\partial}{\partial x^{i_k}} \bigg|_p \right).$$

Equation (21.1) is usually abbreviated

$$(21.3) \qquad \omega = \sum_{i_1 < \cdots < i_k} f_{i_1 \cdots i_k} dx^{i_1} \wedge \cdots \wedge dx^{i_k}.$$

A k-form is (differentiable of class) C^N on U if the coefficients $f_{i_1 \cdots i_k}$ are C^N and the coordinate functions $x^1, \ldots, x^n$ are C^{N+1} on U. (The reason it is required that $x^1, \ldots, x^n$ be C^{N+1} is that this ensures the coefficients of ω with respect to a cartesian coordinate system will be C^N.) Notice that according to the remarks at the end of Section 19 a 0-form is just a real-valued function on U.

The exterior product of the k-form α and the m-form β is the $(k + m)$-form $\alpha \wedge \beta$ which assigns the $(k + m)$-covector

$$(21.4) \qquad (\alpha \wedge \beta)_p = \alpha_p \wedge \beta_p$$

to the point $p \in U$. It satisfies all the properties (18.2) of the exterior product of k-covectors.

If $X_1, \ldots, X_k$ are vector fields on U, $X_1 \wedge \cdots \wedge X_k$ represents the map which assigns to each $p \in U$ the k-vector $X_1|_p \wedge \cdots \wedge X_k|_p$.

In this situation it is convenient to use the notation

$$\langle X_1|_p \wedge \cdots \wedge X_k|_p, \, \omega_p\rangle = \langle X_1 \wedge \cdots \wedge X_k, \, \omega\rangle(p)$$

(21.5)
$$= \langle X_1 \wedge \cdots \wedge X_k, \, \omega_p\rangle$$

$$= \langle X_1|_p \wedge \cdots \wedge X_k|_p, \, \omega\rangle$$

where the left-hand side of (21.5) is taken as the definition of each of the three expressions on the right-hand side. In particular the function

$$p \rightarrow \langle X_1|_p \wedge \cdots \wedge X_k|_p, \, \omega_p\rangle$$

is denoted by

$$\langle X_1 \wedge \cdots \wedge X_k, \, \omega\rangle.$$

The exterior derivative of the C^1 k-form ω given by (21.3) is the $(k + 1)$-form

(21.6)
$$d\omega = \sum_{i_1 < \cdots < i_k} (df_{i_1 \ldots i_k}) \wedge dx^{i_1} \wedge \cdots \wedge dx^{i_k}.$$

For the moment it is not clear whether $d\omega$ depends on the particular coordinate system chosen in (21.6) or not; so until this question is settled by Theorem (21.7) consider the coordinate system $x^1, \ldots, x^n$ as fixed. Note that if ω is C^N, $d\omega$ is C^{N-1} [cf. (15.6)], and that if ω is the 0-form given by the function f, its exterior derivative is just the 1-form df defined in Section 15.

(21.7) Theorem. The exterior derivative d is the only operator defined on the C^1 differential forms on U with the properties:

(i) $d(\alpha + \beta) = d\alpha + d\beta$.

(ii) For each C^1 function f and each vector $X_p \in T_p(\mathbf{R}^n)$

(21.8)
$$\langle X_p, df\rangle = X_p f.$$

(iii) $d(d\omega) = 0$ whenever ω is C^2.

(iv) $d(\alpha \wedge \beta) = d\alpha \wedge \beta + (-1)^a \alpha \wedge d\beta$, $a = \text{degree } (\alpha)$.

In particular, the operator d does not depend on the coordinate system used in (21.3) and (21.6).

PROOF.   First it is shown that d satisfies (i)–(iv). Properties (i) and (ii) follow easily from the definition, and because of (i) and (18.2)(i) it suffices to establish (iv) when

$$\alpha = f \, dx^{i_1} \wedge \cdots \wedge dx^{i_k};$$

$$\beta = g \, dx^{j_1} \wedge \cdots \wedge dx^{j_m}.$$

Then

(21.9) $\quad \alpha \wedge \beta = fg \, dx^{i_1} \wedge \cdots \wedge dx^{i_k} \wedge dx^{j_1} \wedge \cdots \wedge dx^{j_m}$

$$= fg \text{ sign } (\sigma) \, dx^{\phi_1} \wedge \cdots \wedge dx^{\phi_{m+k}}$$

where the integers $\phi_1 < \cdots < \phi_{k+m}$ are just the numbers $i_1, \ldots, i_k$, $j_1, \ldots, j_m$ written in ascending order and σ is the permutation of the integers $1, 2, \ldots, k + m$ determined by $\phi_{\sigma(1)} = i_1, \ldots, \phi_{\sigma(k)} = i_k, \ldots, \phi_{\sigma(m+k)} = j_m$. Equation (21.9) has the form (21.3), so that d can be applied to give

$$d(\alpha \wedge \beta) = d(fg) \wedge \text{sign } (\sigma) \, dx^{\phi_1} \wedge \cdots \wedge dx^{\phi_{k+m}}$$

$$= (g \, df + f \, dg) \, dx^{i_1} \wedge \cdots \wedge dx^{i_k} \wedge dx^{j_1} \wedge \cdots \wedge dx^{j_m}$$

$$= (df \wedge dx^{i_1} \wedge \cdots \wedge ds^{i_k}) \wedge (g \, dx^{j_1} \wedge \cdots \wedge dx^{j_m})$$

$$+ (-1)^k (f \, dx^{i_1} \wedge \cdots \wedge dx^{i_k}) \wedge (dg \wedge dx^{j_1} \wedge \cdots \wedge dx^{j_m})$$

$$= d\alpha \wedge \beta + (-1)^k \alpha \wedge d\beta.$$

Property (iii) is also established by direct computation, which because of (i) only needs to be carried out when $\omega = f \, dx^{i_1} \wedge \cdots \wedge dx^{i_k}$.

$$\omega = f \, dx^{i_1} \wedge \cdots \wedge dx^{i_k}, \qquad i_1 < \cdots < i_k;$$

$$d\omega = df \wedge (dx^{i_1} \wedge \cdots \wedge dx^{i_k}).$$

By (iv) and the fact that $d(dx^{i_1} \wedge \cdots \wedge dx^{i_k}) = 0$

$$d(d\omega) = d(df) \wedge (dx^{i_1} \wedge \cdots \wedge dx^{i_k}) + df \wedge 0;$$

so it suffices to show $d(df) = 0$.

$$df = \sum_{j=1}^{n} \frac{\partial f}{\partial x^j} dx^j;$$

$$d(df) = \sum_{j=1}^{n} d \, \frac{\partial f}{\partial x^j} \wedge dx^j$$

$$= \sum_{i,j=1}^{n} \frac{\partial^2 f}{\partial x^i \, \partial x^j} dx^i \wedge dx^j$$

$$= \sum_{i<j} \frac{\partial^2 f}{\partial x^i \, \partial x^j} dx^i \wedge dx^j + \sum_{j<i} \frac{\partial^2 f}{\partial x^i \, \partial x^j} (-1) \, dx^j \wedge dx^i$$

$$= \sum_{i<j} \left(\frac{\partial^2 f}{\partial x^i \, \partial x^j} - \frac{\partial^2 f}{\partial x^j \, \partial x^i} \right) dx^i \wedge dx^j$$

$$= 0.$$

If d' is another operator with properties (i)–(iv) (for example, the exterior derivative associated with another coordinate system), then $d'f = df$ when f is a C^1 function on U by (ii), and $d'\omega = d\omega = 0$ when $\omega = dg$ for some C^2 function g on U by (iii). Furthermore the set of all C^1 differential forms ω for which $d\omega = d'\omega$ is closed under addition by (i) and exterior multiplication by (iv). Putting these observations together shows that $d'\omega = d\omega$ whenever ω can be built up from f's and dg's using addition and exterior multiplication. According to (21.3) every differential form ω can be built up in this way, and the uniqueness of d has been established. $\blacklozenge$

If $\phi: U \to V$ is a C^1-map of the open set U of $\mathbf{R}^m$ into $\mathbf{R}^n$, the map ϕ^* which carries k-forms on V into k-forms on U is defined by

$$(\textbf{21.10}) \qquad \langle X_1|_p \wedge \cdots \wedge X_k|_p, \; \phi^*\omega\rangle(p)$$
$$= \langle \phi^*(X_1|_p) \wedge \cdots \wedge \phi^*(X_k|_p), \; \omega\rangle(\phi[p])$$

whenever $X_1|_p, \ldots, X_k|_p$ are vectors at $p \in U$. It is an extension of the ϕ^* defined in Section 15 and satisfies the properties:

$$\text{(i)} \quad \phi^*(\alpha + \beta) = \phi^*\alpha + \phi^*\beta.$$

$$\text{(ii)} \quad \phi^*(\alpha \wedge \beta) = \phi^*\alpha \wedge \phi^*\beta.$$

$(\textbf{21.11})$

$$\text{(iii)} \quad \phi^*(d\alpha) = d\phi^*\alpha.$$

$$\text{(iv)} \quad (\psi \circ \phi)^* = \phi^*\psi^*,$$

where in (iv) $\phi: U \to V$ and $\psi: V \to W$. The verification of (21.11) (i)–(iv) is left to the exercises.

$(\textbf{21.12})$ **Example.** If $y^1, \ldots, y^m$ is a system of coordinates for U and $x^1, \ldots, x^n$ a system of coordinates for V and

$$\omega = dx^{i_1} \wedge \cdots \wedge dx^{i_k} \qquad \text{on } V,$$

then when $\phi: U \to V$,

$$\phi^*\omega = \phi^* dx^{i_1} \wedge \cdots \wedge \phi^* dx^{i_k}$$

$$= \sum_{j_1 < \cdots < j_k} \left\langle \frac{\partial}{\partial y^{j_1}} \wedge \cdots \wedge \frac{\partial}{\partial y^{j_k}}, \; d(x^{i_1} \circ \phi) \wedge \cdots \wedge d(x^{i_k} \circ \phi) \right\rangle dy^{j_1} \wedge \cdots \wedge dy^{j_k}$$

$$= \sum_{j_1 < \cdots < j_k} \det \begin{bmatrix} \dfrac{\partial x^{i_1} \circ \phi}{\partial y^{j_1}} & \cdots & \dfrac{\partial x^{i_k} \circ \phi}{\partial y^{j_1}} \\ \cdot & & \cdot \\ \cdot & & \cdot \\ \cdot & & \cdot \\ \dfrac{\partial x^{i_1} \circ \phi}{\partial y^{j_k}} & \cdots & \dfrac{\partial x^{i_k} \circ \phi}{\partial y^{j_k}} \end{bmatrix} dy^{j_1} \wedge \cdots \wedge dy^{j_k}.$$

Exercises

21.1 Prove (21.11)(i)–(iv).

21.2 Show that $\langle X \wedge Y, \ d(f\,dg) \rangle = X(fYg) - Y(fXg) - f[X, Y]g$ where $[X, Y]h = X(Yh) - Y(Xh)$ for suitably differentiable functions f, g and vector fields X, Y.

21.3 Use the result of Exercise 21.2 to show

$$\langle X \wedge Y, d\omega \rangle = X\langle Y, \omega \rangle - Y\langle X, \omega \rangle - \langle [X, Y], \omega \rangle$$

when ω is a 1-form. This formula is often used as the definition of $d\omega$ in this case.

21.4 If $f^1, \ldots, f^k$ are differentiable functions on the open set $U \subset \mathbf{R}^n$, show that the $k \times n$ matrix $(\partial f^i / \partial x^j)$ has rank k if and only if

$$df^1 \wedge \cdots \wedge df^k \neq 0.$$

21.5 Suppose df is not zero at $p \in U$, U open, and that $dg \wedge df = 0$ on U. Show that there is an open set V containing p and a differentiable function h on $f(V)$ such that $g(q) = h(f(q))$, $q \in V$. That is, g is locally a differentiable function of f alone. [HINT: Choose a local coordinate system $z^1, \ldots, z^n$ in which $f = z^1$ and let V be a cubical neighborhood in the z's. Note that $dg \wedge dz^1 = 0$ implies $\partial g / \partial z^k = 0$, $k > 1$ (cf. Exercise 6.7).]

21.6 If $g, f^1, \ldots, f^k$ are differentiable functions on the open set U, $df^1 \wedge \cdots \wedge df^k \neq 0$ on U, and $dg \wedge df^1 \wedge \cdots \wedge df^k = 0$ on U, show that each point $p \in U$ has a neighborhood V on which g is a differentiable function of $f^1, \ldots, f^k$. See Exercise 21.5 to clarify terminology.

21.7 (Based on Exercise 21.3.) Suppose $X_1, \ldots, X_n$ are vector fields on $U \subset \mathbf{R}^n$ whose associated vectors $X_1|_p, \ldots, X_n|_p$ are linearly independent at each $p \in U$ and suppose $\omega^1, \ldots, \omega^n$ is the dual basis of 1-forms. That is, $\langle X_i, \omega^i \rangle(p) = \delta_i^j$, $p \in U$. $[X_i, X_j]$ is a vector field; so

$$[X_i, X_j] = \sum_{k=1}^{n} C_{ij}^k X_k$$

for some functions C_{ij}^k on U. Show that

$$d\omega^k = -\sum_{i<j} C_{ij}^k \omega^i \wedge \omega^j.$$

22 The scalar product

The scalar product introduced in Sections 13 and 15 for vectors and co-vectors, respectively, can be extended to k-vectors and k-covectors. Throughout this section let $x^1, \ldots, x^n$ be cartesian coordinates for $\mathbf{R}^n$. If

(22.1)

$$\omega = \sum_{i_1 < \cdots < i_k} w_{i_1 \cdots i_k}\, dx^{i_1} \wedge \cdots \wedge dx^{i_k},$$

$$\alpha = \sum_{j_1 < \cdots < j_k} a_{j_1 \cdots j_k}\, dx^{j_1} \wedge \cdots \wedge dx^{j_k}$$

are k-forms on some open subset U of $\mathbf{R}^n$, the scalar product of the two k-covectors ω_p and α_p associated with ω and α at $p \in U$ is

$$(\omega_p, \alpha_p) = \sum_{i_1 < \cdots < i_k} \omega_{i_1 \cdots i_k}(p) a_{i_1 \cdots i_k}(p),$$

and as a function of p it is denoted by $(\omega, \alpha)(p)$, $p \in U$, or (ω, α). Similarly if

$$F = \sum_{i_1 < \cdots < i_k} f^{i_1 \cdots i_k} \frac{\partial}{\partial x^{i_1}} \wedge \cdots \wedge \frac{\partial}{\partial x^{i_k}},$$

(22.2)

$$G = \sum_{j_1 < \cdots < j_k} g^{j_1 \cdots j_k} \frac{\partial}{\partial x^{j_1}} \wedge \cdots \wedge \frac{\partial}{\partial x^{j_k}}$$

are two fields of k-vectors on U, the scalar product of their associated k-vectors F_p, G_p at p is

$$(F_p, G_p) = \sum_{i_1 < \cdots < i_k} f^{i_1 \cdots i_k}(p) g^{i_1 \cdots i_k}(p),$$

and as a function of p it is denoted by $(F, G)(p)$, $p \in U$, or (F, G). The field of k-vectors

(22.3)
$$\omega^{\#} = \sum_{i_1 < \cdots < i_k} w_{i_1 \cdots i_k} \frac{\partial}{\partial x^{i_1}} \wedge \cdots \wedge \frac{\partial}{\partial x^{i_k}}$$

is uniquely specified by the condition

(22.4)
$$(\omega, \alpha) = \langle \omega^{\#}, \alpha \rangle$$

for each k-form α on U. Indeed if F is any field of k-vectors with components given by (22.2) which satisfies the relation (22.4), then putting $\alpha = dx^{k_1} \wedge \cdots \wedge dx^{i_k}$, $i_1 < i_2 < \cdots < i_k$, gives

$$f^{i_1 \cdots i_k} = \langle F, dx^{i_1} \wedge \cdots \wedge dx^{i_k} \rangle = (\omega, dx^{i_1} \wedge \cdots \wedge dx^{i_k})$$

$$= w_{i_1 \cdots i_k};$$

so $F = \omega^{\#}$.

(22.5)   Theorem.   (1) $(\alpha \wedge \omega)^{\#} = \alpha^{\#} \wedge \omega^{\#}$ for any two differential forms on U. (2) if $\alpha_1, \ldots, \alpha_k$ and $\omega_1, \ldots, \omega_k$ are 1-forms, then

(22.6) $(\alpha_1 \wedge \cdots \wedge \alpha_k, \omega_1 \wedge \cdots \wedge \omega_k) = \det [(\alpha_i, \omega_j)].$

PROOF.   (1) follows directly from the definition, the observation that the map $\beta \to \beta^{\#}$ is linear and

$$(dx^{i_1} \wedge \cdots \wedge dx^{i_n})^{\#} = \frac{\partial}{\partial x^{i_1}} \wedge \cdots \wedge \frac{\partial}{\partial x^{i_m}}$$

whether the i's are listed in increasing order or not. Equation (22.6) is obtained using (1) and (22.4) by the chain of equalities

$$(\alpha_1 \wedge \cdots \wedge \alpha_k, \omega_1 \wedge \cdots \wedge \omega_k) = \langle (\alpha_1 \wedge \cdots \wedge \alpha_k)^\#, \omega_1 \wedge \cdots \wedge \omega_k \rangle$$

$$= \langle \alpha_1^\# \wedge \cdots \wedge \alpha_\beta^\#, \omega_1 \wedge \cdots \wedge \omega_k \rangle$$

$$= \det [\alpha_i^\#, \omega_j]$$

$$= \det [(\alpha_i, \omega_j)]. \qquad \blacklozenge$$

(22.7) Definition. The dual of the k-form ω of (22.1) is the $(n - k)$-form $*\omega$ defined by

(22.8) $\qquad *\omega = \displaystyle\sum_{i_1 < \cdots < i_k} w_{i_1 \cdots i_k} \varepsilon(i_1, \ldots, i_k) \, dx^{j_i} \wedge \cdots \wedge dx^{j_{n-k}}$

where $\{j_1, \ldots, j_{n-k}\}$ is the set complementary to $\{i_1, \ldots, i_k\}$ in $\{1, 2, \ldots, n\}$, $j_1 < j_2 < \cdots < j_n$, and $\varepsilon(i_1, \ldots, i_k) = \pm 1$ is chosen so that

(22.9) $\qquad \varepsilon(i_1, \ldots, i_k) \, dx^{i_1} \wedge \cdots \wedge dx^{i_k} \wedge dx^{j_1} \wedge \cdots \wedge dx^{j_{n-k}}$

$$= dx^1 \wedge dx^2 \wedge \cdots \wedge dx^n.$$

(22.10) Example. If $n = 3$; $*dx^1 = dx^2 \wedge dx^3$; $*dx^2 = -dx^1 \wedge dx^3$; $*dx^3 = dx^1 \wedge dx^2$; $*(dx^1 \wedge dx^2) = dx^3$; $*(dx^1 \wedge dx^3) = -dx^2$; $*(dx^2 \wedge dx^3) = dx^1$; $*(dx^1 \wedge dx^2 \wedge dx^3) = 1$; $*1 = dx^1 \wedge dx^2 \wedge dx^3$.

(22.11) Theorem. $*\omega$ is the only k-form on U which satisfies

(22.12) $\qquad \alpha \wedge *\omega = (\alpha, \omega) \, dx^1 \wedge \cdots \wedge dx^n$

for each k-form α. Equivalently,

(22.13) $\qquad *\omega = \omega^\# \lrcorner (dx^1 \wedge \cdots \wedge dx^n).$

Remark. Either (22.12) or (22.13) could have been used instead of (22.8) to define $*\omega$.

PROOF. Straightforward computation shows when $b_1 < \cdots < b_k$ and $i_1 < \cdots < i_k$ that

$$(dx^{b_1} \wedge \cdots \wedge dx^{b_k}) \wedge *(dx^{i_1} \wedge \cdots \wedge dx^{i_k})$$

$$= \varepsilon(i_1, \ldots, i_k) \, dx^{b_1} \wedge \cdots \wedge dx^{b_k} \wedge dx^{j_1} \wedge \cdots \wedge dx^{j_{n-k}}$$

$$= \delta_{i_1}^{b_1} \delta_{i_2}^{b_2} \cdots \delta_{i_k}^{b_k} \, dx^1 \wedge \cdots \wedge dx^n,$$

and (22.12) is an immediate consequence of this relation. If there were two k-forms ω_1 and ω_2 satisfying (22.12), then $(\alpha, \omega_1 - \omega_2) = 0$ for each k-form α. In particular $(\omega_1 - \omega_2, \omega_1 - \omega_2) = 0$, which clearly implies

$\omega_1 - \omega_2 = 0$. Equation (22.13) is just an application of the definition of the inner product to (22.12) using (22.4).   ◆

(22.14)   Properties of *∗*

(1) $*(f\alpha) = f*\alpha$.

(2) $*(\alpha + \beta) = *\alpha + *\beta$.

(3) $**\alpha = (-1)^{k(n-k)}\alpha$ when α has degree k.

(4) $\alpha \wedge *\beta = \beta \wedge *\alpha$ when α and β both have degree k.

(5)   The map $\alpha \rightarrow *\alpha$ is an isomorphism of k-forms onto $(n - k)$-forms.

(6) $|\alpha| = |*\alpha|$.

These properties are all more or less evident from (22.8) and (22.12), but for the sake of illustration (3), (4), and (6) are proved below. Since for each set $i_1 < \cdots < i_k$ there is just one complementary set $j_1 < \cdots < j_{n-k}$ matching the requirements of (22.8), the sum in (22.8) could equally well have been extended over all $(n - k)$-tuples $(j_1, \ldots, j_{n-k})$ of integers with $1 \leq j_1 < \cdots < j_{n-k} \leq n$. Thus

(22.15) $*(*\omega) = \sum\limits_{i_1 < \cdots < i_k} w_{i_1 \cdots i_k}\varepsilon(i_1, \ldots, i_k)\varepsilon(j_1, \ldots, j_{n-k}) \, dx^{i_1} \wedge \cdots \wedge dx^{i_k}.$

Now for each $i_1 < \cdots < i_k$

$dx^1 \wedge \cdots \wedge dx^n$

$\quad = \varepsilon(i_1, \ldots, i_k) \, dx^{i_1} \wedge \cdots \wedge dx^{i_k} \wedge dx^{j_1} \wedge \cdots \wedge dx^{j_{n-k}}$

$\quad = \varepsilon(i_1, \ldots, i_k)(-1)^{k(n-k)} \, dx^{j_1} \wedge \cdots \wedge dx^{j_{n-k}} \wedge dx^{i_1} \wedge \cdots \wedge dx^{i_k}$

$\quad = (-1)^{k(n-k)}\varepsilon(i_1, \ldots, i_k)\varepsilon(j_1, \ldots, j_{n-k}) \, dx^1 \wedge \cdots \wedge dx^n;$

so

$$\varepsilon(i_1, \ldots, i_k)\varepsilon(j_1, \ldots, j_{n-k}) = (-1)^{k(n-k)},$$

and used in (22.15) this establishes (3). Property (4) follows from the symmetry of (α, β) and (22.12).

$$\alpha \wedge *\beta = (\alpha, \beta) \, dx^1 \wedge \cdots \wedge dx^n = (\beta, \alpha) \, dx^1 \wedge \cdots \wedge dx^n = \beta \wedge *\alpha.$$

Property (6) is a consequence of (3), (4), (18.2)(iii), and (22.12):

$$(\alpha, \alpha) \, dx^1 \wedge \cdots \wedge dx^n = \alpha \wedge *\alpha = (-1)^{k(n-k)}**\alpha \wedge *\alpha$$

$$= *\alpha \wedge *(*\alpha) = (*\alpha, *\alpha) \, dx^1 \wedge \cdots \wedge dx^n.$$

The $*$-operation can be combined with exterior differentiation and exterior multiplication to yield all the classical vector operations in $\mathbf{R}^3$. These are defined below and computed in the cartesian coordinate system x^1, x^2, x^3.

(1) The gradient of a function f is

(**22.16**) $$\operatorname{grad} f = df = \frac{\partial f}{\partial x^1} dx^1 + \frac{\partial f}{\partial x^2} dx^2 + \frac{\partial f}{\partial x^3} dx^3.$$

(2) The vector product or cross product $\alpha \times \beta$ of two covectors $\alpha = a_1 dx^1 + a_2 dx^2 + a_3 dx^3$, $\beta = b_1 dx^1 + b_2 dx^2 + b_3 dx^3$, is

$$\alpha \times \beta = *(\alpha \wedge \beta)$$

$$= *\{ (a_2 b_3 - a_3 b_2) \, dx^2 \wedge dx^3 + (a_3 b_1 - a_1 b_3) \, dx^3 \wedge dx^1$$

$$+ (a_1 b_2 - a_2 b_1) \, dx^1 \wedge dx^2 \}$$

(**22.17**) $$= (a_2 b_3 - a_3 b_2) \, dx^1 + (a_3 b_1 - a_1 b_3) \, dx^2 + (a_1 b_2 - a_2 b_1) \, dx^3$$

$$= \det \begin{bmatrix} dx^1 & dx^2 & dx^3 \\ a_1 & a_2 & a_3 \\ b_1 & b_2 & b_3 \end{bmatrix}.$$

(3) The divergence of a 1-form $\alpha = a_1 dx^1 + a_2 dx^2 + a_3 dx^3$ is

$$\operatorname{div} \alpha = *d*\alpha$$

$$= *d(a_1 dx^2 \wedge dx^3 + a_2 dx^3 \wedge dx^1 + a_3 dx^1 \wedge dx^2)$$

(**22.18**) $$= * \left(\frac{\partial a_1}{\partial x^1} + \frac{\partial a_2}{\partial x^2} + \frac{\partial a_3}{\partial x^3} \right) dx^1 \wedge dx^2 \wedge dx^3$$

$$= \frac{\partial a_1}{\partial x^1} + \frac{\partial a_2}{\partial x^2} + \frac{\partial a_3}{\partial x^3}.$$

(4) The curl of a 1-form $\alpha = a_1 dx^1 + a_2 dx^2 + a_3 dx^3$ is

$$\operatorname{curl} \alpha = *d\alpha$$

$$= * \left\{ \left(\frac{\partial a_3}{\partial x^2} - \frac{\partial a_2}{\partial x^3} \right) dx^2 \wedge dx^3 + \left(\frac{\partial a_1}{\partial x^3} - \frac{\partial a_3}{\partial x^1} \right) dx^3 \wedge dx^1 \right.$$

$$\left. + \left(\frac{\partial a_2}{\partial x^1} - \frac{\partial a_1}{\partial x^2} \right) dx^1 \wedge dx^2 \right\}$$

(**22.19**) $$= \left(\frac{\partial a_3}{\partial x^2} - \frac{\partial a_2}{\partial x^3} \right) dx^1 + \left(\frac{\partial a_1}{\partial x^3} - \frac{\partial a_3}{\partial x^1} \right) dx^2$$

$$+ \left(\frac{\partial a_2}{\partial x^1} - \frac{\partial a_1}{\partial x^2} \right) dx^3$$

$$= \det \begin{bmatrix} dx^1 & dx^2 & dx^3 \\ \dfrac{\partial}{\partial x^1} & \dfrac{\partial}{\partial x^2} & \dfrac{\partial}{\partial x^3} \\ a_1 & a_2 & a_3 \end{bmatrix}$$

where this last determinant is expanded in accordance with the line which precedes it.

Using (22.13), we can compute the $*$-operation in other coordinate systems. The computation is generally rather involved, but it is worth carrying out in detail in a few specific cases.

(22.20)   Example. Let ρ, θ, ϕ be spherical coordinates on the subset $\{p:x^1(p) \neq 0 \text{ or } x^2(p) > 0\}$ of $\mathbf{R}^3$. It has been shown that

$$(d\rho, d\rho) = 1; \qquad (d\theta, d\theta) = \{\rho \sin \phi\}^{-2}; \qquad (d\phi, d\phi) = \rho^{-2};$$

$$(d\rho, d\theta) = (d\rho, d\phi) = (d\theta, d\phi) = 0;$$

$$dx^1 \wedge dx^2 \wedge dx^3 = \rho^2 \sin \phi \, d\rho \wedge d\theta \wedge d\phi.$$

Thus

$$d\rho^{\#} = \langle d\rho^{\#}, d\rho \rangle \frac{\partial}{\partial \rho} + \langle d\rho^{\#}, d\theta \rangle \frac{\partial}{\partial \theta} + \langle d\rho^{\#}, d\phi \rangle \frac{\partial}{\partial \phi}$$

$$= (d\rho, d\rho) \frac{\partial}{\partial \rho} + (d\rho, d\theta) \frac{\partial}{\partial \theta} + (d\rho, d\phi) \frac{\partial}{\partial \phi}$$

$$= \frac{\partial}{\partial \rho},$$

and similarly

$$d\theta^{\#} = (\rho \sin \phi)^{-2} \frac{\partial}{\partial \theta}; \qquad d\phi^{\#} = \rho^{-2} \frac{\partial}{\partial \phi}.$$

Using these results

$$*d\rho = d\rho^{\#} \;\lrcorner\; dx^1 \wedge dx^2 \wedge dx^3 = \frac{\partial}{\partial \rho} \;\lrcorner\; \rho^2 \sin \phi \, d\rho \wedge d\theta \wedge d\phi$$

$$= \rho^2 \sin \phi \, d\theta \wedge d\phi.$$

$$*d\theta = -(\sin \phi)^{-1} d\rho \wedge d\phi; \qquad *d\phi = \sin \phi \, d\rho \wedge d\theta.$$

Exercises

22.1   In $\mathbf{R}^5$ calculate (a) $*(dx^1 \wedge dx^3)$; (b) $*(dx^2 \wedge dx^4 \wedge dx^5)$.

22.2   Show that the identities curl (grad f) $= 0$ and div (curl α) $= 0$ in $\mathbf{R}^3$ are consequences of the fact that $**\omega = (-1)^{k(3-k)}\omega = \omega$ and $d^2 = 0$.

22.3   Show in $\mathbf{R}^3$ that $\alpha \wedge \beta \wedge \gamma = (\alpha, \beta \times \gamma) \, dx^1 \wedge dx^2 \wedge dx^3$ where x^1, x^2, x^3 are cartesian coordinates and α, β, γ are 1-forms.

22.4   (Based on Exercise 22.3.)   Show that $(\beta, \beta \times \gamma) = (\gamma, \beta \times \gamma) = 0$, so that the covector $\beta \times \gamma$ is perpendicular to both β and γ.

22.5   If $\omega = \alpha^1 \wedge \cdots \wedge \alpha^n$ where the α's are 1-forms on $\mathbf{R}$, show that $*\omega = \det(\langle \partial/\partial x^i, \alpha^i \rangle)$.

22.6   If $Z_1, \ldots, Z_n$ are vector fields on the open subset U of $\mathbf{R}^n$, show that

$$\det \{ (Z_i, Z_j) : 1 \leq i, j \leq n \} = [\det \{ \langle Z_i, dx^j \rangle : 1 \leq i, j \leq n \}]^2$$

when $x^1, \ldots, x^n$ are cartesian coordinates for $\mathbf{R}^n$. [HINT:

$$(Z_i, Z_j) = \sum_{k=1}^{n} \langle Z_i, dx^k \rangle \langle Z_j, dx^k \rangle .]$$

22.7 If $\alpha^1, \ldots, \alpha^n$ are 1-forms on the open subset U of $\mathbf{R}^n$, show that

$$\det \{(\alpha^i, \alpha^j)\} = \left[\det \left\{ \left\langle \frac{\partial}{\partial x^i}, \alpha^j \right\rangle \right\} \right]^2.$$

[HINT: See the hint for Exercise 22.6.]

22.8 (Based on Exercises 22.5 and 22.7.) If $\omega = \alpha^1 \wedge \cdots \wedge \alpha^n$ where $\alpha^1, \ldots, \alpha^n$ are 1-forms on $\mathbf{R}$, show that

$$(\omega, \omega) = \det \{(\alpha^i, \alpha^j)\} \, dx^1 \wedge \cdots \wedge dx^n.$$

In particular, if the α^i's form an orthonormal set, ω has unit length.

22.9 Write out the expression for $*d*df$ in terms of cartesian coordinates and partial derivatives of f.

22.10 If r, θ are polar coordinates on $\mathbf{R}^2$, show that

$$dr^{\#} = \frac{\partial}{\partial r}; \quad d\theta^{\#} = \frac{1}{r^2} \frac{\partial}{\partial \theta}; \quad *dr = r \, d\theta; \quad *d\theta = \frac{1}{r} \, dr.$$

23 The standard *m*-simplex

The *standard m-simplex* Δ^m is the point set in $\mathbf{R}^m$ consisting of those m-tuples $(a^1, \ldots, a^m)$ for which

(23.1)
$$a^1 > 0; \quad a^2 \geq 0; \quad \ldots; \quad a^m \geq 0;$$
$$a^1 + a^2 + \cdots + a^m \leq 1.$$

It is a generalized triangle or tetrahedron. A *singular C^K m-simplex* ϕ^m in U is a map of Δ^m into U defined and C^K is some open neighborhood of Δ^m.

According to Theorem (16.11) each C^N m-form β on the open set $V \supset \Delta^m$ has the form

$$\beta = g \, dx^1 \wedge \cdots \wedge dx^m$$

where $x^1, \ldots, x^m$ are cartesian coordinates in $\mathbf{R}^m$ and $g \in C^N(V)$. The integral $\int_{\Delta^m} \beta$ is defined by

(23.2) $\displaystyle \int_{\Delta^m} \beta = \int \cdots \int_{\Delta^m} g(x^1, \ldots, x^m) \, dx^1 \, dx^2 \cdots dx^m$

where the integral on the right in (23.2) is the ordinary m-dimensional volume integral over the point set Δ^m or, equivalently, over interior (Δ^m). If $m = 0$, $\int_{\Delta^0} g = g(\Delta^0)$. ($\Delta^0$ is a single point.)

If ϕ is a singular C^K m-simplex in U ($K > 0$) and ω is an m-form on U (of class C^N, $N \geq 0$), the integral of ω over ϕ, $\int_\phi \omega$, is defined by

(23.3) $\displaystyle \int_\phi \omega = \int_{\Delta^m} \phi^* \omega.$

(23.4) Example. Consider   the $(m - 1)$-simplices $\{\sigma_k^m, \; k = 1, \; 2, \ldots, \; m + 1\}$ in $\mathbf{R}^m$ which are on the boundary of Δ^m, and which are defined by the equations

$$\sigma_1^m(t^1, \ldots, t^{m-1}) = (0, t^1, \ldots, t^{m-1});$$

$$\sigma_2^m(t^1, \ldots, t^{m-1}) = (t^1, 0, t^2, \ldots, t^{m-1});$$

(23.5)

$$\sigma_m^m(t^1, \ldots, t^{m-1}) = (t^1, \ldots, t^{m-1}, 0);$$

$$\sigma_{m+1}^m(t^1, \ldots, t^{m-1}) = (t^1, \ldots, t^{m-1}, 1 - [t^1 + \cdots + t^{m-1}]).$$

In (23.5) the right-hand side of each equation represents the m-tuple $(x^1, \ldots, x^m)$ as functions of $(t^1, \ldots, t^{m-1}) \in \Delta^{m-1} \subset \mathbf{R}^{m-1}$. To make this notation complete, Δ^0 is a single point and

$$\sigma_1^1(\Delta^0) = 0, \qquad \sigma_2^1(\Delta^0) = 1.$$

It will prove useful later on to note that

(23.6) $$\sigma_k^m \circ \sigma_j^{m-1} = \sigma_{j+1}^m \circ \sigma_k^{m-1}, \qquad 1 \leq k \leq j \leq m.$$

If ϕ is a singular C^K m-simplex $(k > 1)$ in U defined on the open set $V \supset \Delta^m$, ϕ is *imbedded* if (i) ϕ is one-one on V and (ii) $\phi_*(X_p) \neq 0$ for any vector $X_p \in T_p(\mathbf{R}^m)$, $p \in V$. Condition (ii) is equivalent to the requirement that ϕ has rank m at each point of V. The following theorem provides a geometric basis for $\int_\phi \omega$, stating as it does that to within a sign the integral of the m-form ω over the imbedded m-simplex ϕ depends only on ω and the geometric object $\phi(\Delta^m)$.

(23.7) Theorem. Suppose ϕ_1 and ϕ_2 are imbedded m-simplices $(m > 0)$ in U and $\phi_1(\Delta^m) = \phi_2(\Delta^m)$; then for each m-form ω on U

(23.8) $$\int_{\phi_1} \omega = \varepsilon \int_{\phi_2} \omega$$

where ε is the sign of the Jacobian of the map $\phi_2^{-1} \circ \phi_1$ of $\Delta^m \to \Delta^m$.

PROOF.   Suppose $\phi_2 : V \to U$, where V is open and contains Δ^m. Put $W = $ interior (Δ^m). Theorem (12.5) states explicitly that $f = \phi_2^{-1} \circ \phi_1 : \Delta^m \to V$ has rank m at each point of W. It follows that $f(W)$ is open (inverse function theorem) and a subset of Δ^m, so that $f(W) \subset W$. Since the same reasoning applies to f^{-1}, $f(W) = W$, and both the maps f and f^{-1} of W onto W are differentiable. According to (21.22)(iv)

(23.9) $$f^*(\phi_2^* \omega) = \phi_1^*(\phi_2^{-1})^* \phi_2^* \omega = \phi_1^*(\phi_2 \circ \phi_2^{-1})^* \omega = \phi_1^* \omega.$$

on W. Suppose that

(23.10)
$$\phi_1^*\omega = h_1(t^1, \ldots, t^m)\, dt^1 \wedge \cdots \wedge dt^m,$$
$$\phi_2^*\omega = h_2(t^1, \ldots, t^m)\, dt^1 \wedge \cdots \wedge dt^m$$

where $t^1, \ldots, t^m$ are cartesian coordinates on $\mathbf{R}^m$. Put $f^k = t^k \circ f$ $(k = 1, \ldots, m)$, so that

$$(t^1, \ldots, t^m) \to (f^1(t^1, \ldots, t^m), \ldots, f^m(t^1, \ldots, t^m))$$

describes the map f. Since $f^*(dt^k) = d(t^k \circ f) = df^k$,

$$f^*(\phi_2^*\omega) = f^*h_2 f^*(dt^1) \wedge \cdots \wedge f^*(dt^m)$$
$$= h_2(f^1, \ldots, f^m)\, df^1 \wedge \cdots \wedge df^m$$
(23.11)
$$= h_2 \circ f \det\left[\frac{\partial f^j}{\partial t^k}\right] dt^1 \wedge \cdots \wedge dt^m.$$

Comparing (23.9), (23.10), and (23.11) shows that

(23.12)
$$h_1 = h_2 \circ f \det\left[\frac{\partial f^j}{\partial t^k}\right].$$

Equation (23.8) follows from two observations: (i) $\det [\partial f^j/\partial t^k(p)] \neq 0$ for each $p \in W$ (cf. Exercise 8.2). Thus if $p, q \in W$,

(23.13)
$$\text{sign} \det\left[\frac{\partial f^j}{\partial t^k}(p)\right] = \text{sign} \det\left[\frac{\partial f^j}{\partial t^k}(q)\right],$$

so that the function $\varepsilon = \varepsilon(p) = \text{sign} \det [\partial f^j/\partial t^k(p)]$ is just a constant $= \pm 1$ on W. The only alternative to (23.13) would be for the continuous function $\det [\partial f^j/\partial t^k(p)]$ to vanish somewhere on the segment $\overline{pq} \subset W$ in keeping with the intermediate value theorem. (ii) The basic theorem for changing variables in multiple integrals states that

(23.14)
$$\int \cdots \int_{\{(f^1,\ldots,f^m):(f^1,\ldots,f^m)\varepsilon W\}} h_2(f^1, \ldots, f^m)\, df^1 \cdots df^m$$
$$= \int \cdots \int_{\{(t^1,\ldots,t^m):f(t^1,\ldots,t^m)\varepsilon W\}} h_2 \circ f \left| \det \frac{\partial f^j}{\partial t^k} \right| dt^1 \cdots dt^m.$$

Putting these together yields (23.8) via the sequence of equalities

$$\int_{\phi_2}\omega = \int_{\Delta^m}\phi_2^*\omega = \int_W h_2(f^1, \ldots, f^m)\, df^1 \cdots df^m$$
$$= \int_W h_2 \circ f\varepsilon \det\left(\frac{\partial f^j}{\partial t^k}\right) dt^1 \cdots dt^m$$
$$= \varepsilon \int_W h_1(t^1, \ldots, t^m)\, dt^1 \cdots dt^m = \varepsilon \int_{\phi_1}\omega. \qquad \blacklozenge$$

Theorem (23.7) is responsible for some additional terminology. If ϕ_1 and ϕ_2 are imbedded k-simplices with $\phi_1(\Delta^k) = \phi_2(\Delta^k)$, ϕ_1 and ϕ_2 have the *same orientation* if the ε of (23.8) is $+1$ and *opposite orientation* if $\varepsilon = -1$. According to this terminology all 0-simplices with the same image have the same orientation, while for higher dimensions the imbedded k-simplices with the same image set divide into two orientation classes. The concept of orientation is developed further in Section 24.

If ϕ is a singular C^K m-simplex in the open set U of $\mathbf{R}^n$ and ψ is a C^K map of U into the open set V of $\mathbf{R}^k$, then $\psi \circ \phi$ is a singular C^K m-simplex in V. It is called the image of ϕ under the map ψ. There is an important relation between these simplices. If ω is an m-form on V, then

(23.15)
$$\int_\phi \psi^*\omega = \int_{\psi \circ \phi} \omega,$$

because $\qquad \int_{\psi \circ \phi} \omega = \int_{\Delta^m} (\psi \circ \phi)^*\omega = \int_{\Delta^m} \phi^*(\psi^*\omega) = \int_\phi \psi^*\omega$

according to the definition (23.3) and the relation (22.11)(iv).

24   *m*-chains. The boundary operator ∂

The singular simplices by themselves are not a sufficiently rich class of objects to describe all the integrals of the form (23.3) to which the mathematician attributes a meaning. For example, "integration of a 1-form around a circle" does not have the form (23.3). It is necessary to piece simplices together or to cut up the figure over which integration extends into simplices. This leads directly to the notion of an m-chain.

m-chains are presented abstractly below, but the reader is cautioned to bear in mind that in the applications in this book an m-chain represents a piecewise parametrization of a subset of $\mathbf{R}^n$, and this parametrization is used almost exclusively to evaluate integrals of m-forms over the chain. The m-simplices are the fundamental building blocks of this parametrization. They are particularly suitable. The m-chains that result can be used to describe integration over a very rich class of hypersurfaces, curves, and smoothly bounded regions in $\mathbf{R}^n$.

A *singular C^K m-chain in U* is described by an abstract linear combination

(24.1)
$$a_1\sigma_1 + a_2\sigma_2 + \cdots + a_k\sigma_k$$

where the a_j's are integers and the σ_i's C^K m-simplices in U. The symbols "$+$" in (24.1) are a form of punctuation indicating symbolically the type of rearrangements and substitutions that can be made without changing the underlying m-chain. These take the following forms:

(i)   The positions of two terms $a_i\sigma_i$ and $a_j\sigma_j$ can be interchanged.

(24.2)   (ii)   "$a\sigma + b\sigma$" can be substituted for "$(a + b)\sigma$."

(iii)   "0σ" can be dropped from (24.1) except when it is the only term and then it can be replaced by "0."

Two expressions $a_1\sigma_1 + \cdots + a_k\sigma_k$ and $b_1\tau_1 + \cdots + b_j\tau_j$ are equivalent or represent the same underlying m-chain if one can be reduced to the other by using the operations (24.2). Their *sum* is the m-chain described by

$$a_1\sigma_1 + \cdots + a_k\sigma_k + b_1\tau_1 + \cdots + b_j\tau_j.$$

As a matter of notation, $a(a_1\sigma_1 + \cdots + a_k\sigma_k) = (aa_1)\sigma_1 + \cdots + (aa_k)\sigma_k$ as usual when a is an integer.

If ω is an m-form on U and c^m an m-chain represented by the expression $a_1\sigma_1 + \cdots + a_k\sigma_k$, the integral of ω over c^m is defined by

$$(24.3) \qquad \int_{c^m} \omega = \sum_{j=1}^{k} a_j \int_{\sigma_j} \omega.$$

The substitutions in (24.2) are compatible with (24.3), so that the integral in (24.3) depends only on the underlying m-chain and not on the particular expression of type (24.1) used to represent it. If ϕ is a C^K map of U into V, the *image of c^m under ϕ* is the m-chain in V described by $a_1(\phi \circ \sigma_1) + \cdots + a_k(\phi \circ \sigma_k)$ and denoted by $\phi \circ c^m$.

The boundary operator ∂. The boundary $\partial\Delta^m$ of the standard m-simplex is the singular $(m-1)$-chain

$$(24.4) \qquad \partial\Delta^m = \sum_{k=1}^{m+1} (-1)^k \sigma_k^m$$

where the σ_k^m's are the singular $(m-1)$-simplices given in Example (23.4). If τ is a singular C^K m-simplex in U its boundary $\partial\tau$ is the $(m-1)$-chain defined by

$$(24.5) \qquad \partial\tau = \tau \circ \partial\Delta^m,$$

and if $c = a_1\tau_1 + \cdots + a_j\tau_j$ is an m-chain in U, its boundary is the $(m-1)$-chain.

$$(24.6) \qquad \partial c = a_1\,\partial\tau_1 + \cdots + a_j\,\partial\tau_j.$$

If c is any m-chain in U

$$(24.7) \qquad \partial(\partial c) = 0.$$

Preliminary reductions show that when $c = a_1\tau_1 + \cdots + a_k\tau_k$,

$$\partial(\partial c) = \partial(a_1\,\partial\tau_1 + \cdots + a_k\,\partial\tau_k)$$
$$= a_1\,\partial(\partial\tau_1) + \cdots + a_k\,\partial(\partial\tau_k)$$
$$= a_1\tau_1 \circ (\partial[\partial\Delta^m]) + \cdots + a_k\tau_k \circ (\partial[\partial\Delta^m]);$$

so it suffices to prove $\partial(\partial\Delta^m) = 0$. But

$$\partial(\partial\Delta^m) = \sum_{k=1}^{m+1} (-1)^k \, \partial\sigma_k^m$$

$$= \sum_{k=1}^{m+1} (-1)^k \sigma_k^m \circ \sum_{j=1}^{m} (-1)^j \sigma_j^{m-1}$$

$$= \sum_{k=1}^{m+1} (-1)^k \sum_{j=1}^{m} (-1)^j \sigma_k^m \circ \sigma_j^{m-1}$$

$$= \sum_{1 \le k \le j \le m} [(-1)^{k+j} \sigma_k^m \circ \sigma_j^{m-1} + (-1)^{k+j+1} \sigma_{j+1}^m \circ \sigma_k^{m-1}]$$

$$= 0$$

by (23.6).

The boundary operator ∂ is closely related to the concept of orientation mentioned in Section 23. Consider for example the three cases of Δ^1, Δ^2, and Δ^3. In these examples the zero simplex which maps the point Δ^0 into the point q is denoted by $\{q\}$, so that $\{q\}(\Delta^0) = q$.

$\Delta^1 = [0, 1]$ in $\mathbf{R}$. $\partial\Delta^1 = \sigma_2^1 - \sigma_1^1$, which can be written $\partial\Delta^1 = \{1\} - \{0\}$. For graphical purposes Δ^1 is represented as a directed line segment, an arrow directed from 0 to 1. The general 1-simplex is a continuous image of Δ^1, $\phi: \Delta^1 \to \mathbf{R}^m$, and is usually represented by an arc directed from $\phi(0)$ to $\phi(1)$.

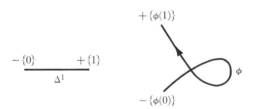

Δ^2 is a triangular region described graphically by a triangle containing an oriented circle usually drawn as a partially open circle with an arrowhead showing how the simplices in the bounding 1-chain are directed. The general imbedded 2-simplex ψ is a continuous image of Δ^2 and can be thought of as a warped copy of Δ^2, the oriented circle being carried along by the map ψ in a suggestive manner (see Figure 9).

Δ^3 is a tetrahedral region. It is described graphically by a tetrahedron with a symbol, consisting of an oriented circle whose plane is pierced at right angles through the circle's center by an arrow, showing how to orient the simplices in the bounding 2-chain. The manner in which this is done should be clear from Figure 10. Roughly speaking, the oriented circle is

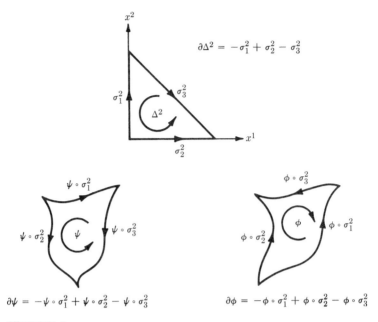

$$\partial \Delta^2 = -\sigma_1^2 + \sigma_2^2 - \sigma_3^2$$

$$\partial \psi = -\psi \circ \sigma_1^2 + \psi \circ \sigma_2^2 - \psi \circ \sigma_3^2 \qquad \partial \phi = -\phi \circ \sigma_1^2 + \phi \circ \sigma_2^2 - \phi \circ \sigma_3^2$$

FIGURE 9

projected on the bounding 2-simplices from inside Δ^3 in the direction of the arrow.

k-chains are built up from k-simplices which may abut, overlap, and cancel one another out in quite complicated patterns. The general

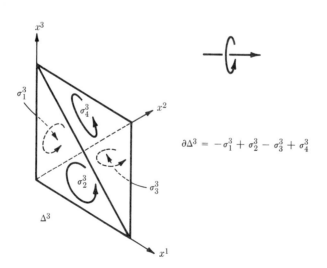

$$\partial \Delta^3 = -\sigma_1^3 + \sigma_2^3 - \sigma_3^3 + \sigma_4^3$$

FIGURE 10

possibilities should be clear from the discussion above and the examples which follow later.

A useful concept associated with a chain c in U is the subset of U on which c is concentrated or the *support of c*. This is a closed subset of U. It is conveniently described by its complement: A point p of U does not belong to the support of the k-chain c if there is a neighborhood V of p such that

$$\int_c \omega = 0$$

whenever ω is a k-form on U which vanishes outside V in the sense that the associated k-covector $\omega_q = 0$, $q \notin V$. Every point in the interior of a set V of the type described above is excluded from the support of c, so that support (c) is relatively closed in U. If c is represented by the expression

$$c = a_1\tau_1 + \cdots + a_m\tau_m$$

where the a_j's are integers and the τ_i's are singular k-simplices in U, it is rather easy to see using (23.2), (23.3), and (24.3) that support (c) is a subset of the compact set $D = \bigcup_{j=1}^{m} \tau_j(\Delta^k)$. In some cases support (c) will actually be equal to D, but, because of cancellations which can occur in the expressions representing c and the possibility that $\tau_i(\Delta^k)$ and $\tau_j(\Delta^k)$ may overlap with opposite orientations, this is not generally so. As a relatively closed subset of D, however, support (c) is closed and even compact.

As the examples below demonstrate, it is a distinct possibility that two distinct m-chains c and b may nevertheless be indistinguishable as far as integration is concerned, by which it is meant that

$$\int_c \omega = \int_b \omega$$

for every m-form ω for which the integrals make sense. In this case c and b are called *equivalent with respect to integration* or just plain *equivalent*, and this relation is denoted by $c \sim b$.

In actually evaluating the integral $\int_c \omega$ of an m-form ω over an m-chain c it is often convenient to use (23.15) to put the chain together in an open set U, which is usually chosen because a particular type of coordinate system simplifies evaluating the integrals concerned. Technically this amounts to finding a map $\phi: U \to \mathbf{R}^n$ and a chain c_0 in U such that $c = \phi \circ c_0$ and then using the relation

$$\int_{\phi \circ c_0} \omega = \int_{c_0} \phi^*\omega$$

to evaluate the integral. The possibilities are illustrated in the examples below. In some cases the results are outlined and the details left to the exercises.

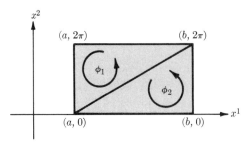

FIGURE 11

(24.8) **Example.** Let p_0, p_1, and p_2 be three points in $\mathbf{R}^2$, and $\phi: \Delta^2 \to \mathbf{R}^2$ the 2-simplex described in vector notation by

$$\phi(t^1, t^2) = t^1 p_0 + t^2 p_1 + (1 - t^1 - t^2) p_2.$$

If $\omega = f(x^1, x^2) \, dx^1 \wedge dx^2$ where x^1 and x^2 are cartesian coordinates in $\mathbf{R}^2$, then

(24.9) $$\int_\phi \omega = \pm \int_{\Delta(p_0, p_1, p_2)} f(x^1, x^2) \, dx^1 \, dx^2$$

where $\Delta(p_0, p_1, p_2)$ is the triangle determined by the three points p_0, p_1, and p_2. The sign in (24.9) is plus if p_0, p_1, p_2 taken in that order circumscribe the triangle in the counterclockwise sense and minus if they circumscribe the triangle in the clockwise sense. The second integral in (24.9) is just an ordinary area integral in $\mathbf{R}^2$.

By joining several simplices of the type in Example (24.8) together in a chain it is possible to describe the integral of a function over any region of $\mathbf{R}^2$ which can be triangulated in the form $\int_\phi \omega$.

(24.10) **Example.** Let ϕ_1 and ϕ_2 be the 2-simplices in $\mathbf{R}^2$ described by (the points are written below as 2-tuples of real numbers)

$$\phi_1(t^1, t^2) = t^1(a, 0) + t^2(b, 2\pi) + [1 - t^1 - t^2](a, 2\pi);$$

$$\phi_2(t^1, t^2) = t^1(a, 0) + t^2(b, 0) + [1 - t^1 - t^2](b, 2\pi).$$

If $\omega = f(x^1, x^2) \, dx^1 \wedge dx^2$ with x^1 and x^2 cartesian coordinates, and $b > a$, then the integral of ω over the chain $c = \phi_1 + \phi_2$ is just the ordinary area integral (see Figure 11)

$$\int_0^{2\pi} \int_a^b f(x^1, x^2) \, dx^1 \, dx^2 = \int_c \omega.$$

(24.11) **Example.** Let $\psi: \mathbf{R}^2 \to \mathbf{R}^2$ be described in terms of cartesian coordinates x^1, x^2 on $\mathbf{R}^2$ by

$$x^1 \circ \psi = x^1 \cos x^2; \qquad x^2 \circ \psi = x^1 \sin x^2.$$

If c is the chain $\phi_1 + \phi_2$ of Example (24.10) and $\omega = f(x^1, x^2) \, dx^1 \wedge dx^2$, then

(24.12) $$\int_{\psi \circ c} \omega = \int_0^{2\pi} \int_a^b f(r \cos \theta, r \sin \theta) r \, dr \, d\theta,$$

so that integration of ω over $\psi \circ c$ corresponds to evaluating the ordinary area

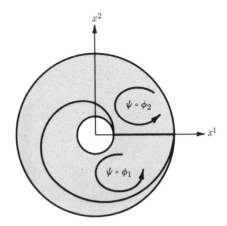

FIGURE 12

integral of f over the annulus described in polar coordinates by $a \leq r \leq b$ (see Figure 12).

(24.13)   Example.   Let $\psi: \mathbf{R}^2 \to \mathbf{R}^3$ be described by

$$y^1 \circ \psi = \rho \cos x^1 \sin x^2; \quad y^2 \circ \psi = \rho \sin x^1 \sin x^2; \quad y^3 \circ \psi = \rho \cos x^1,$$

where y^1, y^2, and y^3 are cartesian coordinates for $\mathbf{R}^3$ and x^1, x^2 cartesian coordinates for $\mathbf{R}^2$. Let $\tau = \phi_1 + \phi_2$ be the 2-chain in $\mathbf{R}^2$ described by $a < b$, $c < d$ (see Figure 13),

$$\phi_1(t^1, t^2) = t^1(a, c) + t^2(b, d) + [1 - t^1 - t^2](a, d),$$

$$\phi_2(t^1, t^2) = t^1(a, c) + t^2(b, c) + [1 - t^1 - t^2](b, d),$$

and suppose

$$\omega = \left(\frac{y^1}{\rho} \frac{\partial}{\partial y^1} + \frac{y^2}{\rho} \frac{\partial}{\partial y^2} + \frac{y^3}{\rho} \frac{\partial}{\partial y^3} \right) \lrcorner \; dy^1 \wedge dy^2 \wedge dy^3$$

$$= \frac{y^1}{\rho} dy^2 \wedge dy^3 + \frac{y^2}{\rho} dy^3 \wedge dy^1 + \frac{y^3}{\rho} dy^1 \wedge dy^2.$$

Then

(24.14)
$$\int_{\psi \circ \tau} \omega = \int_c^d \int_a^b \rho \sin^2 \phi \, d\theta \, d\phi.$$

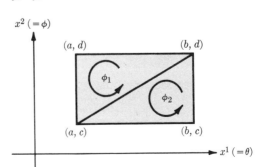

FIGURE 13

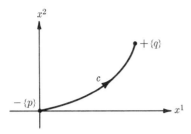

FIGURE 14

Note that the unnumbered formula preceding (24.14) exhibits ω as the inner product of a unit outer normal vector field N on the sphere of radius ρ centered at the origin and the 3-form $dy^1 \wedge dy^2 \wedge dy^3$. Equation (24.14) gives the area of that portion of the 2-sphere $x^2 + y^2 + z^2 = \rho^2$ described in spherical coordinates by $a \leq \theta \leq b, c \leq \phi \leq d$.

When working with m-chains $m \leq 3$ it is often quite helpful to use an orienting symbol designed (1) to keep track of the sign involved in integration over the chain and (2) to describe the boundary of the chain. Since they are used in graphic depiction of a chain, such orienting symbols are not mathematical objects in themselves but are used to describe mathematical relationships. Their use is illustrated in the following examples.

(24.15) Example. Let $\phi: [0, 1] \to \mathbf{R}^2$ be the 1-simplex described by $x^1 \circ \phi(t) = t$; $x^2 \circ \phi(t) = t^2$, and let c be the chain $c = +1\phi$ represented by $+1$ times ϕ. The boundary of c consists of two 0-simplices $p(\Delta^\circ) = (0,0)$ and $p(\Delta^\circ) = (1,1)$ and is represented by $\partial c = (+1)q + (-1)p$, usually abbreviated $\partial c = \{q\} - \{p\}$. Graphically c together with its boundary ∂c is described in Figure 14.

If $\psi: [0, 1] \to \mathbf{R}^2$ is given by $\psi(t) = \phi(1 - t)$, then the chain $b = +1\psi$ has boundary $\partial b = \{p\} - \{q\}$ and is represented graphically in Figure 15. b has the same representation and the same boundary as the chain $-c = (-1)\phi$, and it is even true that

$$\int_b \omega = \int_{-c} \omega$$

for every 1-form ω on $\mathbf{R}^2$, yet in the above treatment b and $-c$ are distinguished as chains but equivalent with respect to integration, $b \sim -c$.

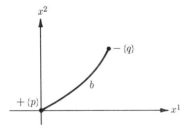

FIGURE 15

(24.16)   **Example.**   Let $c = \phi_1 + \phi_2$ be the 2-chain in $\mathbf{R}^2$ described by

$$\phi_1(t^1, t^2) = t^1(0, 0) + t^2\left(1, \frac{\pi}{2}\right) + (1 - t^1 - t^2)\left(0, \frac{\pi}{2}\right);$$

$$\phi_2(t^1, t^2) = t^1(0, 0) + t^2(1, 0) + (1 - t^1 - t^2)\left(1, \frac{\pi}{2}\right).$$

If x^1 and x^2 are cartesian coordinates in $\mathbf{R}^2$, then

$$\int_c f(x^1, x^2)\, dx^1\, dx^2 = \int_0^{\pi/2} \int_0^1 f(x^1, x^2)\, dx^1\, dx^2,$$

so that c is related to integration over the rectangle $0 \le x^1 \le 1$, $0 \le x^2 \le \pi/2$. For any 2-simplex ϕ, the boundary of ϕ is given by $\partial\phi = \phi \circ \sigma_1^2 + \phi \circ \sigma_2^2 - \phi \circ \sigma_3^2$. Now

$$\phi_1 \circ \sigma_1^2(t) = t\left(1, \frac{\pi}{2}\right) + (1 - t)\left(0, \frac{\pi}{2}\right);$$

$$\phi_1 \circ \sigma_2^2(t) = t(0, 0) + (1 - t)\left(0, \frac{\pi}{2}\right);$$

$$\phi_1 \circ \sigma_3^2(t) = t(0, 0) + (1 - t)\left(1, \frac{\pi}{2}\right);$$

$$\phi_2 \circ \sigma_1^2(t) = t(1, 0) + (1 - t)\left(1, \frac{\pi}{2}\right);$$

$$\phi_2 \circ \sigma_2^2(t) = t(0, 0) + (1 - t)\left(1, \frac{\pi}{2}\right);$$

$$\phi_2 \circ \sigma_3^2(t) = t(0, 0) + (1 - t)(1, 0).$$

Evidently $\phi_2 \circ \sigma_2^2 = \phi_1 \circ \sigma_3^2$; thus

$$\partial c = \partial\phi_1 + \partial\phi_2$$
$$= -\phi_1 \circ \sigma_1^2 + \phi_1 \circ \sigma_2^2 - \phi_1 \circ \sigma_3^2 - \phi_2 \circ \sigma_2^2 + \phi_2 \circ \sigma_2^2 - \phi_2 \circ \sigma_3^2$$
$$= -\phi_1 \circ \sigma_1^2 + \phi_1 \circ \sigma_2^2 - \phi_2 \circ \sigma_1^2 - \phi_2 \circ \sigma_3^2,$$

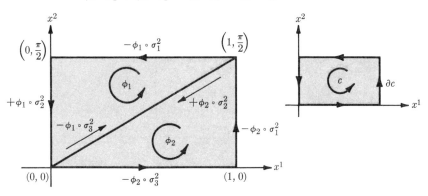

FIGURE 16

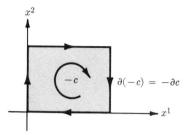

FIGURE 17

where the last simplification has been made using the operations permitted by (24.2) together with the fact that $\phi_1 \circ \sigma_3^2 = \phi_2 \circ \sigma_2^2$. The 1-simplices remaining in ∂c represent the four sides of the rectangle represented by c (see Figure 16).

The chain $-c = -\phi_1 - \phi_2$ is represented graphically by Figure 17.

If $\beta_1(t^1, t^2) = \phi_1(t^2, t^1)$, $\beta_2(t^1, t^2) = \phi_2(t^2, t^1)$, then $-c$ and the 2-chain $b = \beta_1 + \beta_2$ have the same effect as far as integrating forms is concerned and they are represented by the same diagram. $b \sim -c$.

(24.17) Example. Let $\psi: \mathbf{R}^2 \to \mathbf{R}^2$ be the map described in Example (24.11) by

$$x^1 \circ \psi = x^1 \cos x^2, \qquad x^2 \circ \psi = x^1 \sin x^2,$$

and let c be the 2-chain of Example (24.16). Then $\psi \circ c = \psi \circ \phi_1 + \psi \circ \phi_2$ is a 2-chain in $\mathbf{R}^2$ which is closely related to integration over the first quadrant of the unit disk according to Example (24.11) (see Figure 18). $\partial(\psi \circ c) = \psi \circ \partial c$ as always, and this would not require further emphasis except that the 1-simplex $\psi \circ \phi_1 \circ \sigma_2^2$ is given by

$$\psi \circ \phi_1 \circ \sigma_2^2(t) = (0, 0), \qquad 0 \le t \le 1,$$

and can be considered collapsed at the origin.

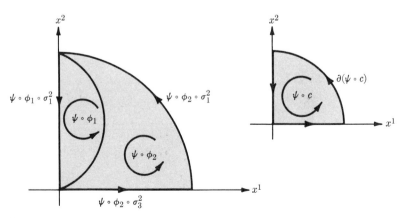

FIGURE 18

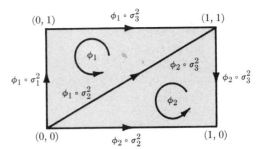

FIGURE 19

(24.18)   **Example.**   Let $\psi = \phi_1 + \phi_2$ be the 2-chain in $\mathbf{R}^2$ described by

(24.19)
$$\phi_1(t^1, t^2) = t^1(1, 1) + t^2(0, 1),$$
$$\phi_2(t^1, t^2) = t^1(1, 0) + t^2(1, 1).$$

ψ represents integration over the unit square $0 \le x^1 \le 1, 0 \le x^2 \le 1$ in $\mathbf{R}^2$ (see Figure 19). Now let $C_i(s) = (a_i + r_i \cos 2\pi s, \ b_i + r_i \sin 2\pi s)$, $i = 1, 2$; $s \in [0, 1]$. C_i is a parametrization of the circle of radius r_i centered at (a_i, b_i). Let $F: \mathbf{R}^2 \to \mathbf{R}^2$ be the map

$$F(s^1, s^2) = s^2 C_1(s^1) + (1 - s^2) C_2(s^1),$$

and consider the 2-chain $F \circ \psi$ (see Figure 20).

$$\partial(F \circ \psi) = F \circ (\partial\psi)$$
$$= F \circ (\partial\phi_1 + \partial\phi_2)$$
$$= F \circ (-\phi_1 \circ \sigma_1^2 + \phi_1 \circ \sigma_2^2 - \phi_1 \circ \sigma_3^2 - \phi_2 \circ \sigma_1^2 + \phi_2 \circ \sigma_2^2 - \phi_2 \circ \sigma_3^2).$$

Now
$$\phi_1 \circ \sigma_2^2(t) = t(1, 1) = \phi_2 \circ \sigma_1^2(t),$$

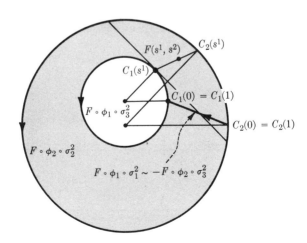

FIGURE 20

while

$$F \circ \phi_1 \circ \sigma_1^2(t) = F \circ \phi_1(0, t) = F(0, t) = tC_1(0) + (1 - t)C_2(0);$$

$$F \circ \phi_2 \circ \sigma_3^2(t) = F \circ \phi_2(t, 1 - t) = F(1, 1 - t) = (1 - t)C_1(1) + tC_2(1);$$

$$F \circ \phi_1 \circ \sigma_3^2(t) = F \circ \phi_1(t, 1 - t) = F(t, 1) = C_1(t);$$

$$F \circ \phi_2 \circ \sigma_3^2(t) = F \circ \phi_2(t, 0) = F(t, 0) = C_2(t).$$

Notice that $\phi_1 \circ \sigma_2^2 - \phi_2 \circ \sigma_1^2 = 0$ while $-F \circ \phi_1 \circ \sigma_1^2 - F \circ \phi_2 \circ \sigma_3^2 \sim 0$ since these last simplices represent integration over the line segment joining $C_1(0)$

(1) 1-chains:

(2) 2-chains:

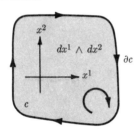
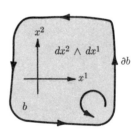

(3) 3-chains:

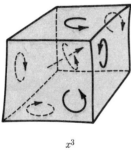

$$dx^1 \wedge dx^2 \wedge dx^3$$

$$-dx^1 \wedge dx^2 \wedge dx^3$$

FIGURE 21

to $C_2(0)$ in opposite directions. As a consequence

(24.20) $$\partial(F \circ \psi) \sim F \circ \phi_2 \circ \sigma_2^2 - F \circ \phi_1 \circ \sigma_3^2$$

and represents integration over the circle C_2 minus integration over C_1. Of particular importance is the case where C_1 lies inside C_2. Then $C_2(s)$ bisects the arc cut off from C_2 by the chord tangent to C_1 at $C_1(s)$ and as a consequence the support of the 2-chain $F \circ \psi$ is the set of points between C_1 and C_2 and including these circles.

In summary these orienting symbols are illustrated in Figure 21. Given with each of them is an indication of a coordinate grid and an *m*-form of the type that would have a positive integral over a chain with the indicated orientation—that is, a chain made up of simplices with the indicated orientation. The symbols themselves are immersed in the outline of an *m*-chain with which they are associated, the boundary of which is oriented in a manner consistent with the orientation of the chain itself. As is to be expected, two orientations are given for each dimension.

Exercises

In the following construct a chain c which represents integration over the specified set H with the orientation prescribed. Then perform the indicated integration. Unless otherwise specified $x^1, \ldots, x^n$ are cartesian coordinates.

24.1 H is the triangle with vertices $(1, 1)$, $(2, 1)$, and $(1, 3)$ in $\mathbf{R}^2$ and c is oriented so that

$$\int_c dx^1 \wedge dx^2 = \text{volume } (H).$$

Evaluate $\int_{3c} (x^1)^2 \, dx^1 \wedge dx^2$.

24.2 c is the 2-chain of Exercise 24.1. Find ∂c and evaluate:

$$\int_{\partial c} (x^1 \, dx^2 + x^2 \, dx^1).$$

24.3 H is the tetrahedron with vertices $(0, 0, 0)$, $(1, 2, 1)$, $(1, -1, 1)$, and $(3, 1, 1)$ in $\mathbf{R}^3$.

$$\int_c dx^1 \wedge dx^2 \wedge dx^3 = \text{volume } (H).$$

Evaluate $\int_c (x^1 - x^2) x^3 \, dx^1 \wedge dx^2 \wedge dx^3$.

24.4 H is the ball of radius b centered at $(0, 0, 0)$ in $\mathbf{R}^3$.

$$\int_c dx^1 \wedge dx^2 \wedge dx^3 = \tfrac{4}{3}\pi b^3.$$

Evaluate: (a) $\int_c x^1 x^2 x^3 \, dx^1 \wedge dx^2 \wedge dx^3$; (b) $\int_{\partial c} x^1 \, dx^2 \wedge dx^3$.

24.5 H is the box $0 \leq x^1 \leq a^1, 0 \leq x^2 \leq a^2, 0 \leq x^3 \leq a^3$.

$$\int_c dx^1 \wedge dx^2 \wedge dx^3 = a^1 a^2 a^3.$$

Give a detailed description of c.

Section 24 appendix. Exercises on chains.
Simplicial subdivision. Affine chains

The contents of this section are not used in the remainder of this book. They describe a method by which any chain c can be replaced by a chain c' which is equivalent for the purposes of integration, $c \sim c'$, and is made up of simplices whose diameters are all less than any prescribed $\varepsilon > 0$. Geometrically this is accomplished by successively subdividing the simplices of the original chain c. The procedure is described below and furnishes many exercises on manipulation of chains.

The Cone Construction. If ϕ is an m-simplex in $\mathbf{R}^n$ and p is a point of $\mathbf{R}^n$, the cone with base ϕ and vertex p is the $(m + 1)$-simplex $p \times \phi$ defined by

$$(p \times \phi)(t^1, \ldots, t^{m+1}) = (1 - [t^1 + \cdots + t^{m+1}])p$$

$$+ [t^1 + \cdots + t^{m+1}]\phi \left(\frac{t^1}{t^1 + \cdots + t^{m+1}}, \cdots, \frac{t^m}{t^1 + \cdots + t^{m+1}} \right)$$

where $(t^1, \ldots, t^{m+1}) \in \Delta^{m+1}$.

Exercise 1. Show that $(p \times \phi) \circ \sigma_k^{m+1} = p \times (\phi \circ \sigma_k^m)$, $k \leq m + 1$.

Exercise 2. Show that $(p \times \phi) \circ \sigma_{m+2}^{m+1} = \phi$.

Exercise 3. Show that $\partial(p \times \phi) = p \times \partial\phi + (-1)^{m+2}\phi$. [HINT: See Exercises 1 and 2.]

Exercise 4. Illustrate $p \times \phi$ when (a) ϕ is a 1-simplex; (b) ϕ is a 2-simplex. Show in these illustrations why the result of Exercise 3 holds.

If $c = a_1\phi_1 + \cdots + a_k\phi_k$ is an m-chain, $p \times c$ is defined by $p \times c = a_1(p \times \phi_1) + \cdots + a_k(p \times \phi_k)$, $p \times 0 = 0$.

Exercise 5. Show that $p \times c$ depends only on the chain underlying the expression $a_1\phi_1 + \cdots + a_k\phi_k$ used to represent c and not on that expression itself. That is, show that $p \times c$ is well defined.

Simplicial Subdivision. The subdivision operator S is defined inductively: If b is a 0-chain, $Sb = b$. Suppose that S has been defined for $(m - 1)$-chains and let $c = a_1\phi_1 + \cdots + a_k\phi_k$ be an m-chain. Sc is then defined by the requirements:

(i) $S(a_1\phi_1 + \cdots + a_k\phi_k) = a_1 S\phi_1 + \cdots + a_k S\phi_k$.

(ii) $S\phi = \phi \cdot S \Delta^m$ when ϕ is an m-simplex.

(iii) $S\Delta^m = p_m \times S \partial\Delta^m$ where $p_m = \left(\dfrac{1}{m + 1}, \cdots, \dfrac{1}{m + 1} \right) \in \mathbf{R}^m$.

The case where c is a 2-simplex is illustrated in Figure 22 and should indicate the geometrical nature of S to the reader.

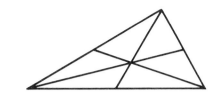

FIGURE 22

Exercise 6. Show that Sc is well defined. See Exercise 5 for the meaning here of "well defined."

Exercise 7. Show that $f \circ Sc = S(f \circ c)$ whenever c is an m-chain in U and $f: U \to \mathbf{R}^n$. In other words $f \circ S = S \circ f$.

Exercise 8. Show that $\partial S = S\partial$. [HINT: Establish this fact by induction on the dimension of the chain on which both sides act.]

Exercise 9. Show that $Sc \sim c$. That is, for each m-chain c in U and each m-form ω on U, $\int_{Sc} \omega = \int_c \omega$.

Affine Chains. A simplex $\phi: \Delta^m \to \mathbf{R}^n$ is *affine* if

(A.1) $\qquad \phi[sp + (1 - s)q] = s\phi(p) + (1 - s)\phi(q)$

whenever $0 \le s \le 1$ and $p, q \in \Delta^m$. A chain is affine if it can be expressed as a sum of affine simplices.

Exercise 10. Show that ϕ is affine if and only if $\phi(t^1, \ldots, t^m) = t^1 p_1 + \cdots + t^m p_m + (1 - [t^1 + \cdots + t^m])p_{m+1}$ whenever $(t^1, \ldots, t^m) \in \Delta^m$ for some points $p_1, \ldots, p_{m+1}$ in $\mathbf{R}^n$.

Exercise 11. Show that the $(m - 1)$-simplices σ_k^m, $1 \le k \le m + 1$, are affine and hence that $\partial \Delta^m$ is an affine chain.

Exercise 12. Show that $p \times \phi$ is affine when ϕ is affine.

Exercise 13. Suppose $f: U \to \mathbf{R}^n$ satisfies condition (A.1) above. [Assume $sp + (1 - s)q \in U$ whenever $0 \le s \le 1$ and p, q are points of U.] Show that $f \circ \phi$ is an affine simplex whenever ϕ is an affine simplex in U.

Exercise 14. Using the results of Exercises 11–13, show that Sc is an affine chain if c is affine.

Recall that the diameter of a subset E of $\mathbf{R}^n$ is the least upper bound of the distance between two points of E. In particular the diameter of a triangular region is just the length of its longest side. Suppose the m-chain c is represented by the expression $a_1\phi_1 + \cdots + a_k\phi_k$ and that $\phi_i \ne \phi_j$ if $i \ne j$. Put

$$\text{mesh } (c) = \text{maximum } \{\text{diameter } \phi_i(\Delta^m), 1 \le i \le k\}.$$

Exercise 15. Show that mesh (c) is well defined.

Exercise 16. If ϕ is an affine m-simplex (considered as a chain), show that

$$\text{mesh } (S\phi) \le \left(\frac{m}{m + 1}\right) \text{mesh } (\phi).$$

Exercise 17. If $\varepsilon > 0$ and ϕ is an m-simplex in U, show that mesh $(S^k\phi) < \varepsilon$ for some k. [HINT: Using uniform continuity of ϕ on the compact set Δ^m choose

$\delta > 0$ so that $\|\phi(p) - \phi(q)\| < \varepsilon$ if $\|p - q\| < \delta$, then

$$\text{mesh } (S^k \Delta^m) \leq \left(\frac{m}{m+1}\right)^k \sqrt{2} < \delta$$

if k is large enough. Show that this k will work.]

Exercise 18. If c is an m-chain in U and $\varepsilon > 0$, show that mesh $(S^k c) < \varepsilon$ for some k. [HINT: See Exercise 17. Since $S^k c \sim c$ by Exercise 9, this establishes the result promised in the introductory paragraph to this section.]

25 Stokes' theorem

If ω is a C^1 $(m-1)$-form on U and c is a C^1 m-chain in U, the relation

(25.1) $$\int_c d\omega = \int_{\partial c} \omega$$

is known as Stokes' theorem and has many important applications. To prove it suppose that $c = a_1\tau_1 + \cdots + a_k\tau_k$ where the τ_i's are singular m-simplices in U and note that

$$\int_c d\omega = \sum_{j=1}^{k} a_j \int_{\tau_j} d\omega = \sum_{j=1}^{k} a_j \int_{\Delta^m} \tau_j^*(d\omega)$$

$$= \sum_{j=1}^{k} a_j \int_{\Delta^m} d(\tau_j^* \omega),$$

while similarly

$$\int_{\partial c} \omega = \sum_{j=1}^{k} a_j \int_{\partial \Delta^m} \tau_j^* \omega.$$

Thus it is sufficient to prove

(25.2) $$\int_{\Delta^m} d\alpha = \int_{\partial \Delta^m} \alpha$$

for each C^1 $(m-1)$-form α defined on some open set containing Δ^m. [To complete the proof from (25.2) it is only necessary to apply (25.2) k times with the choices $\alpha = \tau_j^* \omega$, $i = 1, \ldots, k$, in the expression for $\int_c d\omega$ above.]

If $x^1, \ldots, x^m$ denote cartesian coordinate functions in $\mathbf{R}^m$, α has the form

(25.3) $$\alpha = f\,dx^2 \wedge \cdots \wedge dx^m + g\,dx^1 \wedge dx^3 \wedge \cdots \wedge dx^m + \cdots$$
$$+ h\,dx^1 \wedge \cdots \wedge dx^{m-1}$$

according to (21.3) where f, g, . . . , h are C^1 functions on some neighborhood of Δ^m. Equation (25.2) is a consequence of the m-equations

$$\int_{\Delta^m} d(f \, dx^2 \wedge \cdots \wedge dx^m) = \int_{\partial \Delta^m} f \, dx^2 \wedge \cdots \wedge dx^m,$$

(25.4)

$$\cdot$$
$$\cdot$$
$$\cdot$$

$$\int_{\Delta^m} d(h \, dx^1 \wedge \cdots \wedge dx^{m-1}) = \int_{\partial \Delta^m} h \, dx^1 \wedge \cdots \wedge dx^{m-1}.$$

The first equation in (25.4) is established below. The others have almost identical derivations except for the variables involved. Since

$$\partial \Delta^m = \sum_{j=1}^{m+1} (-1)^j \sigma_j^m,$$

$$\int_{\partial \Delta^m} f \, dx^2 \wedge \cdots \wedge dx^m$$

(25.5)

$$= \sum_{j=1}^{m+1} (-1)^j \int_{\Delta^{m-1}} (\sigma_j^m)^*(f \, dx^2 \wedge \cdots \wedge dx^m)$$

$$= \sum_{j=1}^{m+1} (-1)^j \int_{\Delta^{m-1}} (\sigma_j^m)^*(f)(\sigma_j^m)^*(dx^2) \wedge \cdots \wedge (\sigma_j^m)^*(dx^m).$$

From (23.5) it is readily seen that $(\sigma_j^m)^*(dx^j) = 0$ when $j < m+1$, so that (25.5) reduces to two terms, those with $j = 1$, $m+1$. Equations (23.5) also yield

(25.6)

$$(\sigma_1^m)^*(dx^k) = dt^{k-1}, \qquad k = 2, \ldots, m;$$

$$(\sigma_{m+1}^m)^*(dx^k) = dt^k, \qquad \text{when } k < m;$$

$$(\sigma_{m+1}^m)^*(dx^m) = -(dt^1 + dt^2 + \cdots + dt^{m-1}).$$

Substituting (25.6) in (25.5) and making the appropriate cancellations yields

$$\int_{\partial \Delta^m} f \, dx^2 \wedge \cdots \wedge dx^m$$

(25.7)

$$= \int_{\Delta^{m-1}} f(t^1, \ldots, t^{m-1}, 1 - [t^1 + \cdots + t^{m-1}]) \, dt^1 \cdots dt^{m-1}$$

$$- \int \cdots \int_{\Delta^{m-1}} f(0, t^1, \ldots, t^{m-1}) \, dt^1 \cdots dt^{m-1}.$$

When we notice that

$$d(f \, dx^2 \wedge \cdots \wedge dx^m) = \frac{\partial f}{\partial x^1} \, dx^1 \wedge dx^2 \wedge \cdots \wedge dx^m,$$

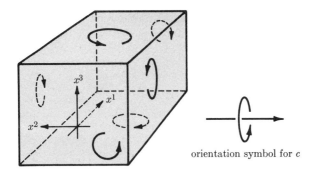

orientation symbol for c

FIGURE 23

the left-hand side of the first equation in (25.4) becomes

$$\int \cdots \int_G \left(\int_0^{1-(x^2+\cdots+x^m)} \frac{\partial f}{\partial x^1}\, dx^1 \right) dx^2 \cdots dx^m$$

$$(25.8) \quad = \int \cdots \int_G f(1 - [x^2 + \cdots + x^m], x^2, \ldots, x^m)\, dx^2 \cdots dx^m$$

$$- \int \cdots \int_G f(0, x^2, \ldots, x^m)\, dx^2 \cdots dx^m$$

where

$$G = \{(x^2, \ldots, x^m) : 0 \le x^2, \ldots, 0 \le x^m, x^2 + \cdots + x^m \le 1\}.$$

The second integral in (25.8) is identical with the second integral on the right-hand side of (25.7) except for the dummy variables used in the integration. The proof of (25.1) is now completed by showing that the first integral in (25.8) and the first integral on the right-hand side of (25.7) also coincide by using the coordinate transformation

$$(25.9) \quad \begin{array}{cc} x^2 = t^2, & x^3 = t^3, \quad \ldots, \\ x^{m-1} = t^{m-1}, & x^m = 1 - [t^1 + \cdots + t^{m-1}], \end{array}$$

which implies $1 - [x^2 + \cdots + x^m] = t^1$, maps Δ^{m-1} in a one-to-one manner onto G, and has Jacobian 1. ◆

If two k-chains b and c are equivalent, $b \sim c$, Stokes' theorem shows that $\partial b \sim \partial c$ because for any $(k-1)$-form ω

$$\int_{\partial b} \omega = \int_b d\omega = \int_c d\omega = \int_{\partial c} \omega.$$

(25.10) Example. Let c be a 3-chain in $\mathbf{R}^3$ such that

$$\int_c f(x^1, x^2, x^3)\, dx^1 \wedge dx^2 \wedge dx^3 = \int_{-\pi}^{\pi} d\beta \int_{-\pi}^{\pi} d\theta \int_0^a f(w, \theta, \beta)\, dw$$

for every differentiable f where x^1, x^2, x^3 are a fixed cartesian coordinate system. c is represented by a box (see Figure 23) and ∂c is represented by the six faces of this box taken with proper orientations. To be more specific let

$$\partial c = b(x^1 = 0) + b(x^1 = a) + b(x^3 = -\pi) + b(x^3 = +\pi) + b(x^2 = -\pi)$$
$$+ b(x^2 = +\pi),$$

where, for example, $b(x^3 = -\pi)$ is the 2-chain describing integration over the face on which $x^3 = -\pi$ taken with the orientation it gets as part of ∂c. According to the figure this orientation is opposite to that induced by $dx^1 \wedge dx^2$, so that

$$\int_{b(x^3 = -\pi)} g(x^1, x^2, x^3)\, dx^1 \wedge dx^2 = -\int_0^a dx^1 \int_{-\pi}^{\pi} g(x^1, x^2, -\pi)\, dx^2.$$

Stokes' theorem is easily verified for such a chain. If

$$\omega = f_3\, dx^1 \wedge dx^2 + f_2\, dx^3 \wedge dx^1 + f_1\, dx^2 \wedge dx^3$$

is any 2-form, then

$$d\omega = \left(\frac{\partial f_3}{\partial x^3} + \frac{\partial f_2}{\partial x^2} + \frac{\partial f_1}{\partial x^1} \right) dx^1 \wedge dx^2 \wedge dx^3.$$

Now

$$\int_c \frac{\partial f_3}{\partial x^3}\, dx^1 \wedge dx^2 \wedge dx^3 = \int_0^a dx^1 \int_{-\pi}^{\pi} dx^2 \int_{-\pi}^{\pi} \frac{\partial f_3}{\partial x^3}\, (x^1, x^2, x^3)\, dx^3$$

$$= \int_0^a dx^1 \int_{-\pi}^{\pi} [f_3(x^1, x^2, \pi) - f_3(x^1, x^2, -\pi)] dx^2$$

$$= \int_{b(x^3 = \pi)} f_3\, dx^1 \wedge dx^2 + \int_{b(x^3 = -\pi)} f_3\, dx^1 \wedge dx^2$$

$$= \int_{\partial c} f_3\, dx^1 \wedge dx^2$$

because the integrals of $f_3\, dx^1 \wedge dx^2$ over the other faces vanish since either x^1 or x^2 is constant on each of these other faces. The remaining terms in $\int_c d\omega$ behave similarly, giving

$$\int_c d\omega = \int_{\partial c} \omega.$$

Although at first this example may seem quite special, most applications of Stokes' theorem to 3-chains follow from it. If $h: U \to \mathbf{R}^n$ is defined and differentiable in a neighborhood U of the set $0 \le x^1 \le a,\ -\pi \le x^2 \le \pi$, $-\pi \le x^3 \le \pi$ representing c, then whenever ω is a 2-form in $\mathbf{R}^n$

$$\int_{h \circ c} d\omega = \int_c h^* \, d\omega = \int_c dh^* \omega$$

$$= \int_{\partial c} h^* \omega = \int_{h \circ \partial c} \omega = \int_{\partial(h \circ c)} \omega.$$

The transition from the first to the second line above is by way of the result of Example (25.10), so that in a way Example (25.10) is a verification of Stokes' theorem for all three chains of the form $h \circ c$. Two illustrations follow.

(25.11) **Example** (Stokes' theorem for the 3-ball.) Let $h: \mathbf{R}^3 \to \mathbf{R}^3$ be described by

$$x^1 \circ h = x^1 \sin \frac{x^3 + \pi}{2} \cos x^2;$$

$$x^2 \circ h = x^1 \sin \frac{x^3 + \pi}{2} \sin x^2;$$

$$x^3 \circ h = x^1 \cos \frac{x^3 + \pi}{2}.$$

Then the chain $h \circ c$ [c as in Example (25.10)] represents integration over the ball of radius a centered at the origin in $\mathbf{R}^3$. Indeed

$$\rho = x^1 \circ h^{-1}, \qquad \phi = \frac{x^3 + \pi}{2} \circ h^{-1}, \quad \text{and} \quad \theta = x^2 \circ h^{-1}$$

are the usual spherical coordinates on this ball. For ∂c, $h \circ b(x^3 = \pi)$, $h \circ b(x^3 = -\pi)$, and $h \circ b(x^1 = 0)$ collapse into one-dimensional image sets while $h \circ b(x^2 = -\pi)$ and $h \circ b(x^2 = \pi)$ are 2-chains with the same image set (the set $\theta = \pm\pi$ in the ball) but with opposite orientations. They therefore contribute nothing to $\int_{\partial c} \omega$, cancelling each other's effect. The only term in ∂c which is left to contribute anything is $h \circ b(x^1 = a)$, representing integration over the surface of the ball.

(25.12) **Example** (Stokes' theorem for solid tori.) Let $h: \mathbf{R}^3 \to \mathbf{R}^3$ be described by

$$x^1 \circ h = (b + x^1 \cos x^3) \cos x^2;$$

$$x^2 \circ h = (b + x^1 \cos x^3) \sin x^2;$$

$$x^3 \circ h = x^1 \sin x^3.$$

Then the 3-chain $h \circ c$ [c as in Example (25.10)] represents integration over the solid torus generated by rotating the disk of radius a in the x^1,x^3-plane with center at $(b, 0, 0)$ about the x^3-axis. In this case the pair $h \circ b(x^3 = \pi)$, $h \circ b(x^3 = -\pi)$ have the same image set with opposite orientations and hence cancel each other in the integral over $\partial(h \circ c)$ as does the pair $h \circ b(x^2 = -\pi)$, $h \circ b(x^2 = \pi)$. The 2-chain $h \circ b(x^1 = 0)$ collapses into the central circle of the torus, and all that is left to contribute to the integral $\int_{\partial(h \circ c)} \omega$ is the 2-chain $h \circ b(x^1 = a)$, representing integration over the surface of the torus.

(25.13) **Example.** Consider the 1-simplices C_1, C_2 of Example (24.18) and regard them as 1-chains. Suppose the circle C_1 lies inside the circle C_2 and that ω is a 1-form on an open set containing C_1, C_2 and the region between them. If $d\omega = 0$, then

$$\int_{C_2} \omega = \int_{C_1} \omega,$$

because, in the language of Example (24.18),

$$\int_{C_2} \omega - \int_{C_1} \omega = \int_{\partial(F \circ \psi)} \omega = \int_{F \circ \psi} d\omega = \int_{F \circ \psi} 0 = 0.$$

Exercises

25.1 Verify Stokes' theorem when c is the 1-chain consisting of the 1-simplex ϕ given by $\phi(t) = (1 - t)a + tb$, $t \in [0, 1]$, and ω is the 0-form $\omega = fg$ where f and g are differentiable functions on $[a, b]$.

25.2 Suppose ω is a k-form on the open set U in $\mathbf{R}^n$. Show that $\int_{\partial c} \omega = 0$ for every $(k + 1)$-chain c in U if and only if $d\omega = 0$ on U.

26 Volume, surface area, and the flux of a vector field

If $e_1, \ldots, e_k$ are vectors in $\mathbf{R}^n$, let $\square(e_1, \ldots, e_k)$ denote the generalized parallelogram with sides parallel to $e_1, \ldots, e_k$ consisting of the vectors which can be written as $\lambda^1 e_1 + \cdots + \lambda^k e_k$ with $0 \leq \lambda^j \leq 1$ for each $1 \leq j \leq k$. Its k-dimensional volume is the square root of the determinant of the $k \times k$ matrix $\{(e_i, e_j)\}_{1 \leq i, j \leq k}$ where (e_i, e_j) is the scalar product of e_i and e_j.

(26.1) $\qquad \{k\text{-volume } \square(e_1, \ldots, e_k)\}^2 = \det (e_i, e_j).$

(26.2) Example. If $t \to C(t)$ is a differentiable curve in $\mathbf{R}^n$ whose tangent vector at t_0 is

$$C'(t_0) = \sum_{j=1}^{n} \left(\frac{dx^j \circ C}{dt} \right) (t_0) \frac{\partial}{\partial x^j} \Bigg|_{C(t_0)},$$

the 1-volume or arc length of the point set $\{\lambda C'(t_0) : 0 \leq \lambda \leq 1\}$ in $T_{C(t_0)}(\mathbf{R}^n)$ is just the length of the tangent vector $C'(t_0)$. It is the square root of the determinant of the 1×1 matrix $(C'(t_0), C'(t_0))$.

$$\{1\text{-volume } \square(C'(t_0))\}^2 = (C'(t_0), C'(t_0)) = \sum_{j=1}^{n} \left[\frac{dx^{j} \circ C}{dt} (t_0) \right]^2$$

if $x^1, \ldots, x^n$ are cartesian coordinates.

(26.3) Example. If θ is the angle between e_1 and e_2 then 2-volume $\square(e_1, e_2) = |e_1| \, |e_2| \sin \theta$ as is evident from Figure 24.

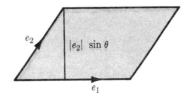

FIGURE 24

Now

$$|e_1|^2 e_2|^2 \sin^2 \theta = (1 - \cos^2 \theta)|e_1|^2|e_2|^2$$

$$= |e_1|^2|e_2|^2 - (|e_1|\,|e_2|\cos \theta)^2$$

or

$$\{2\text{-volume } \square(e_1, e_2)\}^2 = |e_1|^2|e_2|^2 - (e_1, e_2)^2$$

$$= \det \begin{bmatrix} (e_1, e_1) & (e_1, e_2) \\ (e_2, e_1) & (e_2, e_2) \end{bmatrix}.$$

Equation (26.1) has an infinitesimal analog which is taken in the following as the definition for the k-volume of a large class of objects. More specifically,

(26.4) **Definition.** Let $\phi: \Delta^k \to \mathbf{R}^n$ be an imbedded k-simplex. Then

(26.5) $\quad k$-volume (ϕ)

$$= \int \cdots \int_{\Delta^k} \left\{ \det \phi^* \left(\phi_* \left[\frac{\partial}{\partial t^i} \right], \phi_* \left[\frac{\partial}{\partial t^j} \right] \right) \right\}^{1/2} dt^1 \cdots dt^k,$$

where $\phi^*(\phi_*[\partial/\partial t^i], \phi_*[\partial/\partial t^j])$ is the function on Δ^k whose value at $p \in \Delta^k$ is the scalar product of $\phi_*[\partial/\partial t^i|_p]$ and $\phi_*[\partial/\partial t^j|_p]$.

The integrand in (26.5) is closely related to (26.1), so that (26.5) can be regarded as an infinitesimal analog of (26.1). It is important from geometrical considerations that the k-volume of the imbedded k-simplex ϕ really only depends on $\phi(\Delta^k)$. More precisely,

(26.6) **Theorem.** If ϕ and ψ are both imbedded k-simplices in $\mathbf{R}^n$ and $\phi(\Delta^k) = \psi(\Delta^k)$, then k-volume $(\phi) = k$-volume (ψ).

In the proof given here use is made of the concept of a k-form on $\phi(\Delta^k)$. Strictly speaking, until now differential forms have been defined only on open subsets of $\mathbf{R}^n$, so that it is necessary to clarify this term. Let $W = $ interior (Δ^k). A "k-form ω on $\phi(\Delta^k)$" is a map $p \to \omega_p \in \wedge^k T_p^*(\mathbf{R}^n)$, $p \in \phi(\Delta^k)$, with the property that $\phi^*\omega$, defined as usual, is a k-form on W. The initial argument in the proof of Theorem (23.7) shows that when ψ is another imbedded simplex with $\psi(\Delta^k) = \phi(\Delta^k)$, $h = (\phi|_W)^{-1} \circ (\psi|_W)$ and h^{-1} are both differentiable, and it follows that the property of being a k-form on $\phi(\Delta^k)$ really depends only upon the point set $\phi(\Delta^k)$. Theorem (23.7) is valid as it stands for such ω's.

PROOF. It suffices to construct a k-form ω on $\phi(\Delta^k)$ with the property that

(26.7) $\qquad\qquad k$-volume $(\psi) = \left| \int_\psi \omega \right|$

for each imbedded k-simplex ψ with $\psi(\Delta^k) = \phi(\Delta^k)$. Because, given such an ω,

$$(26.8) \qquad \int_\psi \omega = \pm \int_\phi \omega$$

by Theorem (23.7), and Theorem (26.6) then follows from the relations

$$k\text{-volume } (\psi) = \left| \int_\psi \omega \right| = \left| \int_\phi \omega \right| = k\text{-volume } (\phi).$$

Construction of ω: Let ϕ be a fixed imbedded k-simplex and let $Z_1, \ldots,$ Z_k be orthonormal vector fields on $\phi(\Delta^k)$ which at each $p \in \phi(\Delta^k)$ span the linear space generated by $\phi_*(\partial/\partial t^1), \ldots, \phi_*(\partial/\partial t^k)$. $[Z_1, \ldots, Z_k$ can be obtained, for example, by using the Gram-Schmidt process to orthonormalize $\phi_*(\partial/\partial t^1), \ldots, \phi_*(\partial/\partial t^k)$—cf. Exercise 13.11.] Put

$$\alpha^j = Z_j^\#, \qquad\qquad 1 \leq j \leq k,$$

and

$$\omega = \alpha^1 \wedge \cdots \wedge \alpha^k \qquad \text{on } \phi(\Delta^k).$$

It remains to show that ω satisfies (26.7) for each imbedded k-simplex ψ with $\psi(\Delta^k) = \phi(\Delta^k)$. Using the notation above, where $h = \phi^{-1} \circ \psi$ restricted to $W =$ interior (Δ^k), $h_*(\partial/\partial t^i)|_q$ is a linear combination of $(\partial/\partial t^i)|_q$, $1 \leq i \leq k$, when $q \in W$. Consequently, $\psi_*(\partial/\partial t^j)|_p = \phi_* h_*(\partial/\partial t^j)|_p$ can be expressed as a linear combination of $\phi_*(\partial/\partial t^j)|_p$, $1 \leq j \leq k$, and hence of $Z_1|_p, \ldots, Z_k|_p$.

$$(26.9) \qquad \psi_*\left(\frac{\partial}{\partial t^j}\right) = \sum_{m=1}^{k} \left\langle \psi_*\left(\frac{\partial}{\partial t^j}\right), \alpha^m \right\rangle Z_m, \qquad 1 \leq j \leq k,$$

on $\psi(W)$, where the coefficients in (26.9) are easily checked.

$$(26.10) \qquad \left(\psi_*\left(\frac{\partial}{\partial t^i}\right), \psi_*\left(\frac{\partial}{\partial t^j}\right) \right) = \sum_{m=1}^{k} \left\langle \psi_*\left(\frac{\partial}{\partial t^i}\right), \alpha^m \right\rangle \left\langle \psi_*\left(\frac{\partial}{\partial t^j}\right), \alpha^m \right\rangle;$$

so

$$(26.11) \qquad \det\left(\psi_*\left(\frac{\partial}{\partial t^i}\right), \psi_*\left(\frac{\partial}{\partial t^j}\right) \right) = \left\{ \det\left\langle \psi_*\left(\frac{\partial}{\partial t^j}\right), \alpha^m \right\rangle \right\}^2.$$

From this it follows that

$$(26.12) \qquad \begin{aligned} \left\langle \frac{\partial}{\partial t^1} \wedge \cdots \wedge \frac{\partial}{\partial t^k}, \psi^*\omega \right\rangle &= \psi^* \left\langle \psi_*\left(\frac{\partial}{\partial t^1}\right) \wedge \cdots \wedge \psi_*\left(\frac{\partial}{\partial t^k}\right), \omega \right\rangle \\ &= \psi^* \left\{ \det\left\langle \psi_*\left(\frac{\partial}{\partial t^i}\right), \alpha^j \right\rangle \right\} \\ &= h\psi^* \left\{ \det\left(\psi_*\left(\frac{\partial}{\partial t^i}\right), \psi_*\left(\frac{\partial}{\partial t^j}\right) \right) \right\}^{1/2}, \end{aligned}$$

where $h(t^1, \ldots, t^k) = \pm 1$. Since h is continuous it must be constant on W, and (26.7) follows on comparing (26.12) with (26.5). $\blacklozenge$

The notation and formulas developed here are useful in discussing the flux of a vector field X. If f is a function on the range $\phi(\Delta^k)$ of the imbedded k-simplex ϕ and $\alpha^1, \ldots, \alpha^k$ are chosen as above with the additional stipulation that

$$\left\langle \frac{\partial}{\partial t^1} \wedge \cdots \wedge \frac{\partial}{\partial t^k}, \phi^*(\alpha^1 \wedge \cdots \wedge \alpha^k) \right\rangle > 0 \qquad \text{on } \Delta^k,$$

which is just a way of ensuring that

$$\phi^*(\alpha^1 \wedge \cdots \wedge \alpha^k) = \left\{ \det \left(\phi_* \left(\frac{\partial}{\partial t^i} \right), \phi_* \left(\frac{\partial}{\partial t^j} \right) \right) \right\}^{1/2} dt^1 \wedge \cdots \wedge dt^k,$$

then

$$\int_\phi f \alpha^1 \wedge \cdots \wedge \alpha^k$$

is called the integral of f over $\phi(\Delta^k)$ with respect to k-volume.

(26.13) Definition. The flux of the vector field X is the $(n-1)$-form $X \lrcorner \, dx^1 \wedge \cdots \wedge dx^n$ where $x^1, \ldots, x^n$ are cartesian coordinates on $\mathbf{R}^n$.

In physics if X is the velocity field of a streaming fluid, so that X_p is the velocity of the fluid at the point p, the integral

$$\int_b X \lrcorner \, dx^1 \cdots dx^n$$

of the flux over an $(n-1)$-chain b represents the rate at which fluid is passing through the $(n-1)$-chain b. It is referred to in the following as the total flux of X through b.

The flux of a vector field is closely related to the concept of surface area. In fact if ϕ is an imbedded $(n-1)$-simplex and N is a unit normal vector field to $\phi(\Delta^{n-1})$, then $N^\# \wedge \alpha^1 \wedge \cdots \wedge \alpha^{n-1}$ is an n-form of unit length everywhere on $\phi(\Delta^{n-1})$ and consequently

$$N^\# \wedge \alpha^1 \wedge \cdots \wedge \alpha^{n-1} = \varepsilon \, dx^1 \wedge \cdots \wedge dx^n, \quad \varepsilon = \pm 1, \quad \text{on } \phi(\Delta^{n-1}).$$

Taking the inner product with X and using Section 20 (iv) gives

$$\varepsilon(X \lrcorner \, dx^1 \wedge \cdots \wedge dx^n) = X \lrcorner \, (N^\# \wedge \alpha^1 \wedge \cdots \wedge \alpha^{n-1})$$
$$= \langle X, N^\# \rangle \alpha^1 \wedge \cdots \wedge \alpha^{n-1}$$
$$- N^\# \wedge (X \lrcorner \, \alpha^1 \wedge \cdots \wedge \alpha^{n-1}).$$

Applying ϕ^* to both sides of the preceding equation and noting that $\phi^*(N^\#) = 0$ [$\langle T, \phi^* N^\# \rangle = \langle \phi_*(T), N^\# \rangle = (\phi_*(T), N) = 0$ for any vector field T on Δ^{n-1}] gives

(26.14) $\qquad \varepsilon \phi^*(X \lrcorner \, dx^1 \wedge \cdots \wedge dx^n) = \phi^*(X, N) \phi^*(\alpha^1 \wedge \cdots \wedge \alpha^{n-1})$

or

(26.15) $\qquad \int_\phi X \lrcorner \, dx^1 \wedge \cdots \wedge dx^n = \pm \int_\phi (X, N) \alpha^1 \wedge \cdots \wedge \alpha^{n-1}.$

That is, the integral of the flux of X over any imbedded $(n - 1)$-simplex ϕ is to within a sign (depending on the normal chosen) just the integral of the normal component of X over the surface $\phi(\Delta^{n-1})$ with respect to $(n - 1)$-dimensional volume. Formula (26.15) will be reinterpreted and rederived later, but for the moment consider the following special case:

(26.16) Example. The vector field $(dh)^{\#}$ is normal to the level surfaces of h (Exercise 15.8), and where dh does not vanish $N = (dh, dh)^{-1/2}(dh)^{\#}$ represents a unit vector field normal to the level surfaces of h. Its flux

$$N \lrcorner dx^1 \wedge \cdots \wedge dx^n = (dh, dh)^{-1/2} *dh$$

has a ready interpretation. When integrated over an imbedded $(n - 1)$-simplex ϕ lying on one of the level surfaces of h it gives the surface area $[(n - 1)$-volume] of ϕ to within a sign.

Exercises

26.1 Express the 2-form $(dh, dh)^{-1/2} *dh$ which gives surface area in $\mathbf{R}^3$ in terms of dx^1, dx^2, dx^3, and the partial derivatives of h, where the x's are cartesian coordinates.

26.2 Find a unit normal vector field N on the surface described by the equation $x^3 = (x^1)^2 - 3(x^2)^2 + x^1x^2$.

26.3 Suppose ω is a 1-form on the open subset U of $\mathbf{R}^n$ and that the total flux,

$$\int_{\partial\phi} \omega^{\#} \lrcorner dx^1 \wedge \cdots \wedge dx^n,$$

of ω through the boundary of any n-simplex ϕ in U is zero. Show that $d*\omega = 0$ on U.

26.4 Suppose X is a vector field and h is a differentiable function and both are defined on the open subset U of $\mathbf{R}^n$. Suppose $dh \neq 0$ at any point of U and $Xh = 0$ on U. Show that there is an $(n - 2)$-form α on U such that $X \lrcorner dx^1 \wedge \cdots \wedge dx^n = dh \wedge \alpha$.

26.5 (Based on Exercise 26.4.) If, in addition to the conditions in Exercise 26.4, ϕ is an $(n - 1)$-simplex with $h \circ \phi = $ a constant on Δ^{n-1}, show that

$$\int_\phi \text{flux of } X = 0.$$

Give a geometrical interpretation of this result.

27 Green's identities

For the moment let $p = (a^1, \ldots, a^n)$ be a fixed point in $\mathbf{R}^n$. The homothetic transformation H_t centered at p is the map

$$H_t(q) = p + t(q - p), \qquad t > 0, q \in \mathbf{R}^n,$$

of $\mathbf{R}^n$ onto itself. Suppose that b [or $b(p)$] is an n-chain in $\mathbf{R}^n$ representing integration over the 1-ball centered at p, so that in particular the integral of the n-form $dx^1 \wedge dx^2 \wedge \cdots \wedge dx^n$ over b gives the volume of this 1-ball—$x^1, \ldots, x^n$ are cartesian coordinates for $\mathbf{R}^n$.

(27.1) $\qquad H_t^* \, dx^k = d(x^k \circ H_t) = d(a^k + t[x^k - a^k]) = t \, dx^k;$

so if

$$\rho^2 = (x^1 - a^1)^2 + \cdots + (x^n - a^n)^2;$$

$$2\rho \, d\rho = 2(x^1 - a^1) \, dx^1 + \cdots + 2(x^n - a^n) \, dx^n;$$

$$d\rho = \frac{x^1 - a^1}{\rho} \, dx^1 + \cdots + \frac{x^n - a^n}{\rho} \, dx^n;$$

$$*d\rho = \frac{x^1 - a^1}{\rho} \, dx^2 \wedge \cdots \wedge dx^n + \cdots$$

$$+ \frac{x^n - a^n}{\rho} (-1)^{n-1} \, dx^1 \wedge \cdots \wedge dx^{n-1};$$

and using $H_t^*(x^1 - a^1) = t(x^1 - a^1)$, $H_t^* \rho = t\rho$, this gives

(27.2) $\qquad H_t^*(*d\rho) = t^{n-1} *d\rho.$

These calculations also yield $d\rho \wedge *d\rho = dx^1 \wedge \cdots \wedge dx^n$; thus from Theorem 21.11 it follows that $(d\rho, d\rho) = 1$ and then using Example 26.16 that

$$\int_{\partial b} *d\rho = \omega_n,$$

the surface area of the unit sphere in $\mathbf{R}^n$. Let h_n, $n = 1, 2, \ldots$, be the function defined on $(0, +\infty)$ by

$$h_1(t) = \frac{1}{2} t;$$

$$h_2(t) = \frac{1}{2\pi} \log t;$$

$$h_n(t) = \frac{1}{(2 - n)\omega_n} t^{2-n}, \qquad n > 2.$$

Put

(27.3) $\qquad S_p(q) = h_n(\|p - q\|) = h_n(\rho)$

for $q \in \mathbf{R}^n \sim \{p\}$ [$\mathbf{R}^n$ with the point p deleted]. S_p is differentiable on $\mathbf{R}^n \sim \{p\}$ and possesses the fundamental property

(27.4) $\qquad *dS_p = \frac{1}{\omega_n} \rho^{1-n} *d\rho.$

(27.5) **Lemma.** $*dS_p$ has in addition to (27.4) the properties:

(i) $H_t^*(*dS_p) = *dS_p$.

(ii) $\int_{\partial b} *dS_p = 1$.

(iii) $d*dS_p = 0$.

PROOF. Property (i) follows from (27.2) and the observation that $H_t^* \rho^{1-n} = t^{1-n} \rho^{1-n}$. Property (ii) is a consequence of

$$\int_{\partial b} *d\rho = \omega_n$$

together with the fact that $\rho = 1$ on the support of ∂b. To establish property (iii), calculate directly

(27.6) $\qquad d(*dS_p) = \dfrac{1}{\omega_n}[(1-n)\rho^{-n}\, d\rho \wedge *d\rho + \rho^{1-n}\, d*d\rho].$

Now from the equations preceding (27.2)

$$d(\rho *d\rho) = n\, dx^1 \wedge \cdots \wedge dx^n = n\, d\rho \wedge *d\rho;$$

so

$$d\rho \wedge *d\rho + \rho\, d*d\rho = n\, d\rho \wedge *d\rho;$$

$$\rho^{1-n}\, d*d\rho = \rho^{-n}\rho\, d*d\rho = (n-1)\rho^{-n}\, d\rho \wedge *d\rho,$$

which yields (iii) when combined with (27.6). ◆

(27.7) **Theorem** (Green's third identity.) If c is an n-chain in $\mathbf{R}^n$ representing integration over the region G which contains p in its interior, then for each differentiable function f on $\mathbf{R}^n$

(27.8) $\qquad f(p) = \displaystyle\int_c S_p\, d*df + \int_{\partial c} (f *dS_p - S_p *df).$

The first integral on the right-hand side of (27.8) is a convergent improper integral. $\lim_{q \to p} S_p(q) = +\infty$ if $n > 2$ and $-\infty$ if $n = 2$; its convergence is verified in the proof. The main difficulty in the proof arises because Stokes' theorem cannot be applied to such improper integrands.

PROOF. For each $t > 0$, $c - H_t \circ b$ is an n-chain in $R^n \sim \{p\}$—if t is small enough it represents integration over $G \sim$ (the t-ball centered at p)—and the forms involved are perfectly regular on $\mathbf{R}^n \sim \{p\}$, so that Stokes' theorem can be applied to yield

(27.9)
$$\int_{\partial(c - H_t \circ b)} (f *dS_p - S_p *df) = \int_{c - H_t \circ b} d(f *dS_p - S_p *df)$$
$$= \int_{c - H_t \circ b} (f\, d*dS_p - S_p\, d*df)$$
$$= -\int^{c - H_t \circ b} S_p\, d*df,$$

because $df \wedge *dS_p = dS_p \wedge *df$ [(22.14), property (4)] and $d *dS_p = 0$.

$$\int_{\partial H_t \circ b} f *dS_p = \int_{\partial b} H_t^*(f *dS_p)$$

$$= \int_{\partial b} (H_t^* f) *dS_p,$$

because $H_t^*(*dS_p) = *dS_p$. Since $H_t^* f \cdot (q) = f[p + t(q - p)] \to f(p)$ uniformly on the support of ∂b, it follows that

(**27.10**) $$\lim_{t \to 0} \int_{\partial H_t \circ b} f *dS_p = f(p) \int_{\partial b} *dS_p = f(p).$$

Using the fact that $H_t^* dx^i = t dx^i$ for each i, we obtain

$$\int_{\partial H_t \circ b} S_p *df = \sum_{j=1}^{n} \int_{\partial b} t^{n-1}(H_t^* S_p) \left(H_t^* \frac{\partial f}{\partial x^j} \right) (-1)^{j-1} dx^1 \wedge \cdots \wedge dx^{j-1}$$

$$\wedge dx^{j+1} \wedge \cdots \wedge dx^n.$$

Now as $t \to 0$, $H_t^*(\partial f/\partial x^j) \to (\partial f/\partial x^j)(p)$ uniformly on the support of ∂b, while for each n, $t^{n-1}(H_t^* S_p) \to 0$ uniformly on the support of ∂b. Thus

(**27.11**) $$\lim_{t \to 0} \int_{\partial H_t \circ b} S_p *df = 0.$$

Passing to the limit in (27.9) using these relations then gives

$$\int_{\partial c} (f *dS_p - S_p *df) - f(p) = -\lim_{t \to 0} \int_{c - H_t \circ b} S_p d*df,$$

which is just a rephrasing of (27.8). ◆

There is a more primitive identity then (27.8). It states that whenever f is differentiable and the n-chain c represents integration over the region G containing p, then

(**27.12**) $$f(p) = \int_{\partial c} f *dS_p - \int_c df \wedge *dS_p.$$

To prove it let b represent integration over $B_1(p)$ as before and apply Stokes' theorem to get

$$\int_{\partial(c - H_t b)} f *dS_p = \int_{c - H_t b} df \wedge *dS_p,$$

because $p \notin \text{support} \ (c - H_t b)$ and $d*dS_p = 0$. This equality can be rearranged to read

$$\int_{\partial H_t b} f *dS_p = \int_{\partial c} f *dS_p - \int_{c - H_t b} df \wedge *dS_p$$

which yields (27.12) when we let $t \to 0$ and use (27.10).

Exercises

27.1 Derive Green's first identity:

$$\int_{\partial c} f *dg = \int_c (df \wedge *dg + f\, d*dg).$$

27.2 Derive Green's second identity:

$$\int_{\partial c} (f *dg - g *df) = \int_c (f\, d*dg - g\, d*df).$$

27.3 Show that

$$\omega_n = \frac{2\pi^{n/2}}{\Gamma\left(\dfrac{n}{2}\right)}$$

where Γ denotes the gamma function.

A C^2 function f is *subharmonic* on the open subset G of $\mathbf{R}^n$ if $d*df \geq 0$ on G. In the following exercises suppose c is an n-chain in the open set U in $\mathbf{R}^n$ representing integration over the open subset G of U and oriented so that $\int_c dx^1 \wedge \cdots \wedge dx^n > 0$.

27.4 If f is subharmonic on G and C^2 on U, show that

$$\int_{\partial c} *df \geq 0.$$

27.5 If f is subharmonic and C^2 on U and $b_r(q)$ is an n-chain representing integration over $B_r(q)$, the ball of radius r centered at q, show

$$f(q) \leq \int_{\partial b_r(q)} f *dS_q, \qquad B_r(q) \subset U.$$

[HINT: $S_q = \lambda$, a constant, on support $[b_r(q)]$ and $S_q - \lambda \leq 0$ on $B_r(q)$. Use these observations and (27.8).]

27.6 Show in the notation of Exercise 27.5 that

$$\int_{\partial b_r(p)} *dS_p = 1$$

using only the properties of $*dS_p$ given in Lemma (27.5).

27.7 (Based on Exercises 27.5 and 27.6.) Show that if f is C^2 and subharmonic on the open subset U of $\mathbf{R}^n$, then f attains its maximum on an open subset of U. Show that if U is connected, either f is constant or it does not attain its maximum at any point of U. [HINT: If f attains its maximum at $q \in U$, then $f - f(q)$ is subharmonic and

$$0 = f(q) - f(q) \leq \int_{\partial b_r(q)} [f - f(q)] *dS_p \leq 0, \qquad B_r(q) \subset U,$$

implying $f - f(q) = 0$ on $\{p : \|p - q\| = r\}$.]

28 Harmonic functions. Poisson's integral formula

A function f is *harmonic* on the open set U if $d*df = 0$ on U. In this case if c is an n-chain representing integration over the region G in U and p is an interior point of G, Green's third identity (27.8) becomes

$$(28.1) \qquad f(p) = \int_{\partial c} (f *dS_p - S_p *df).$$

If h_p is another harmonic function on U, Green's second identity yields

$$\int_{\partial c} (f *dh_p - h_p *df) = 0.$$

Adding this to (28.1) gives

$$(28.2) \qquad f(p) = \int_{\partial c} (f *dg_p - g_p *df)$$

where $g_p(q) = S_p(q) + h_p(q)$. Suppose it is possible for each $p \in G$ to choose h_p so that $g_p = 0$ on the support of ∂c, that is, on the boundary of the region G. Then the function $(p, q) \to g_p(q)$ of p and q is called Green's function for the region G. From (28.2) it follows then that

$$(28.3) \qquad f(p) = \int_{\partial c} f *dg_p$$

whenever f is harmonic on G. Theorem (28.5), known as Poisson's integral formula, illustrates (28.3) when G is the ball $B_r(0)$ of radius r centered at the origin. Let $\rho = \|q - p\|$ and $\rho' = \|q - \lambda^2 p\|$ with $\lambda = r/\|p\|$. In the notation of (28.3) the function $h_n(\rho'/\lambda)$ is harmonic except at the point $\lambda^2 p$ where it is not defined and

$$(28.4) \qquad g_p(q) = h_n(\rho) - h_n\left(\frac{\rho'}{\lambda}\right) = S_p(q) - h_n\left(\frac{\rho'}{\lambda}\right)$$

is a candidate for Green's function for $B_r(0)$.

Now, referring to Figure 25, the triangles $\triangle qop$ and $\triangle(\lambda^2 p)oq$ are similar when $\|q\| = r$ because $\lambda = r/\|p\| = \|\lambda^2 p\|/r$.

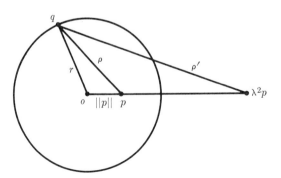

FIGURE 25

In particular $\rho'/\rho = r/\|p\| = \lambda$ when $\|q\| = r$, so that

$$g_p(q) = h_n(\rho) - h_n\left(\frac{\lambda\rho}{\lambda}\right) = 0$$

on the sphere $\{q:\|q\| = r\}$, and $g_\rho(g)$ is indeed Green's function for this sphere.

(28.5)   Theorem (Poisson's integral formula.)   If c is an n-chain representing integration over the ball $B_r(0)$ in $\mathbf{R}^n$ and f is a harmonic function on $B_r(0)$, then

(28.6)
$$f(p) = \frac{r}{\omega_n}\left(1 - \frac{\|p\|^2}{r^2}\right)\int_{\partial c} \rho^{-n}f *ds$$

where $s^2 = (x^1)^2 + \cdots + (x^n)^2$; so $*ds$ describes surface area on the sphere $\{q:\|q\| = r\}$ which is the support of ∂c.

PROOF.   It suffices to use (28.3) with g_p given by (28.4). If $n > 2$,

$$g_p(q) = \frac{1}{(2-n)\omega_n}\left\{\rho^{2-n} - \left(\frac{\rho'}{\lambda}\right)^{2-n}\right\};$$

$$dg_p = \frac{1}{(2-n)\omega_n}\left\{(2-n)\rho^{1-n}\,d\rho - (2-n)\left(\frac{\rho'}{\lambda}\right)^{1-n}\lambda^{-1}\,d\rho'\right\}$$

$$= \frac{1}{\omega_n}\left\{\rho^{1-n}\,d\rho - \left(\frac{\rho'}{\lambda}\right)^{1-n}\lambda^{-1}\,d\rho'\right\}.$$

So

$$*dg_p = \frac{1}{\omega_n}\left\{\rho^{1-n}*d\rho - \left(\frac{\rho'}{\lambda}\right)^{1-n}\lambda^{-1}*d\rho'\right\}.$$

Since $\rho' = \lambda\rho$ when $\|q\| = r$ it follows that on the sphere, $\|q\| = r$,

(28.7)
$$*dg_p = \frac{1}{\omega_n}\rho^{1-n}\{*d\rho - \lambda^{-1}*d\rho'\}.$$

Just as in the computations preceding (28.2)

$$*d\rho = \frac{x^1 - a^1}{\rho}\,dx^2 \wedge \cdots \wedge dx^n + \cdots$$

$$= \frac{x^1 - \lambda^2 a^1}{\rho'}\,dx^2 \wedge \cdots \wedge dx^n + \cdots,$$

and on the sphere $\|q\| = r$

(28.8)
$$*d\rho - \lambda^{-1}*d\rho' = \left(\frac{x^1 - a^1}{\rho} - \frac{x^1 - \lambda^2 a^1}{\lambda^2 \rho}\right)dx^2 \cdots dx^n + \cdots$$

$$= \frac{r}{\rho}\left(\frac{\lambda^2 - 1}{\lambda^2}\right)\left[\frac{x^1}{r}\,dx^2 \wedge \cdots \wedge dx^n + \cdots\right]$$

$$= \frac{r}{\rho}\left(\frac{\lambda^2 - 1}{\lambda^2}\right)*ds$$

where $s(q) = \|q\|$ so that $*ds$ is an $(n - 1)$-form associated with surface area on the sphere $\{q : \|q\| = r\}$. Poisson's integral formula follows directly from (28.3), (28.7), and (28.8). ◆

Exercises

28.1 Show that when $n = 2$ Poisson's integral formula reads

$$f(p) = \frac{r^2 - \|p\|^2}{2\pi} \int_0^{2\pi} \frac{f \circ \phi(\theta)\, d\theta}{r^2 - 2r\|p\| \cos (\theta - \psi) + \|p\|^2}$$

where $\phi(\theta)$ is the point with cartesian coordinates $(r \cos \theta, r \sin \theta)$ on the circle of radius r centered at the origin and $p = (\|p\| \cos \psi, \|p\| \sin \psi)$.

28.2 Show that when $n = 3$ and $p = (0, 0, \|p\|)$, Poisson's integral formula reads

$$f(p) = \frac{r(r^2 - \|p\|^2)}{4\pi} \int_0^{2\pi} \int_0^{\pi} \frac{f \circ \psi(\theta, \phi) \sin \phi\, d\phi\, d\theta}{\{r^2 - 2r\|p\| \cos \phi + \|p\|^2\}^{3/2}}$$

where $\psi(\theta, \phi)$ is the point with spherical coordinates r, θ, ϕ.

28.3 Show that h is harmonic on the open subset U of $\mathbf{R}^n$ if and only if $\int_{\partial c} *dh = 0$ for each n-chain c in U.

In the two following exercises c is an n-chain in the open subset U of $\mathbf{R}^n$ representing integration over the region G. bdry (G) is support (∂c), the boundary of G.

28.4 If h is harmonic on G (and differentiable on U), show the values of h on bdry (G) determine the values of h on G. Specifically, if h_1 and h_2 are both harmonic on G and agree on bdry (G), show $h_1 = h_2$ on G. [HINT: Use Green's first identity, Exercise 27.1, with $f = g = h_1 - h_2$, to get

$$\int_c df \wedge *df = 0.$$

This implies $df = 0$ and f is a constant on G.]

28.5 If h is harmonic on G (and differentiable on U), show that the flux of $(dh)^\#$ through ∂c determines the values of h on G. More specifically, if h_1 and h_2 are both harmonic on G and

$$\int_{\partial c} f *dh_1 = \int_{\partial c} f *dh_2$$

for every differentiable function f, show that $h_1 = h_2$ on G.

28.6 If h is harmonic on U and $b_r(q)$ represents integration over the ball $B_r(q)$, show

(28.9) $$h(q) = \int_{\partial b_r(q)} h *dS_q, \qquad B_r(q) \subset U.$$

28.7 (The maximum principle.) Show that if $h(p) \leq M$, $p \in U$, the set $\{q : h(q) = M\}$ is open in U. Deduce from this that if U is connected, then either

h is constant or it does not attain its maximum at any point of U. (For a more general statement see Exercise 27.7.)

28.8 (Based on Exercise 28.6.) If $b_r(q)$ represents integration over $B_r(q)$ and h is harmonic on U, show that

$$h(q) = \{\text{volume } [B_r(q)]\}^{-1} \int_{b_r(q)} *h.$$

[HINT: Show $\int_0^r [\int_{b_t(q)} f *dS_q] \, dt = \int_{b_r(q)} *f.$]

28.9 (Based on Exercise 28.8.) Suppose h is harmonic on $\mathbf{R}^n$ and bounded, $|h(q)| \leq M$, $q \in \mathbf{R}^n$. Show that h is a constant. [HINT: If p, $q \in \mathbf{R}^n$,

$$\text{volume } [B_t(0)][h(p) - h(q)] = \int_{b_t(p) - b_t(q)} *h;$$

so

$$|h(p) - h(q)| \leq \frac{nM}{\omega_n t^n} \text{ volume } \{[B_t(p) \cup B_t(q)] \cap [B_t(q) \cap B_t(p)]^c\},$$

which approaches zero as $t \to \infty$.]

28.10 Show that a C^2 function h is harmonic on U if and only if (28.9) holds. [HINT: Use the hint to Exercise 27.5.]

CHAPTER SIX

Vector Fields and Differential Forms

29 Flows and vector fields

If U is an open subset of the open set V, a *flow* of U into V is a differentiable map

$$\phi: (-\varepsilon, \varepsilon) \times U \to V \qquad \text{where } \varepsilon > 0$$

with the restrictions that (1) $\phi(0, q) = q$, $q \in U$, and (2) the map ϕ_t: $q \to \phi(t, q)$ of U into V is one-one for each fixed $t \in (-\varepsilon, \varepsilon)$. The terminology is taken from fluid mechanics where points correspond to positions in a moving fluid and the particle in position $\phi(t, q)$ at time t traverses the path $t \to \phi(t, q) = C_q(t)$ as time unfolds (see Figure 26). Condition (2) can be interpreted as stating that distinct positions in the fluid remain distinct throughout the motion. Note that in the notation used here

$$\phi(t, q) = \phi_t(q) = C_q(t);$$

C_q is the curve traced by a point during the flow, and ϕ_t is the displacement of U created by the flow.

The *velocity vector field* $X(t)$ of the flow ϕ is the vector field on $\phi_t(U)$ whose associated vector at $\phi_t(p)$ is the tangent to the curve C_p at $C_p(t)$. That is,

$$X(t)|_{\phi_t(p)} = C'_p(t), \qquad p \in U, |t| < \varepsilon.$$

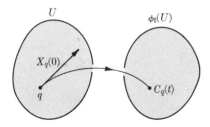

FIGURE 26

120

In other terms, when $q = \phi(t, p)$,

$$X(t)f \cdot (q) = \frac{\partial f \circ \phi}{\partial t}(t, p).$$

The flow is *stationary* if $X(t)|_p = X(s)|_p$ whenever $p \in \phi_t(U) \cap \phi_s(U)$. In most discussions of stationary flows there is a vector field X on V with $X|_p = X(t)|_p$, $p \in \phi_t(U)$, and in this situation in keeping with the usual terminology X is also called the velocity field of the flow ϕ.

If $x^1, \ldots, x^n$ is a coordinate system for V and $p = \phi(t, q)$, a comparison of the two equations

$$X(t)|_p = \sum_{k=1}^{n} [X(t)x^k](p) \left.\frac{\partial}{\partial x^k}\right|_p$$

and

$$X(t)f \cdot (p) = \sum_{k=1}^{n} \frac{\partial f}{\partial x^k}(p) \frac{\partial x^k \circ \phi}{\partial t}(t, q)$$

shows that $X(t)$ is the velocity vector field of the flow ϕ if and only if

$$(\mathbf{29.1}) \qquad \frac{\partial x^k \circ \phi}{\partial t}(t, q) = [X(t)x^k] \circ \phi(t, q), \qquad k = 1, 2, \ldots, n.$$

The system of differential equations (29.1) can be used to determine the flow from the velocity vector field $X(t)$. The technique is illustrated below when $X(t)$ does not depend on t in Theorem (29.2), which is a rephrasing of the fundamental theorem on the existence and uniqueness of solutions for ordinary differential equations.

(29.2)   Theorem.   If X is a C^1 vector field on the open set V, then for each $p \in V$ there is an open neighborhood U of p, a number $\varepsilon > 0$, and a flow $\phi: (-\varepsilon, \varepsilon) \times U \to V$ of U into V with velocity field X.

PROOF.   Let $x^1, \ldots, x^n$ be a coordinate system for V and let X^j be the function defined on the subset $x(V)$ of $\mathbf{R}^n$ by

$$(\mathbf{29.3}) \qquad X^j[x^1(p), \ldots, x^n(p)] = (Xx^j)(p), \qquad p \in V.$$

The fundamental existence and uniqueness theorem for the solutions of ordinary differential equations ensures for each $p \in V$ the existence of an $\varepsilon > 0$ and a C^1 map

$$y: (-\varepsilon, \varepsilon) \times N \to x(V),$$

$$y[t; u^1, \ldots, u^n] = (y^1[t; u^1, \ldots, u^n], \ldots, y^n[t; u^1, \ldots, u^n]),$$

defined on the subset $(-\varepsilon, \varepsilon) \times N$ of $\mathbf{R}^{n+1}$ described by

$$|t| < \varepsilon, \qquad |u^k - x^k(p)| < \varepsilon, \qquad k = 1, 2, \ldots, n,$$

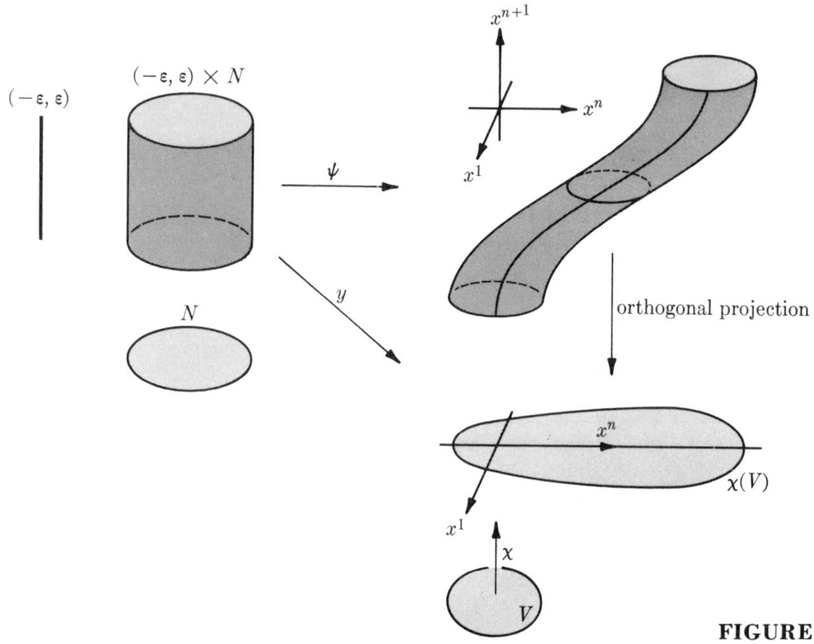

FIGURE 27

and satisfying

(29.4)
$$\frac{\partial y^k}{\partial t} = X^k(y^1, \ldots, y^n)$$

with the initial conditions

(29.5) $y^j(0; u^1, \ldots, u^n) = u^j, \qquad j = 1, \ldots, n.$

Furthermore, y is the only map from $(-\varepsilon, \varepsilon) \times N$ to $x(V)$ satisfying (29.4) and (29.5). Let $\phi(t, q)$ be the unique point in V whose coordinate values are given by

(29.6) $x^k \circ \phi(t, q) = y^k[t; x^1(q), \ldots, x^n(q)], \qquad |t| < \varepsilon, \qquad x(q) \in N;$

that is

$$\phi(t, q) = x^{-1} \circ y[t; x(q)], \qquad |t| < \varepsilon, \qquad q \in x^{-1}(N).$$

Note that (29.5) shows $\phi(0, q) = q$, $q \in x^{-1}(N)$ and (29.4) and (29.3) imply

(29.7) $\dfrac{\partial x^k \circ \phi}{\partial t} (t, q) = X^k\{y[t; x(q)]\} = (Xx^k)[\phi(t, q)],$

so that (29.1) is satisfied.

Let $\psi \colon (-\varepsilon, \varepsilon) \times N \to R^{n+1}$ be the map defined by (see Figure 27)

$$\psi(t, u^1, \ldots, u^n) = (t, y^1[t; u^1, \ldots, u^n], \ldots, y^n[t; u^1, \ldots, u^n]).$$

The Jacobian of ψ is the determinant of the $(n + 1) \times (n + 1)$ matrix

$$\begin{bmatrix} 1 & \dfrac{\partial y^1}{\partial t} & \cdots & \dfrac{\partial y^n}{\partial t} \\[2mm] 0 & \dfrac{\partial y^1}{\partial u^1} & \cdots & \dfrac{\partial y^n}{\partial u^1} \\[1mm] \cdot & \cdot & & \cdot \\ \cdot & \cdot & & \cdot \\ \cdot & \cdot & & \cdot \\[1mm] 0 & \dfrac{\partial y^1}{\partial u^n} & \cdots & \dfrac{\partial y^n}{\partial u^n} \end{bmatrix}$$

whose value at $(0, x^1(p), \ldots, x^n(p))$ is

$$(29.8) \qquad \det \begin{bmatrix} 1 & (Xx^1)(p) & \cdots & (Xx^n)(p) \\ 0 & 1 & \cdots & 0 \\ \cdot & \cdot & & \cdot \\ \cdot & \cdot & & \cdot \\ \cdot & \cdot & & \cdot \\ 0 & 0 & \cdots & 1 \end{bmatrix} = 1$$

where except for the first row and column the matrix in (29.8) is the $n \times n$ identity matrix because of (29.5). Thus according to the inverse function theorem one can choose ε so small that ψ is one-one. Then in particular, whenever $\phi(t, q_1) = \phi(t, q_2)$, $t \in (-\varepsilon, \varepsilon)$, q_1 and q_2 in $x^{-1}(N)$, it follows that

$$\psi(t, x(q_1)) = (t, x \circ \phi(t, q_1)) = (t, x \circ \phi(t, q_2)) = \psi(t, x(q_2))$$

or $x(q_1) = x(q_2)$, and the second condition for ϕ to be a flow is also satisfied. This completes the proof of Theorem (29.2).   ◆

With a few additions the preceding argument can be made to yield somewhat more. A coordinate system $z^1, \ldots, z^n$ valid in a neighborhood W of p is said to be *adapted* to X if $X = \partial/\partial z^1$ throughout W. Another way of describing this condition is by

$$(29.9) \qquad (X_q z^j) = \delta^j_1, \qquad j = 1, 2, \ldots, n, q \in W.$$

So if $C \colon [a, b] \to W$ is an integral curve of the vector field X (recall that C is an integral curve of X if $C'(t) = X|_{c(t)}, t \in [a, b]$),

$$z^j \circ C(b) - z^j \circ C(a) = \int_a^b X_{c(s)} z^j \, dx$$

$$= \int_a^b \delta^j_1 \, dx$$

$$= (b - a)\delta^j_1.$$

If $z^1, \ldots, z^n$ is adapted to X on W, the integral curves C of X have the local coordinate representation

(29.10) $z^j \circ C(t) = z^j \circ C(a) + (t - a)\delta_1^j, \qquad j = 1, 2, \ldots, n.$

In particular, the values of z^j all along such an integral curve are determined by their values at just one point on the curve. For example, if the values $z^1, \ldots, z^n$ are known on the surface $S = \{q \in W: h(a) = 0\}$, (29.10) suffices to give the values of the z^j's at any point of the set F of points which can be connected to S in W by an integral curve of X. If X is not tangent to S at p, it is reasonable to expect F to be a neighborhood of p and to use (29.10) to construct a coordinate system adapted to X and valid on an open set containing p. More precisely:

(29.11) **Theorem.** Let $x^1, \ldots, x^n$ be a local coordinate system for the open set V and X a C^1 vector field on V. If $(Xx^1)(p) \neq 0$, p has a coordinate neighborhood U with coordinate functions $z^1, \ldots, z^n$ such that

(i) $X = \partial/\partial z^1$ on U.
(ii) $z^1(q) = 0$, $q \in U$ implies $z^2(q) = x^2(q), \ldots, z^n(q) = x^n(q)$ and $x^1(q) = x^1(p)$. That is, the level surface $\{q \in U: z^1(q) = 0\}$ is a subset of the level surface $\{q \in U: x^1(q) = x^1(p)\}$ and on the former surface the functions $z^2, \ldots, z^n$ agree with $x^2, \ldots, x^n$, respectively.

PROOF.   Using the notation developed in the proof of Theorem (29.2), let J be the set of n-tuples described by the conditions

$$J = \{(t, u^2, \ldots, u^n): |t| < \varepsilon; |u^j - x^j(p)| < \varepsilon, j = 2, 3, \ldots, n\},$$

and let σ be the map of J into $x(V)$ described by

(29.12) $\sigma(t, u^2, \ldots, u^n)$

$$= (y^1[t; x^1(p), u^2, \ldots, u^n], \ldots, y^n[t; x^1(p), u^2, \ldots, u^n]).$$

[σ is the restriction of the previous map y to the slice of $(-\varepsilon, \varepsilon) \times N$ determined by $u^1 = x^1(p)$.] The Jacobian of σ at $(0, x^2(p), \ldots, x^n(p))$ is $(Xx^1)(p)$, which is not zero by hypothesis. [It is just the determinant of the matrix of (29.8) with the first column and second row deleted.] According to the inverse function theorem there is an open neighborhood W of $(0, x^2(q), \ldots, x^n(p))$ in $\mathbf{R}^n$ such that σ is one-one on W, $\sigma(W)$ is open in $x(V)$, and σ^{-1} is differentiable on $\sigma(W)$.

(29.13) $J \xrightarrow{\sigma} x(V) \xleftarrow{x} V, \qquad W \xrightarrow{\sigma} \sigma(W) \xleftarrow{x} x^{-1} \circ \sigma(W) = U.$

Putting $U = x^{-1} \circ \sigma(W)$, the restrictions of the maps x and σ indicated in the second expression of (29.13) are one-one, differentiable, and have differentiable inverses. Consequently the function $t, u^2, \ldots, u^n$ defined on U by the condition

(29.14) $\qquad \sigma^{-1} \circ x(q) = (t(q), u^2(q), \ldots, u^n(q))$

form a system of local coordinates for U. From (29.14) and (29.12)

$$x^j(q) = y^j(t(p); x^1(p), u^2(q), \ldots, u^n(q)),$$

so that as a function of the values of the coordinates $t, u^2, \ldots, u^n$

(29.15) $\qquad x^j = y^j(t; x^1(p), u^2, \ldots u^n), \qquad j = 1, \ldots, n.$

Consequently,

$$\frac{\partial}{\partial t} = \sum_{j=1}^{n} \frac{\partial x^j}{\partial t} \frac{\partial}{\partial x^j} = \sum_{j=1}^{n} (Xx^j) \frac{\partial}{\partial x^j} = X \qquad \text{on } U,$$

and if $t(q) = 0$, $x^1(q) = y^1(0; x^1(p), u^2(q), \ldots, u^n(q)) = x^1(p), x^2(q) = y^2(0; \ldots) = u^2(q), \ldots, x^n(q) = u^n(q)$. So if $z^1, \ldots, z^n$ are defined by

$$z^1(q) = t(q),$$

$$z^2(q) = u^2(q),$$

$$\cdot$$
$$\cdot$$
$$\cdot$$

$$z^n(q) = u^n(q), \qquad q \in U,$$

the functions $z^1, \ldots, z^n$ form a coordinate system in U with the desired properties. ◆

Addendum. By shrinking U it is possible to strengthen the conclusion of Theorem (29.11) slightly. Specifically, the part of conclusion (ii) which asserts

$$\{q \in U : z^1(q) = 0\} \subset \{q \in U : x^1(q) = x^1(p)\}$$

can be strengthened to

(29.16) $\qquad \{q \in U : z^1(q) = 0\} = \{q \in U : x^1(q) = x^1(p)\}.$

To do this let

$$W(\delta) = \{q \in U : |z^j(q) - z^j(p)| < \delta, 1 \le j \le n\}$$

and suppose $\delta > 0$ is chosen so small that $W(\delta) \subset U$ and

$$Xx^1(q) = \frac{\partial x^1}{\partial z^1}(q) \ne 0, \qquad q \in W(\delta).$$

Equation (29.16) holds with U replaced by $W(\delta)$. Indeed, if $q \in W(\delta)$ and $x^1(q) = x^1(p)$, let q' be the point with z-coordinates $(0, z^2(q), \ldots, z^n(q))$.

Then since $z^1(q') = 0$ it follows that $x^1(q') = x^1(p)$ and according to (6.12)

$$0 = x^1(q) - x^1(q') = \sum_j \frac{\partial x^1}{\partial z^j}(q_0)[z^j(q) - z^j(q')]$$

$$= \frac{\partial x^1}{\partial z^1}(q_0)z^1(q).$$

Since $(\partial x^1/\partial z^1)(q_0) \neq 0$, $z^1(q) = 0$ as asserted.

(29.17) Example. If X is a vector field on the open subset U of $\mathbf{R}^n$, one of the consequences of Theorem (29.11) is that the first-order linear partial differential equation

(29.18) $$XF = f$$

has a local solution F in a neighborhood W of each point p where $X \neq 0$ no matter what the (continuous) function f. Moreover this solution is unique if its values are known on an $(n-1)$-dimensional submanifold $S = \{q \in W : h(q) = 0\}$ to which X is not tangent; i.e., $Xh \neq 0$ on S. To show this let $x^1, \ldots, x^n$ be a local coordinate system at p in which $x^1 = h$. Theorem (29.11) implies W can be chosen so that the map $(-\varepsilon, \varepsilon) \times S \to W$ which maps $(t, q) \to C_q(t)$, the integral curve of X through q, is one-one onto, and in this case F is given by

(29.19) $$F \circ C_q(t) = F \circ C_q(0) + \int_0^t f \circ C_q(s)\, ds, \qquad -\varepsilon < t < \varepsilon, q \in S.$$

It suffices to take W cubical in the coordinate system $z^1, \ldots, z^n$ of Theorem (29.11) and small enough so that the conditions of the addendum hold.

(29.20) Example. An important question easily answered using Theorem (29.2) is to determine how far the integral curves $s \to C_q(s)$ of the vector field X can be extended in the parameter s. Stated precisely, let X be a vector field on the open subset V of $\mathbf{R}^n$ and suppose $p \in V$. Then there is a curve $C_p: (a, b) \to V$ with the properties

    (i) $C_p(0) = p$. In particular, $a < 0 < b$.
    (ii) $C'_p(s) = X_{C_p(s)}$. C_p is an integral curve of X.
    (iii) The limits $\lim_{s \uparrow b} C_p(s)$, $\lim_{s \downarrow a} C_p(s)$ if they exist do not belong to V.

Under these conditions C_p, a, and b are unique.

    PROOF. Theorem (29.2) shows that a curve $C_p: (a, b) \to V$ exists with properties (i) and (ii), and although it is not stated there, the fundamental existence theorem of ordinary differential equations also implies the uniqueness of C_p when X is C^1 on V. It suffices to show that if either of the limits in (iii) exists in V, the parameter set (a, b) for C_p can be enlarged. Suppose, for example, that $\lim_{s \uparrow b} C_p(s) = q \in V$. In accordance with Theorem (29.2) let $\phi: (-\varepsilon, \varepsilon) \times W \to V$ be a flow of the neighborhood W of q into V with velocity field X. If $C_p(b - \delta) \in W$, $0 < \delta < \varepsilon$, the curves

$$t \to \phi(t, C_p(b - \delta)) \qquad \text{and} \qquad t \to C_p(b - \delta + t)$$

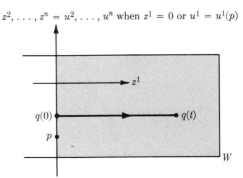

$z^2, \ldots, z^n = u^2, \ldots, u^n$ when $z^1 = 0$ or $u^1 = u^1(p)$

FIGURE 28

are both integral curves of X agreeing when $t = 0$, so by the unstated uniqueness of such curves (cf. Exercise 29.5) they agree for all values of t for which they are both defined.

$$\textbf{(29.21)} \qquad C_p(b - \delta + t) = \phi(t, C_p(b - \delta)), \qquad 0 \le t < \delta,$$
$$= \phi(t - \delta, q)$$

(cf. Exercise 29.6 for this section) and the parameter set for C_p can be extended to $(a, b + \varepsilon)$ by

$$C_p(t) = C_p(t) \qquad \text{as previously defined when } t < b,$$
$$= \phi(t - b, q), \qquad b \le t < b + \varepsilon.$$

(29.22) Example. To close this section a result is proved about the possibility of choosing a coordinate system simultaneously adapted to the k vector fields $X_1, \ldots, X_k$. Besides its inherent interest it serves a pedantic objective, because the proof given here is similar to the proof of the Frobenius theorem in the following section and, being simpler, serves as a natural forerunner to that proof. The result can be stated as follows: Suppose $X_1, \ldots, X_k$ are C^1 vector fields on the open set U in $\mathbf{R}^n$. Then the point $p \in U$ has a coordinate neighborhood W with local coordinates $z^1, \ldots, z^n$ in which $X_1 = \partial/\partial z^1, \ldots, X_k = \partial/\partial z^k$ if and only if

(i) $X_1|_p, \ldots, X_k|_p$ are linearly independent in $T_p(\mathbf{R}^n)$.
(ii) $[X_i, X_j] = 0, 1 \le i, j \le k$, on a neighborhood of p.

(Recall that $[X, Y]$ is the vector field defined by $[X, Y]g = X(Yg) - Y(Xg)$.)

PROOF. First one can assume by shrinking U if necessary that $X_1, \ldots, X_k$ are linearly independent in U and $[X_i, X_j] = 0$ on U. The proof proceeds by induction on k. If $k = 1$ this result is a weak restatement of Theorem (29.11). Now suppose the result holds when $k - 1$ vector fields are involved. In keeping with this choose local coordinates $u^1, \ldots, u^n$ in a neighborhood of p so that $X_2 = \partial/\partial u^2, \ldots, X_k = \partial/\partial u^k$. Since $X_1|_p$ is not linearly dependent on $X_2|_p, \ldots, X_k|_p$ it follows that one of the terms $(X_1 u^1)(p), (X_1 u^{k+1})(p), \ldots,$ $(X_1 u^n)(p)$ is not zero and without loss of generality one can assume $(X_1 u^1)(p) \ne 0$ (Figure 28). Now from Theorem (29.11) there is a coordinate system $z^1, \ldots,$

z^n on some neighborhood of p such that $z'(q) = 0$ implies that $u'(q) = u'(p)$;

(29.23)
$$X_1 = \frac{\partial}{\partial z^1};$$

$$z^i(q) = u^i(q), \quad 2 \le j \le n, \quad \text{when } z^1(q) = 0.$$

One consequence of (29.23) is that when $z^1 = 0$ the other z^i's coincide with the corresponding u^i's, so that

(29.24)
$$\frac{\partial f}{\partial z^i}(q) = \frac{\partial f}{\partial u^i}(q) = X_i f(q), \quad 2 \le j, \, z^1(q) = 0.$$

Now let W be a cubical neighborhood of p in the z's and suppose $q(t)$ has z-coordinates $(t, a^2, \ldots, a^n)$; then

$$(X_j z^k)[q(t)] - (X_j z^k)[q(0)] = \int_0^t \frac{\partial(X_j z^k)}{\partial z^1}[q(s)]\, ds$$

$$= \int_0^t X_1(X_j z^k)\,[q(s)]\, ds$$

$$= \int_0^t \{[X_1, X_j]z^k + X_j(X_1 z^k)\}[q(s)]\, ds$$

$$= 0, \quad j > 1.$$

From (29.24)

$$(X_j z^k)[q(0)] = \frac{\partial z^k}{\partial z^i} = \delta_j^k, \quad j > 1,$$

which shows $X_j = \partial/\partial z^i, \, j > 1$, on all of W.

Exercises

29.1 Find coordinates z^1, z^2 in a neighborhood of $(1, 0)$ adapted to X when

(a)
$$X = \frac{x^1}{r}\frac{\partial}{\partial x^1} + \frac{x^2}{r}\frac{\partial}{\partial x^2} \quad \text{where } r^2 = (x^1)^2 + (x^2)^2, \, r > 0.$$

(b)
$$X = \frac{\partial}{\partial x^1} + \frac{\partial}{\partial x^2}.$$

29.2 If $z^1, \ldots, z^n$ are adapted to X on U and $Xh = 1/f$ where $f \ne 0$ on U, show that $y^1 = h$, $y^2 = z^2, \ldots, y^n = z^n$ form a local coordinate system at each point of U adapted to fX.

29.3 Let r, θ be polar coordinates on $\mathbf{R}^2$. Show that the differential equation $XF = 1$ does not have a solution on the annulus $1 < r < 2$ if $X = \partial/\partial\theta$.

29.4 If $X = -x^2(\partial/\partial x^1) + x^1(\partial/\partial x^2)$, show that the equation $Xf = 1$ does not even have a local solution in a neighborhood of $(0, 0)$.

29.5 Suppose X is a vector field on U and $C_q: (a, b) \to U$, $D_q: (a, b) \to U$ are integral curves of X satisfying $C_q(t_0) = D_q(t_0)$ for some $t_0 \in (a, b)$. Show that $C_q(t) = D_q(t)$ for all $t \in (a, b)$. [HINT: Use a uniqueness theorem from ordinary differential equations.]

29.6   (Based on Exercise 29.5.) If $\phi\colon (-\varepsilon, \varepsilon) \times W \to V$ is a flow with velocity field X on V and $|s|, |t| < \varepsilon/2$, show that $\phi(s, \phi(t, q)) = \phi(s + t, q)$, $q \in W$.

29.7   Suppose $C_q\colon (a, b) \to U$ is an integral curve of the vector field X on U. Suppose $s_m \uparrow b$ and $\lim\limits_{m \to \infty} C_q(s_m) = p \in U$. Show that $\lim\limits_{s \uparrow b} C_q(s) = p$.

29.8   Let f be a differentiable function on the open set U in $\mathbf{R}^n$ and suppose that X is a vector field on U satisfying $Xf(p) = 0$ whenever $p \in S = \{q \in U\colon f(q) = 0\}$. If $C\colon (a, b) \to U$ is an integral curve of X with $C(t_0) \in S$ for some $t_0 \in (a, b)$, show that $C(t) \in S$ for all $t \in (a, b)$.

29.9   (Based on Exercises 29.7 and 29.8.) If S is compact in U, show that each integral curve $C_q\colon (a, b) \to U$ starting at a point $C_q(0) = q \in S$ can be extended to an integral curve $C_q\colon (-\infty, \infty) \to S$.

29.10   If $X_1, \ldots, X_2$ are vector fields on U which are independent at p and $[X_i, X_j] = 0$ all i and j, show that p has a neighborhood with local coordinates $z^1, \ldots, z^n$ on which the partial differential equations $X_1 f = g_1, \ldots, X_k f = g_k$ are equivalent to $\partial f/\partial z^1 = g_1, \ldots, \partial f/\partial z^k = g_k$.

30   Frobenius' theorem

There is a very important generalization of Theorem (29.11) which encompasses one of the basic theorems for systems of first-order partial differential equations. The system $X_1, \ldots, X_k$ of k vector fields on U is said to be involutive if (1) the vectors $X_1|_q, \ldots, X_k|_q$, are linearly independent [in $T_q(U)$] at each point $q \in U$, and (2) the Lie bracket of any two of the X's can be written as a linear combination of $X_1, \ldots, X_k$,

$$(\mathbf{30.1}) \qquad [X_i, X_j] = \sum_{m=1}^{k} C_{ij}^m X_m, \qquad i, j = 1, \ldots, k$$

where the C_{ij}^m's are differentiable functions on U.

   If the vector fields $Y_1, \ldots, Y_k$ are nonsingular linear combinations of $X_1, \ldots, X_k$ with differentiable coefficients,

$$Y_j = \sum_{\alpha=1}^{k} a_j^\alpha X_\alpha, \qquad \det [a_j^\alpha(q)] \neq 0,$$

and the system $X_1, \ldots, X_k$ is involutive, then so is the system $Y_1, \ldots, Y_k$. Namely,

$$[Y_i, Y_j] = \sum_{\alpha,\beta=1}^{k} [a_i^\alpha X_\alpha, a_j^\beta X_\beta]$$

$$(\mathbf{30.2}) \qquad = \sum_{\alpha,\beta=1}^{k} \{a_i^\alpha a_j^\beta [X_\alpha, X_\beta] + a_i^\alpha (X_\alpha a_j^\beta) X_\beta - a_j^\beta (X_\beta a_i^\alpha) X_\alpha\}.$$

If we use (30.1), this last expression is certainly a linear combination of the X_j's, and then if we use

$$X_i = \sum_{m=1}^{k} b_i^m Y_m, \qquad [b_i^m(q)] = [a_j^\alpha(q)]^{-1},$$

$[Y_i, Y_j]$ can be written as a linear combination of the Y_i's with differentiable coefficients.

If the functions $z^1, \ldots, z^n$ form a coordinate system for U, the system $\partial/\partial z^1, \ldots, \partial/\partial x^k$ is involutive on U and, as the following theorem shows, all involutive systems are closely related to this simple example.

(30.3) **Theorem** (Frobenius' theorem.) Suppose the system $X_1, \ldots,$ X_k of vector fields on U is involutive. Then each $p \in U$ has a coordinate neighborhood V with coordinates $z^1, \ldots, z^n$ such that each X_j is a linear combination of $\partial/\partial z^1, \ldots, \partial/\partial z^k$ on V with differentiable coefficients.

Remark. The proof shows that one can even require that $X_1 = \partial/\partial z^1$.

PROOF. The proof is by induction on k. When $k = 1$, Theorem (30.3) is a consequence of the existence of a coordinate system adapted to X_1 ($X_1 = \partial/\partial z^1$) on some neighborhood of p. In general let $y^1, \ldots, y^n$ be local coordinates at p such that $X_1 = \partial/\partial y^1$. Put

$$Y_1 = X_1;$$

$$Y_j = \sum_{m=2}^{n} (X_j y^m) \frac{\partial}{\partial y^m} = X_j - (X_j y^1) X_1, \qquad j > 1.$$

The X_j's are linear combinations of the Y_i's:

$$X_1 = Y_1;$$

$$X_j = Y_j + (X_j y^1) Y_1, \qquad j > 1.$$

So it suffices to show the existence of a coordinate system $z^1, \ldots, z^n$ at p in terms of which each Y_j is a linear combination of $\partial/\partial x^1, \ldots, \partial/\partial z^n$. Note that for each $q \in U$ the sets $X_1|_q, \ldots, X_k|_q$ and $Y_1|_q, \ldots, Y_k|_q$, span the same subspace in $T_q(U)$ of vectors at q. Since $X_1|_q, \ldots, X_k|_q$ are linearly independent by hypothesis, the vectors $Y_1|_q, \ldots, Y_k|_q$ are linearly independent as are the vectors $Y_2|_q, \ldots, Y_k|_q$.

The system $Y_1, \ldots, Y_k$ is involutive according to the argument that precedes the statement of the theorem and when expressed in terms of the $\partial/\partial y^j$'s none of the vector fields $Y_2, \ldots, Y_k$ involves $\partial/\partial y^1$; so none of the brackets $[Y_j, Y_m]$ ($j, m = 1, \ldots, k$) involves $Y_1 = \partial/\partial y^1$. That is,

(30.4) $$[Y_i, Y_j] = \sum_{m=2}^{k} D_{ij}^m Y_m, \qquad i, j = 1, 2, \ldots, k.$$

In particular, the system $Y_2, \ldots, Y_k$ is involutive.

Applying the inductive assumption to $Y_2, \ldots, Y_k$ with a slight renumbering of coordinates, there is a coordinate system $u^1, \ldots, u^n$ valid in a neighborhood W of p such that each Y_j, $j > 1$, is a linear combination of $\partial/\partial u^2, \ldots, \partial/\partial u^k$ and $Y_1 u^1(p) \neq 0$. [Since $Y_1|_p$ is independent of $\partial/\partial u^2|_p, \ldots, \partial/\partial u^k|_p$, certainly $Y_1 u^m(p) \neq 0$ for some $m = 1, k+1, \ldots, n$ and this u^m can be relabeled as u^1.] Theorem (29.11) guarantees the existence of a coordinate neighborhood $V \subset W$ of p with coordinate functions $z^1, \ldots, z^n$ such that (1) $Y_1 = \partial/\partial z^1$ on V and (2) if $z^1(q) = 0$, $q \in V$, then $u^1(q) = u^1(p)$, $z^2(q) = u^2(q), \ldots, z^n(q) = u^n(q)$. Without loss of generality one can assume that the range $z(V)$ of z is a cube centered at $z^1(p), \ldots, z^n(p)$,

$$(30.5) \quad \{(z^1(q), \ldots, z^n(q)) : q \in V\}$$

$$= \{(a^1, \ldots, a^n) : |a^j - z^j(p)| < \varepsilon, j = 1, 2, \ldots, n\}.$$

From the fact that $(z^2(q), \ldots, z^n(q)) = (u^2(q), \ldots, u^n(q))$ and $u^1(q) = u^1(p)$ when $z^1(q) = 0$, $q \in V$, it follows immediately for each differentiable function f on V that on the slice $S = \{q \in V : z^1(q) = 0\}$

$$\frac{\partial f}{\partial z^j}(q) = \frac{\partial f}{\partial u^j}(q), \qquad j > 1.$$

In particular $\partial z^m/\partial u^j = \delta_j^m$ on S when $j > 1$. Since $Y_2, \ldots, Y_k$ are linear combinations of $\partial/\partial u^2, \ldots, \partial/\partial u^k$ on $W \supset V$,

$$(30.6) \qquad Y_j z^m = \sum_{i=2}^{k} (Y_j u^i) \frac{\partial z^m}{\partial u^i} = 0, \qquad m > k \geq j > 1$$

on S. To extend (30.6) to V note that (30.4) together with the relation $Y_1 z^m = \partial z^m/\partial z^1 = 0 \ (m > k)$ implies

$$(30.7) \qquad \frac{\partial}{\partial z^1}(Y_j z^m) = [Y_1, Y_j] z^m + Y_j Y_1 z^m$$

$$= \sum_{\alpha=2}^{k} D_{1j}^\alpha (Y_\alpha z^m).$$

Fix $a^2, \ldots, a^n$ with $|a^j - z^j(p)| < \varepsilon$, $j = 2, \ldots, n$, and let $q(t)$ be the point in V whose z-coordinates are $(t, a^2, \ldots, a^n)$, $-\varepsilon < t < \varepsilon$. Put $f_j(t) = (Y_j z^m)[q(t)]$ and $B_{1j}^\alpha(t) = D_{1j}^\alpha[q(t)]$; then (30.7) and (30.6) state that

$$(30.8) \qquad \frac{df_j}{dt}(t) = \sum_{\alpha=2}^{k} B_{1j}^\alpha(t) f_\alpha(t), \qquad j = 2, 3, \ldots, k,$$

and

$$(30.9) \qquad f_j(0) = 0, \qquad j = 2, 3, \ldots, k.$$

Now the solutions of (30.8) satisfying (30.9) are unique, so that

$$(30.10) \qquad f_j(t) = 0, \qquad t \in (-\varepsilon, \varepsilon), k \geq j > 1.$$

Since every point in V has z-coordinates of the form $(a^1, a^2, \ldots, a^n)$ with $a^1 \in (-\varepsilon, \varepsilon)$ and $|a^j - z^j(p)| < \varepsilon = (j = 2, \ldots, n)$, it follows that (30.6) is valid throughout V. This means

$$Y_j = (Y_j z^1) \frac{\partial}{\partial x^1} + (Y_j z^2) \frac{\partial}{\partial x^2} + \cdots + (Y_j z^k) \frac{\partial}{\partial z^k} \qquad \text{on } V,$$

and the proof of Theorem (30.3) is finished. ◆

(30.11) Corollary. If $X_1, \ldots, X_k$ is an involutive system of vector fields on U, each point $p \in U$ has a coordinate neighborhood V with local coordinates $z^1, \ldots, z^n$ such that

(30.12) $\qquad X_1 f = 0, \quad X_2 f = 0, \quad \ldots, \quad X_k f = 0 \qquad \text{on } V$

if and only if

(30.13) $\qquad \frac{\partial f}{\partial z^1} = 0, \quad \ldots, \quad \frac{\partial f}{\partial z^k} = 0 \qquad \text{on } V.$

PROOF. According to Theorem (30.3), p has a coordinate neighborhood V such that

$$X_j = \sum_{m=1}^{k} (X_j z^m) \frac{\partial}{\partial z^m}.$$

Since the X_j's are linearly independent, the $(k \times k)$-matrix $(X_j z^m)$ must be nonsingular on V, so that

$$\frac{\partial}{\partial z^j} = \sum_{m=1}^{k} b_j^m X_m, \qquad j < k.$$

The equivalence of (30.12) and (30.13) follows immediately from these relations. ◆

Exercises

30.1 Suppose that ω^3 is a 1-form on the open set $U \subset R^3$ whose associated covector $\omega_p^3 \neq 0$, $p \in U$. Let $\omega^1, \omega^2, \omega^3$ be linearly independent 1-forms and let X_1, X_2, X_3 be the dual basis of vector fields, that is, $\langle X_i, \omega^j \rangle = \delta_i^j$ on U.

(a) Show that $\langle [X_1, X_2], \omega^3 \rangle = -\langle X_1 \wedge X_2, d\omega^3 \rangle$. (Cf. Exercise 21.3.)
(b) Show that the vector fields X_1, X_2 are involutive if and only if $d\omega^3 = \omega^3 \wedge \alpha$ for some 1-form α.
(c) Under the condition in (b), $d\omega^3 = \omega^3 \wedge \alpha$, show that each point $p \in U$ has a neighborhood W with a local coordinate system u^1, u^2, u^3 in terms of which $\omega^3 = f \, du^3$ for some differentiable function f.
(d) Show that $\omega^3 = f \, du$ for some functions f and u if and only if $\omega^3 \wedge d\omega^3 = 0$.

30.2 (Based on Exercise 21.7.) Suppose $\omega^1, \ldots, \omega^n$ and $X_1, \ldots, X_n$ are bases for the 1-forms and vector fields on $U \subset \mathbf{R}^n$, respectively, which are dual in the sense that at each p the associated covectors and vectors form a basis for $T_p^*(\mathbf{R}^n)$ or $T_p(\mathbf{R}^n)$, and $\langle X_i, \omega^\partial \rangle = \delta_i^\partial$. Show that

(a) $d(\omega^1 \wedge \omega^2) = \alpha \wedge \omega^1 \wedge \omega^2$ for some 1-form α if and only if $X_3, X_4, \ldots,$ X_n is involutive.

(b) $d(\omega^1 \wedge \cdots \wedge \omega^k) = \alpha \wedge \omega^1 \wedge \cdots \wedge \omega^k$ for some 1-form α if and only if $X_{k+1}, \ldots, X_n$ is involutive.

30.3   (Based on Exercise 30.2.) Suppose that at each $p \in U \subset \mathbf{R}^n$ the covectors associated with the 1-forms $\omega^1, \ldots, \omega^k$ are linearly independent. Show that each point $p \in U$ has a neighborhood V with functions $g, f^1, \ldots,$ f^k such that $\omega^1 \wedge \cdots \wedge \omega^k = g\, df^1 \wedge \cdots \wedge df^k$ if and only if

$$d(\omega^1 \wedge \cdots \wedge \omega^k) = \alpha \wedge \omega^1 \wedge \cdots \wedge \omega^k$$

for some 1-form α on U.

Applications of Exercise 30.3.   To find a solution of the system of equations

(30.14)
$$\frac{\partial g}{\partial x^j} = f_j(x^1, \ldots, x^n; g), \qquad 1 \le j \le n,$$

with the initial condition $g(x_0^1, \ldots, x_0^n) = g_0$ when the functions $f_1,$ $\ldots, f_n$ are defined on the open neighborhood W of $(x_0^1, \ldots, x_0^n, g_0)$ in $\mathbf{R}^{n+1}$, one can proceed as follows. Let

(30.15)
$$\omega = dx^{n+1} - (f_1\, dx^1 + \cdots + f_n\, dx^n).$$

If $d\omega = \alpha \wedge \omega$ or equivalently $d\omega \wedge \omega = 0$, Exercise 30.3 shows that $(x_0^1, \ldots, x_0^n, g_0)$ has a coordinate neighborhood with coordinates $z^1,$ $\ldots, z^{n+1}$ such that $\omega = f\, dz^{n+1}$ for some f. Now it is easily checked that

$$f\, dx^1 \wedge \cdots \wedge dx^n \wedge dz^{n+1} = dx^1 \wedge \cdots \wedge dx^n \wedge \omega$$

$$= dx^1 \wedge \cdots \wedge dx^n \wedge dx^{n+1}$$

$$\ne 0$$

at $(x_0^1, \ldots, x_0^n, g_0)$. So (Exercise 21.4) the functions $\dot{y}^1 = x^1, \ldots,$ $y^n = x^n, y^{n+1} = z^{n+1}$ form a coordinate system in some neighborhood of $(x_0^1, \ldots, x_0^n, g_0)$. In terms of these coordinates, remembering that $dx^k = dy^k$ when $k < n + 1$,

$$\omega = f\, dz^{n+1} = f\, dy^{n+1}$$

$$= dx^{n+1} - (f_1\, dx^1 + \cdots + f_n\, dx^n)$$

$$= \frac{\partial x^{n+1}}{\partial y^{n+1}}\, dy^{n+1} + \left(\frac{\partial x^{n+1}}{\partial y^1} - f_1\right) dy^1 + \cdots + \left(\frac{\partial x^{n+1}}{\partial y^n} - f_n\right) dy^n.$$

This implies $\partial x^{n+1}/\partial y^j = f_j$, $j < n + 1$. If $(x_0^1, \ldots, x_0^n, b)$ are the y-coordinates of the point $(x_0^1, \ldots, x_0^n, g_0)$, the required g can be taken as the function which assigns to $(a^1, \ldots, a^n)$ the value of x^{n+1} at the point with y-coordinates $(a^1, \ldots, a^n, b)$. To elaborate on this let y denote the

map of the y-coordinate neighborhood into $\mathbf{R}^{n+1}$ defined by $y(p) = (y^1(p),$
$\ldots, y^{n+1}(p))$. b and g are then defined by the relations

$$y(x_0^1, \ldots, x_0^n, g_0) = (x_0^1, \ldots, x_0^n, b);$$

$$y^{-1}(a^1, \ldots, a^n, b) = (a^1, \ldots, a^n, g[a^1, \ldots, a^n]).$$

Now if $q = (a^1, \ldots, a^n, b)$, (15.1) together with the above shows that
for $j < n + 1$

$$D_j g(a^1, \ldots, a^n) = D_j(x^{n+1} \circ y^{-1})(q)$$

$$= \frac{\partial x^{n+1}}{\partial y^j} [y^{-1}(q)]$$

$$= f_j(a^1, \ldots, a^n, g[a^1, \ldots, a^n]),$$

so that g does indeed satisfy (30.14).

30.4 Show that the integrability condition $d\omega \wedge \omega = 0$ above is equivalent
to

$$f_k \frac{\partial f_i}{\partial x^j} + f_i \frac{\partial f_j}{\partial x^k} + f_j \frac{\partial f_k}{\partial x^i} = 0, \qquad i < j < k;$$

$$\frac{\partial f_i}{\partial x^k} - \frac{\partial f_k}{\partial x_i} + f_k \frac{\partial f_i}{\partial g} - f_i \frac{\partial f_k}{\partial g} = 0, \qquad i < k.$$

30.5 Consider the system of equations

$$(30.16) \qquad \frac{\partial g^k}{\partial x^i} = f_j^k(x^1, \ldots, x^n; g^1, \ldots, g^m),$$

where $1 \le j \le n$, $1 \le k \le m$, with the initial conditions

$$(30.17) \qquad g^k(x_0^1, \ldots, x_0^n) = g_0^k, \qquad 1 \le k \le m.$$

The f_j^k's are differentiable functions defined in the open neighborhood W of the
point $(x_0^1, \ldots, x_0^n, g_0^1, \ldots, g_0^m)$ in $\mathbf{R}^{n+m}$. Set

$$\omega^k = dx^{n+k} - \sum_{j=1}^{n} f_j^k \, dx^j, \qquad 1 \le k \le m,$$

on W and let Ω be the m-form $\Omega = \omega^1 \wedge \cdots \wedge \omega^m$. Show that if $d\Omega = \alpha \wedge \Omega$
for some 1-form α on W, the system (30.16) has a local solution satisfying the
boundary conditions (30.17). [HINT: Using the result of Exercise 30.3, there are
functions $h, h^1, \ldots, h^m$ such that $\Omega = h \, dh^1 \wedge \cdots \wedge dh^m$, and it is easy to
check that

$$0 \neq dx^1 \wedge \cdots \wedge dx^n \wedge \Omega = h \, dx^1 \wedge \cdots \wedge dx^n \wedge dh^1 \wedge \cdots \wedge dh^m,$$

so that $y^1 = x^1, \ldots, y^n = x^n, y^{n+1} = h^1, \ldots, y^{n+m} = h^m$ form a local coordinate system for $\mathbf{R}^{n+m}$ in a neighborhood of $(x_0^1, \ldots, x_0^n, g_0^1, \ldots, g_0^m) = q$.
Regard the x^{n+k}'s as functions of the values of the y's and show that the functions

$$g^k(a^1, \ldots, a^n) = x^{n+k} \circ y^{-1}(a^1, \ldots, a^n, y^{n+1}(q), \ldots, y^{n+m}(q))$$

will work.]

30.6 If $\Omega = \omega^1 \wedge \cdots \wedge \omega^m$ where the covectors associated with $\omega^1, \ldots,$ ω^m are independent at each point of $U \subset \mathbf{R}^N$, that is, $\Omega \neq 0$ on U, show that $d\Omega = \alpha \wedge \Omega$ for some 1-form α if and only if each $d\omega^k$ is a sum of terms of the type $\omega^i \wedge \beta^i$ where the β^i's are 1-forms. This is often expressed $d\omega^k \equiv 0 \mod (\omega^1, \ldots, \omega^m)$. That is, $d\omega^k \equiv 0$ for each k when the relations $\omega^1 \equiv 0, \ldots, \omega^m \equiv 0$ are taken as valid equations for the purposes of substitution. (Cf. Example 30.18 below.)

30.7 Show in $\mathbf{R}^2$, with variables x, y instead of the usual x^1, x^2, that each of the following systems can be prolonged to a system of type (30.16) by introducing extra variables [see Example (30.18)] and investigate whether or not the prolonged system satisfies the integrability conditions $d\Omega = \alpha \wedge \Omega$ or $d\omega^k \equiv 0 \mod (\omega^1, \ldots, \omega^m)$ of Exercises 30.5 and 30.6.

(i) $\dfrac{\partial f}{\partial x} = y^2, \dfrac{\partial f}{\partial y} = 3x.$

(ii) $\dfrac{\partial^2 f}{\partial x^2} + \dfrac{\partial^2 f}{\partial y^2} = e^x.$

(iii) $\dfrac{\partial^2 f}{\partial x^2} - \dfrac{\partial^2 f}{\partial y^2} + 3x\dfrac{\partial f}{\partial x} + e^x = 0, \quad \dfrac{\partial f}{\partial x} + \dfrac{\partial f}{\partial y} = 0.$

(iv) $\dfrac{\partial^3 f}{\partial x^2\, \partial y} = 3f^2 + x.$

(30.18) **Example.** $\partial^2 f/\partial x^2 + 3f = x;\ \partial f/\partial y + \partial f/\partial x = e^x$. Introduce the dependent variable p and consider the system

$$\frac{\partial f}{\partial x} = p, \qquad \frac{\partial p}{\partial x} = x - 3f, \qquad \frac{\partial f}{\partial y} = e^x - p,$$

which is equivalent to the original one. This new system does not have the form (30.16) because $\partial p/\partial y$ is not specified. To allow all possibilities add the equation $\partial p/\partial y = h$ where h is an as yet unspecified function of x, y, f, and p.

$$\omega^1 = df - (p\, dx + [e^x - p]\, dy);$$
$$\omega^2 = dp - ([x - 3f]\, dx + h\, dy).$$

Now

$$d\omega^1 = -dp \wedge dx - e^x\, dx \wedge dy + dp \wedge dy$$
$$\equiv h\, dx \wedge dy - e^x\, dx \wedge dy + (x - 3f)\, dx \wedge dy$$
$$\equiv (h - e^x + x - 3f)\, dx \wedge dy.$$

$d\omega^1 \equiv 0 \mod (\omega^1, \omega^2)$ only if h is chosen to be $h = e^x + 3f - x$. In this case $dh = e^x\, dx + 3\, df - dx$ and

$$d\omega^2 = 3\, df \wedge dx - dh \wedge dy$$
$$\equiv 3(p - e^x)\, dy \wedge dx - (e^x\, dx + 3\, df - dx) \wedge dy$$
$$\equiv (3e^x - 3p - e^x + 3p + 1)\, dx \wedge dy,$$

which is not zero in x, y, f, p space. Consequently the system in the example will not satisfy the integrability conditions above for any choice of h.

30.8 Show directly by differentiating the equations in Example (30.18) and substituting to arrive at a contradiction that this system has no solutions.

31 The operator θ_X

If X is a vector field on U the operator θ_X, extending the action of X on functions to differential forms and vector fields, is defined by

(31.1)
$$\theta_X \omega = d(X \lrcorner \omega) + X \lrcorner d\omega;$$
$$\theta_X Y = [X, Y].$$

If the function f is regarded as a 0-form, $\theta_X f = d(X \lrcorner f) + X \lrcorner df = Xf$.

(31.2) Theorem. θ_X is the only linear operator defined on differential forms and vector fields and satisfying:

(i) $\theta_X(\alpha \wedge \beta) = (\theta_X \alpha) \wedge \beta + \alpha \wedge (\theta_X \beta)$.

(ii) $\theta_X \, d\alpha = d\theta_X \alpha$.

(iii) $\theta_X f = Xf$.

(iv) $\theta_X \langle Y, \omega \rangle = \langle \theta_X Y, \omega \rangle + \langle Y, \theta_X \omega \rangle$ when ω is a 1-form.

PROOF. Straightforward computations, which are left to the exercises, show θ_X satisfies (i)–(iv). If θ'_X is another linear operator satisfying (i)–(iv), it is readily seen using the representation (21.3) and (i)–(iii) that θ_X agrees with θ'_X on differential forms, and if this is applied to (iv)

$$\langle \theta_X Y, \omega \rangle = \langle \theta_X Y, \omega \rangle - \langle Y, \theta_X \omega \rangle$$
$$= \langle \theta'_X Y, \omega \rangle - \langle Y, \theta'_X \omega \rangle = \langle \theta'_X Y, \omega \rangle$$

for each 1-form ω; so $\theta_X Y = \theta'_X Y$, completing the proof. ◆

There is a geometric way of defining θ_X. It depends on the notion of the derivative of a family of forms or vector fields with respect to a parameter. If $\{\omega(t) : t \in (-\delta, \delta)\}$ is a family of k-forms on U, the k-form $\partial\omega(t)/\partial t$ is determined by the relation

(31.3) $$\left\langle X_1 \wedge \cdots \wedge X_k, \frac{\partial\omega(t)}{\partial t} \right\rangle = \frac{\partial}{\partial t} \langle X_1 \wedge \cdots \wedge X_k, \omega(t) \rangle$$

for any k vector fields $X_1, \ldots, X_k$. Similarly if $\{Y(t) : t \in (-\delta, \delta)\}$ is a family of vector fields on U, $\partial Y(t)/\partial t$ is defined by

(31.4) $$\frac{\partial Y(t)}{\partial t} f = \frac{\partial}{\partial t} \{Y(t)f\},$$

or equivalently

(31.5)
$$\left\langle \frac{\partial Y(t)}{\partial t}, \alpha \right\rangle = \frac{\partial}{\partial t} \langle Y(t), \alpha \rangle$$

for each 1-form α.

(31.6) Theorem. Suppose that $\phi: (-\delta, \delta) \times V \to U$ is a flow of the open set V into U with velocity field $X(t)$ and $X = X(0)$; then

(31.7)
$$\theta_X \omega = \frac{\partial}{\partial t} \phi_t^* \omega \Big|_{t=0},$$

$$\theta_X Y = \frac{\partial}{\partial t} (\phi_t^*)^{-1} Y \Big|_{t=0}$$

on V.

PROOF.   The proof consists of showing that the operator θ_X defined by (31.7) satisfies (i)–(iv) of Theorem (31.2). θ_X is clearly linear; (iii) is just a rephrasing of the statement that ϕ has velocity field X when $t = 0$; while (i), (ii), and (iv) are obtained, respectively, by differentiating the relations

$$\phi_t^*(\alpha \wedge \beta) = \phi_t^* \alpha \wedge \phi_t^* \beta,$$

$$\phi_t^* \, d\alpha = d\phi_t^* \alpha,$$

and

$$\langle (\phi_t*)^{-1} Y, \phi_t^* \omega \rangle = \phi_t^* \langle Y, \omega \rangle. \qquad \blacklozenge$$

One consequence of Theorem (31.6) is that

(31.8)
$$\frac{\partial \phi_t^* \omega}{\partial t} = \phi_t^* \theta_{X(t)} \omega \qquad \text{on } V.$$

To derive (31.8) note that for fixed t and small s the map $\psi: (s, \phi(t, p)) \to \phi(t + s, p)$ is a flow of $\phi_t V$ into U whose velocity field is $X(t)$ when $s = 0$. Thus from Theorem (31.6)

$$\frac{\partial}{\partial s} \psi_s^* \omega \Big|_{s=0} = \theta_{X(t)} \omega \qquad \text{on } \phi_t V.$$

Now $\psi_s \circ \phi_t = \phi_{t+s}$; so

$$\phi_t^* \theta_{X(t)} \omega = \phi_t^* \cdot \frac{\partial}{\partial s} \psi_s^* \omega \Big|_{s=0} = \frac{\partial}{\partial s} \phi_t^* \psi_s^* \omega \Big|_{s=0} = \frac{\partial}{\partial s} \phi_{t+s}^* \omega \Big|_{s=0} = \frac{\partial \phi_t^* \omega}{\partial t}$$

on V.

In applications the form ω often depends on t directly, and a somewhat generalized version of (31.8) is needed to cover this situation.

(31.9) Theorem. If $\phi: (-\delta, \delta) \times V \to U$ is a flow of V into U with velocity field $X(t)$, then whenever $\{\omega(t): t \in (-\delta, \delta)\}$ is a family of k-forms on U

$$(31.10) \quad \frac{\partial}{\partial t} \, \phi_t^* \omega(t) = \phi_t^* \left\{ \theta_{X(t)} \omega(t) + \frac{\partial \omega(t)}{\partial t} \right\}$$

$$= \phi_t^* \left\{ d[X(t) \, \lrcorner \, \omega(t)] + X(t) \, \lrcorner \, d\omega(t) + \frac{\partial \omega(t)}{\partial t} \right\} \quad \text{on } V.$$

PROOF. If $Y_1, \ldots, Y_k$ are vector fields on U the function $g(u, v) = \langle Y_1 \wedge \cdots \wedge Y_k, \phi_u^* \omega(v) \rangle$ is continuously differentiable in both u and v, so that when u and v are regarded as functions of t,

$$\frac{dg}{dt} = \frac{\partial g}{\partial u} \frac{du}{dt} + \frac{\partial g}{\partial v} \frac{dv}{dt}.$$

Putting $u = t$, $v = t$ yields (31.10). ◆

Exercises

31.1 If $\{\omega(t) : t \in (-\delta, \delta)\}$ is a family of k-forms on U and c is a k-chain in U, show that

$$\frac{d}{dt} \int_c \omega(t) = \int_c \frac{\partial \omega(t)}{\partial t}.$$

31.2 (Based on Exercise 31.1.) If $\{\omega(t) : t \in (-\delta, \delta)\}$ is a family of k-forms on U, $\phi : (-\varepsilon, \varepsilon) \times V \to U$ is a flow with velocity field $X(t)$, and c is a k-chain in V, show that

$$(31.11) \quad \frac{d}{dt} \int_{\phi_t \circ c} \omega(t) = \int_{\partial(\phi_t \circ c)} X(t) \, \lrcorner \, \omega(t) + \int_{\phi_t \circ c} \left[X(t) \, \lrcorner \, d\omega(t) + \frac{\partial \omega(t)}{\partial t} \right].$$

31.3 Show that Leibnitz's formula [$a = a(t)$, $b = b(t)$]

$$\frac{d}{dt} \int_a^b F(t, s) \, ds = F(t, b) \frac{db}{dt} - F(t, a) \frac{da}{dt} + \int_a^b \frac{\partial F}{\partial t} (t, s) \, ds$$

is a special case of (31.11). [HINT: Let $\phi_t \circ c$ represent integration over $[a(t), b(t)]$.]

31.4 (Equation of continuity.) Let $\phi : (-\varepsilon, \varepsilon) \times V \to U$ describe the flow of an n-fluid with velocity vector field $X(t)$ and density $\omega(t)$. Thus if c represents integration over the region G, $\int_c \omega(t)$ represents the amount of fluid in G at time t. If the fluid has no sources or sinks, $\int_{\phi_t \circ c} \omega(t)$ is a constant since it represents the amount of a common batch of fluid. Show in this case that

$$d[X(t) \, \lrcorner \, \omega(t)] + \frac{\partial \omega(t)}{\partial t} = 0.$$

This is the equation of continuity.

31.5 (Invariant k-forms.) A k-form ω is invariant under the flow ϕ if $\phi_t^* \omega = \omega$ for each t. Show that ω is invariant if and only if $\theta_X \omega = 0$ where X is the velocity field of the flow ϕ.

32 Homotopy and Poincaré's lemma

Two differentiable maps f_0 and f_1 of V into U are (differentiably) *homotopic* if there is a differentiable map $\phi \colon [0, 1] \times V \to U$ such that $f_0(p) = \phi(0, p)$, $p \in V$, and $f_1(q) = \phi(1, q)$, $q \in V$. The map ϕ is called a homotopy of f_0 and f_1. It describes a differentiable deformation of the map f_0 into the map f_1, the intermediate maps f_t being given by $f_t(p) = \phi(t, p)$, $t \in [0, 1]$, $p \in V$.

A simple example of a homotopy stems from a flow $\psi \colon (-\delta, \delta) \times V \to U$ of V into U. The two maps $p \to \psi(0, p)$ and $p \to \psi(s, p)$ are homotopic, and all that is required to show this is a change of scale in the flow parameter s. The indicated homotopy is the map $\phi \colon [0, 1] \times V \to U$ given by $\phi(t, q) = \psi(ts, q)$.

In the space $[0, 1] \times V$, whose points are ordered pairs (a, p) where $a \in [0, 1]$ and $p \in V$, the letter t is used to represent the function $t(a, p) = a$ describing projection onto the first factor $[0, 1]$ and π to describe projection onto V, $\pi(a, q) = q$. The symbol $\partial/\partial t$ by itself is ambiguous, of course, unless the remaining coordinate variables are given, but in such a product space $\partial/\partial t$ will henceforth be used for the unique vector field satisfying

$$\pi_* \left(\frac{\partial}{\partial t} \right) = 0, \qquad \left\langle \frac{\partial}{\partial t}, dt \right\rangle = 1,$$

at every point of $[0, 1] \times V$. If $y^1, \ldots, y^n$ is a coordinate system for V and t, $x^1 = y^1 \circ \pi, \ldots, x^n = y^n \circ \pi$ is used as a coordinate system for $[0, 1] \times V$, $\partial/\partial t$ has its customary interpretation.

The map $p \to (s, p)$ injecting V into the sth coordinate slice of $[0, 1] \times V$ is denoted by i_s, so that $i_s(p) = (s, p)$. Thus if $\phi \colon [0, 1] \times V \to U$ is a homotopy of f_0 and f_1, $f_t = \phi \circ i_t$. Since $t \circ i_s(p) = $ the constant s, $i_s^*(dt) = 0$. If f is a differentiable function on V, $i_s^*(d[f \circ \pi]) = df$ because $\pi \circ i_s$ is the identity map on V. Thus $i_s^*(dx^j) = dy^j$ in the coordinate systems of the preceding paragraph.

(32.1) Lemma. If ω is a differential form on $[0, 1] \times V$,

(32.2)
$$\frac{\partial}{\partial s} i_s^* \omega = i_s^* \theta_{\partial/\partial t} \omega \qquad \text{on } V.$$

PROOF. Using the $(t; x)$ coordinate system introduced above, we find two types of terms in ω: those containing dt and those not containing dt. If

$$\omega = f(t; x)\, dx^{i_1} \wedge \cdots \wedge dx^{i_k},$$

$$d\omega = \sum_j \frac{\partial f}{\partial x^j}\, dx^j \wedge dx^{i_1} \wedge \cdots \wedge dx^{i_k} + \frac{\partial f}{\partial t}\, dt \wedge dx^{i_1} \wedge \cdots \wedge dx^{i_k},$$

and since $\partial/\partial t \lrcorner \omega = 0$,

$$\theta_{\partial/\partial t}\omega = \frac{\partial}{\partial t} \lrcorner d\omega = \frac{\partial f}{\partial t}(t; x) \, dx^{i_1} \wedge \cdots \wedge dx^{i_k};$$

so

$$i_s^* \theta_{\partial/\partial t}\omega = \frac{\partial f}{\partial s}(s; y) \, dy^{i_1} \wedge \cdots \wedge dy^{i_k}$$

$$= \frac{\partial}{\partial s}\{f(s; y) \, dy^{i_1} \wedge \cdots \wedge dy^{i_k}\}$$

$$= \frac{\partial}{\partial s} i_s^* \omega.$$

Whereas if

$$\omega = g(t; x) \, dt \wedge dx^{i_1} \wedge \cdots \wedge dx^{i_{k-1}},$$

$$d\omega = \sum_j \frac{\partial g}{\partial x^j} dx^j \wedge dt \wedge dx^{i_1} \wedge \cdots \wedge dx^{i_{k-1}},$$

and

$$\frac{\partial}{\partial t} \lrcorner d\omega = -\sum_j \frac{\partial g}{\partial x^j} dx^j \wedge x^{i_1} \wedge \cdots \wedge dx^{i_{k-1}}$$

while

$$d\left(\frac{\partial}{\partial t} \lrcorner \omega\right) = d(g \, dx^{i_1} \wedge \cdots \wedge dx^{i_{k-1}}$$

$$= \sum_j \frac{\partial g}{\partial x^j} dx^j \wedge dx^{i_1} \wedge \cdots \wedge dx^{i_{k-1}} + \frac{\partial g}{\partial t} dt \wedge dx^{i_1} \wedge \cdots \wedge dx^{i_{k-1}};$$

so

$$\theta_{\partial/\partial t}\omega = \frac{\partial g}{\partial t} dt \wedge dx^{i_1} \wedge \cdots \wedge dx^{i_{z-1}}$$

and both

$$i_s^* \theta_{\partial/\partial t}\omega = 0 \quad \text{and} \quad \frac{\partial}{\partial s} i_s^* \omega = 0$$

because

$$i_s^*(dt) = 0. \qquad \blacklozenge$$

With the aid of this lemma it is easy to prove the following important result.

(32.3) Theorem. If f_0 and f_1 are homotopic maps of V into U, for each $k = 0, 1, \ldots, n, n+1, \ldots$ there is a linear map D_k of k-forms on U into $(k-1)$-forms on V such that

(32.4) $$f_1^* \omega - f_0^* \omega = dD_k\omega + D_{k+1} \, d\omega$$

whenever ω is a k-form on U. If n is the dimension of U, $D_0 = D_{n+1} = 0$.

PROOF. Let ϕ be a homotopy of f_0 and f_1 as above. The D_k's are easily described by

$$D_k\omega = \int_0^1 i_s^* \left(\frac{\partial}{\partial t} \lrcorner \, \phi^*\omega \right) ds.$$

The verification of (32.4) rests on the following chain of equalities in which essential use is made of (32.2); the fact that $i_t^*\phi^*\omega = f_t^*\omega$ because $\phi \circ i_t = f_t$; and the relations $\phi^*d = d\phi^*$, $i_t^*d = di_t^*$.

$$f_1^*\omega - f_0^*\omega = \int_0^1 \frac{\partial}{\partial t} f_t^*\omega \, dt = \int_0^1 \frac{\partial}{\partial t} i_t^*\phi^*\omega \, dt$$

$$= \int_0^1 i_t^* \theta_{\partial/\partial t} \phi^*\omega$$

$$= \int_0^1 i_t^* \left(\frac{\partial}{\partial t} \lrcorner \, d\phi^*\omega \right) dt + \int_0^1 i_t^* d \left(\frac{\partial}{\partial t} \lrcorner \, \phi^*\omega \right) dt$$

$$= \int_0^1 i_t^* \left(\frac{\partial}{\partial t} \lrcorner \, \phi^* \, d\omega \right) dt + d \int_0^1 i_t^* \left(\frac{\partial}{\partial t} \lrcorner \, \phi^*\omega \right) dt$$

$$= D_{k+1} \, d\omega + dD_k\omega. \qquad \blacklozenge$$

Theorem (32.3) is the basic ingredient for one of the major existence theorems in the theory of partial differential equations to which the remainder of this section is devoted. The subset V of U can be deformed to the point p in U, in symbols $V \simeq \{p\}$, if and only if the identity map $i: V \to U$ is homotopic to the constant map $h_p: V \to U$ which maps V onto p, $h_p(V) = \{p\}$.

(32.5) Theorem. Suppose β is a k-form on U $(k > 0)$ and (i) $d\beta = 0$ on U; (ii) V is an open subset of U which can be deformed to a point in U. Then there is a $(k-1)$-form α on V such that $\beta = d\alpha$ on V.

PROOF. Let $\phi: [0, 1] \times V \to U$ be a homotopy of the identity map f_1, $f_1(p) = p \in V$, and the constant map f_0, $f_0(p) = p_0$, $p \in V$. $f_1^*\beta = \beta$ on V whereas $f_0^*\beta = 0$. Thus according to Theorem (32.3) $\beta = dD_k\beta + D_{k+1} \, d\beta$ on V, but since $d\beta = 0$ this amounts to $\beta = d(D_k\beta)$, and the $(k-1)$-form $\alpha = D_k\beta$ satisfies the conditions of the theorem. $\blacklozenge$

(32.6) Corollary (Poincaré's lemma). Suppose β is a k-form on U $(k > 0)$ and $d\beta = 0$ on U. Then for each point $p \in U$ there is a neighborhood $p \in N_p$ and a $(k-1)$-form α on N_p such that $\beta = d\alpha$ on N_p.

PROOF. Let $x^1, \ldots, x^n$ be a local coordinate system valid in some neighborhood $W \subset U$ of p and suppose ε is small enough so that

$$x(W) \supset \{(a^1, \ldots, a^n): \sum_j (a^j - x^j(p))^2 < \varepsilon^2\} = J_\varepsilon.$$

Then the map $\phi\colon [0, 1] \times x^{-1}(J_e) \to U$ defined by

$$x^j \circ \phi(t, q) = (1 - t)x^j(p) + tx^j(q)$$

is a homotopy showing that $N_p = x^{-1}(J_e) \simeq \{p\}$ in U and Theorem (32.4) applies to yield the desired $(k - 1)$-form α on N_p. ◆

Exercises

32.1 If f_0 and f_1 are homotopic maps of V into U, c is an m-chain in V with $\partial c = 0$, and ω is an m-form on U with $d\omega = 0$, show that $\int_c f_0^* \omega = \int_c f_1^* \omega$.

32.2 Suppose it is known that the two open sets U_1 and U_2 are each homotopic to a constant and that any two points $p, q \in U_1 \cap U_2$ can be joined by a 1-simplex $C_{pq}\colon [0, 1] \to U_1 \cap U_2$, $C_{pq}(0) = p$, $C_{pq}(1) = q$. If ω is a 1-form on $U_1 \cup U_2$ and $d\omega = 0$, show that $\omega = df$ for some function f on $U_1 \cup U_2$.

32.3 Let U be the annulus $1 < (x^1)^2 + (x^2)^2 < 2$ in $\mathbf{R}^2$. If ω is a 1-form on U with $d\omega = 0$, show that $\omega = \lambda\alpha + df$ for some function f on U and some $\lambda \in \mathbf{R}$, where $\alpha = -(x^2)^{-1}\, dx^1 + (x^1)^{-1}\, dx^2$. α is the form usually denoted by $d\theta$ when r and θ are polar coordinates.

32.4 Show that a 1-form $\omega = \Sigma\, g_i\, dx^i$ has the form $\omega = df$ locally if and only if $\partial g_i/\partial x^j - \partial g_j/\partial x^i = 0$, $i < j$.

CHAPTER SEVEN

Applications to Complex Variables

33   Complex structure

The topic "complex structure" as used here divides naturally into two subheadings. The first, and in a way the more superficial of these, is associated with the problem of using the complex numbers $\mathbf{C}$ as the scalar field rather than the real numbers $\mathbf{R}$. The results obtained by doing this do not differ in any outstanding manner from the previous case, but since they form the framework for an exposition of the second subheading, the concept of holomorphy or analyticity, it is worthwhile to consider briefly the modifications needed in the definitions used so far.

Let U be an open subset of $\mathbf{R}^n$ with cartesian coordinates $x^1, \ldots, x^n$. A function f on U is understood now to be a $\mathbf{C}$-valued function $f: U \to \mathbf{C}$ as opposed to the previous interpretation of a function as being real-valued ($\mathbf{R}$-valued). Such a function can be written uniquely as the sum $f = u + iv$ of two real-valued functions u and v known, respectively, as the real and imaginary parts of f. The conjugate of f is the function $\bar{f} = u - iv$, so that f is real-valued if and only if $\bar{f} = f$. f is *differentiable of class* k or C^k on U if both u and v are C^k on U in the previous sense. Alternatively, f is C^k on U if the map $f: U \to \mathbf{C}$ is a C^k map when $\mathbf{C}$ is identified with $\mathbf{R}^{2k}$ in the natural manner.

In this setting a *vector* Z_p at p is a $\mathbf{C}$-valued operator of the form

$$(33.1) \qquad Z_p = a^1 \frac{\partial}{\partial x^1}\bigg|_p + \cdots + a^n \frac{\partial}{\partial x^n}\bigg|_p, \qquad a^j \in \mathbf{C} \text{ all } j,$$

whose domain is the set of all (complex-valued) functions which are $\mathbf{C}^1$ at p. Associated with each vector Z_p is its conjugate

$$(33.2) \qquad \bar{Z}_p = \overline{a^1} \frac{\partial}{\partial x^1}\bigg|_p + \cdots + \overline{a^n} \frac{\partial}{\partial x^n}\bigg|_p.$$

The vector Z_p is called a *real vector* if $\bar{Z}_p = Z_p$. Each vector Z_p can be represented uniquely in the form $Z_p = X_p + iY_p$ where X_p and Y_p are real vectors at p.

As before, the vectors at p form an n-dimensional vector space (over the scalar field **C**) which is denoted by $CT_p(\mathbf{R}^n)$. The real vectors at p form a subset $T_p(\mathbf{R}^n)$ of $CT_p(\mathbf{R}^n)$ which is closed under addition and multiplication by real scalars, but it is not a vector subspace since it is not closed under scalar multiplication by complex scalars. The dual space of $CT_p(\mathbf{R}^n)$ is the space of covectors at p and is denoted by $CT_p^*(\mathbf{R}^n)$. It consists of all **C**-linear maps of $CT_p(\mathbf{R}^n)$ into **C** and has a basis $(dx^1)_p$, $\ldots$, $(dx^n)_p$ where for each differentiable function h at p, the covector $(dh)_p$ is defined by

$$(33.3) \qquad \langle Z_p, (dh)_p \rangle = Z_p h.$$

Thus a typical element $\omega_p \in CT_j^*(\mathbf{R}^n)$ has the form

$$(33.4) \qquad \omega_p = b_1(dx^1)_p + \cdots + b_n(dx^n)_p, \qquad b_k \in \mathbf{C} \text{ all } k.$$

Technically speaking these $(dx^j)_p$'s are not quite the same $(dx^j)_p$'s used earlier because they are defined on the larger space $CT_p(\mathbf{R}^n)$, but their restrictions to $T_p(\mathbf{R}^n)$ are the same as the $(dx^j)_p$'s used earlier. The conjugate $\overline{\omega}_p$ of ω_p, the concept of a real covector at p, exterior products, vector fields, differential forms, the maps f_* and f^*, and the exterior derivative are defined as before and satisfy the same relations with linearity over **C** replacing linearity over **R**.

It is worth noting that if $f : U \to \mathbf{R}^m$ is a differentiable map of the open subset U of $\mathbf{R}^n$ into $\mathbf{R}^m$, then the maps $f_* : CT_p(\mathbf{R}^n) \to CT_{f(p)}(\mathbf{R}^m)$ and $f^* : CT_{f(p)}^*(\mathbf{R}^m) \to CT_p^*(\mathbf{R}^n)$ preserve the realness of a vector or covector, respectively. On the real subsets of $CT_p(\mathbf{R}^n)$ and $CT_{f(p)}^*(\mathbf{R}^m)$ they coincide with the f_* and f^* used earlier.

The scalar product of two vectors X_p, Y_p belonging to $CT_p(\mathbf{R}^n)$ is given by

$$(33.5) \qquad (X_p, Y_p) = \sum_{j=1}^{n} (X_p x^j)(Y_p x^j)^-$$

where the $x^1, \ldots, x^n$ are cartesian coordinates for $\mathbf{R}^n$ and $(****)^-$ is used to denote the conjugate of $(****)$. It is a positive definite Hermitian scalar product satisfying the identities (subscripts p omitted):

$$(33.6)$$
(i) $(aX + bY, Z) = a(X, Z) + b(Y, Z)$;

(ii) $(X, Y) = (\bar{Y}, \bar{X}) = (Y, X)^-$;

(iii) $0 < (X, X)$ unless $X = 0$;

(iv) $(Z, aX + bY) = \bar{a}(Z, X) + \bar{b}(Z, Y)$.

Using this Hermitian scalar product the map $\#: CT_p^*(\mathbf{R}^n) \to CT_p(\mathbf{R}^n)$ is defined as before by

(33.7) $(X, \beta^{\#}) = \langle X, \beta \rangle, \qquad X \in CT_p(\mathbf{R}^n), \, \beta \in CT_p^*(\mathbf{R}^n).$

The chain of equalities

$$(X, [a\beta]^{\#}) = \langle X, a\beta \rangle = a \langle x, \beta \rangle = a(X, \beta^{\#})$$
$$= (X, \bar{a}\beta^{\#})$$

shows that the map is **C**-antilinear, that is,

(33.8) $$(a\beta)^{\#} = \bar{a}\beta^{\#}.$$

The matching scalar product on $CT_p^*(\mathbf{R}^n)$ is defined by

(33.9) $$(\alpha, \beta) = (\beta^{\#}, \alpha^{\#})$$

where the switch in the relative positions of α and β on the two sides of (33.9) is necessary to make (α, β) **C**-linear in α and **C**-antilinear in β. The map $\#: CT_p(\mathbf{R}^n) \to CT_p^*(\mathbf{R}^n)$ is defined by

(33.10) $\langle Y, X^{\#} \rangle = (Y, X), \qquad X, Y \in CT_p(\mathbf{R}^n).$

The relations $(X^{\#})^{\#} = X$, $(\beta^{\#})^{\#} = \beta$ are left to the exercises.

Exercises

33.1 Show that $X, Y \to (X, Y)$ is the only map of ordered pairs from $CT_p(\mathbf{R}^n)$ into **C** which (a) agrees with the previously defined inner product on the real subset $T_p(\mathbf{R}^n)$; (b) is **C**-linear in X and **C**-antilinear in Y.

33.2 If $\alpha = \sum f_{i_1 \ldots i_k} \, dx^{i_1} \wedge \cdots \wedge dx^{i_k}$ is a k-form on U, its conjugate is the k-form

$$\bar{\alpha} = \sum \bar{f}_{i_1 \ldots i_k} \, dx^{i_1} \wedge \cdots \wedge dx^{i_k}.$$

Show this is equivalent to the condition

$$\langle X_1 \wedge \cdots \wedge X_k, \bar{\alpha} \rangle = \langle \bar{X}_1 \wedge \cdots \wedge \bar{X}_k, \alpha \rangle^-.$$

33.3 Show that $d\bar{\alpha} = (d\alpha)^-$. See Exercise 33.2.

33.4 If $Z_p \in CT_p(\mathbf{R}^n)$, show that the definition of $\bar{Z}_p$ is equivalent to the condition $\bar{Z}_p f = (Z_p \bar{f})^-$ for each f which is differentiable in a neighborhood of p.

33.5 Show that there is no scalar product $B(X, Y)$ on $CT_p(\mathbf{R}^n)$ which is both (a) positive definite, $0 < B(X, X)$ unless $X = 0$; and (b) bilinear, that is, **C**-linear in both X and Y.

33.6 Verify that $(\beta^{\#})^{\#} = \beta$, $\beta \in CT_p^*(\mathbf{R}^n)$ and $(X^{\#})^{\#} = X$, $X \in CT_p(\mathbf{R}^n)$.

33.7 If $\alpha = a_1(dx^1)_p + \cdots + a_n(dx^n)_p$ and $\beta = b_1(dx^1)_p + \cdots + b_n(dx^n)_p$ where the x^i's are cartesian coordinates, show that $(\alpha, \beta) = a_1 \bar{b}_1 + \cdots + a_n \bar{b}_n$.

33.8 Using the basis elements $\partial/\partial x^i|_p$ and $(dx^k)_p$, show how to extend $(\cdot, \cdot)$ (a) to a Hermitian scalar product on m-covectors; (b) to a Hermitian scalar product on m-vectors. Show that this extension is unique provided it agrees on the real elements with the one given previously.

33.9 Show that (33.6)(iv) follows from (33.6)(i) and (33.6)(ii).

33.10 Using the extensions in Exercise 33.8, define the map #: $\wedge^k CT_p(\mathbf{R}^n) \to \wedge^k CT_p^*(\mathbf{R}^n)$ and its inverse in the manner indicated by (33.7) and (33.10). Show that they are both **C**-antilinear.

33.11 The duality operator * is defined by

$$(\alpha, *\beta) \, dx^1 \wedge \cdots \wedge dx^n = \alpha \wedge *\beta.$$

Show that $*(a\alpha) = \bar{a} *\alpha$.

34 Analytic coordinates

Suppose $n = 2m$ is even. Put

(34.1) $$z^k(p) = x^{2k-1}(p) + ix^{2k}(p), \qquad 1 \le k \le m.$$

The map $p \to (z^1(p), \ldots, z^m(p))$ of $\mathbf{R}^{2m} \to \mathbf{C}^m$ is one-one onto, so that the m complex numbers $z^1(p), \ldots, z^m(p)$ can serve as coordinates for p in a sense to be made precise below and it is natural to identify $\mathbf{R}^{2m}$ and $\mathbf{C}^m$.

The relations

(34.2)
$$2 \, dx^{2k-1} = dz^k + d\bar{z}^k,$$
$$2i \, dx^{2k} = dz^k - d\bar{z}^k$$

show that the 1-forms $dz^k = dx^{2k-1} + i \, dx^{2k}$, $1 \le k \le m$, and their conjugates $d\bar{z}^k = dx^{2k-1} - i \, dx^{2k}$, $1 \le k \le m$, form a basis for the complex vector space $CT_p^*(\mathbf{R}^n)$. The associated dual basis for $CT_p(\mathbf{R}^n)$ is denoted by

$$\frac{\partial}{\partial z^1}, \, \cdots, \, \frac{\partial}{\partial z^m}, \frac{\partial}{\partial \bar{z}^1}, \, \cdots, \, \frac{\partial}{\partial \bar{z}^m}$$

where the partial-derivative notation is used to serve as a reminder of the equations

(34.3)
$$\left\langle \frac{\partial}{\partial z^j}, dz^k \right\rangle = \delta_j^k; \qquad \left\langle \frac{\partial}{\partial z^j}, d\bar{z}^k \right\rangle = 0;$$
$$\left\langle \frac{\partial}{\partial \bar{z}^j}, dz^k \right\rangle = 0; \qquad \left\langle \frac{\partial}{\partial \bar{z}^j}, d\bar{z}^k \right\rangle = \delta_j^k.$$

From (34.2) and (34.3) it is easy to compute that

$$\left\langle \frac{\partial}{\partial z^j}, dx^{2k-1} \right\rangle = \frac{1}{2} \delta_j^k; \qquad \left\langle \frac{\partial}{\partial z^j}, dx^{2k} \right\rangle = \frac{1}{2i} \delta_j^k;$$

so

(34.4) $$\frac{\partial}{\partial z^j} = \frac{1}{2} \left\{ \frac{\partial}{\partial x^{2j-1}} + \frac{1}{i} \frac{\partial}{\partial x^{2j}} \right\}.$$

Similarly,

(34.5) $$\frac{\partial}{\partial \bar{z}^j} = \frac{1}{2} \left\{ \frac{\partial}{\partial x^{2j-1}} - \frac{1}{i} \frac{\partial}{\partial x^{2j}} \right\}.$$

Note that for every function f

(**34.6**)
$$\frac{\partial \bar{f}}{\partial \bar{z}^k} = \left(\frac{\partial f}{\partial z^k}\right)^-, \qquad 1 \leq k \leq m,$$

and

(**34.7**)
$$df = \sum_{k=1}^{m} \frac{\partial f}{\partial z^k} dz^k + \sum_{k=1}^{m} \frac{\partial f}{\partial \bar{z}^k} d\bar{z}^k$$

because the 1-forms represented by each side of (34.7) agree on the basis

$$\frac{\partial}{\partial z^1}, \cdots, \frac{\partial}{\partial z^m}, \frac{\partial}{\partial \bar{z}^1}, \cdots, \frac{\partial}{\partial \bar{z}^m} \text{ of } CT_p(\mathbf{R}^{2m}).$$

(**34.8**)   **Definition.**   A C^1 function f is *analytic* on the open set U if and only if

(**34.9**)
$$\frac{\partial f}{\partial \bar{z}^k}(p) = 0, \qquad 1 \leq k \leq m, \, p \in U.$$

(**34.10**)   **Definition.**   A family $w^1, \ldots, w^m$ of differentiable functions on the open set $U \subset \mathbf{C}^m$ forms a *local* (complex) *analytic coordinate system* for U if

(i) The map $w: p \rightarrow (w^1(p), \ldots, w^m(p))$ of $U \rightarrow \mathbf{C}^m$ is one-one.
(ii) The functions $w^1, \ldots, w^m$ are analytic.
(iii) $\det \{(\partial w^j/\partial z^k)(q), 1 \leq j, k \leq m\} \neq 0, q \in U$.

If $w^1, \ldots, w^m$ is an analytic coordinate system for $U \subset \mathbf{C}^m$, according to (34.7) and (34.9)

(**34.11**)
$$(dw^k)_p = \sum_{j=1}^{m} \frac{\partial w^k}{\partial z^j}(p)(dz^j)_p, \qquad 1 \leq k \leq m, \, p \in U.$$

Since the matrix $(\partial w^k/\partial z^j)(p)$ is nonsingular it follows from (34.11) that $(dw^1)_p, \ldots, (dw^m)_p$ span the same subspace of $CT_p^*(\mathbf{C}^m)$ as $(dz^1)_p, \ldots, (dz^m)_p, \, p \in U$. Inverting (34.11) yields

(**34.12**)
$$(dz^j)_p = \sum_{k=1}^{m} \lambda_k^j(p)(dw^k)_p, \qquad p \in U, \, 1 \leq j \leq m,$$

where the $m \times m$ matrix $(\lambda_k^j(p))$ is the inverse of $[(\partial w^k/\partial z^j)(p)]$; so

(**34.13**)
$$(d\bar{z}^j)_p = \sum_{k=1}^{m} \bar{\lambda}_k^j(p)(d\bar{w}^k)_p$$

[because $d\bar{f} = (df)^-$]. Equations (34.12) and (34.13) show that $(dw^1)_p, \ldots, (dw^m)_p, (d\bar{w}^1)_p, \ldots, (d\bar{w}^m)_p$ form a basis for $CT_p^*(\mathbf{C}^m)$, and in keeping with this notation the dual basis for $CT_p(\mathbf{C}^m)$ is denoted by

$$\frac{\partial}{\partial w^1}\Big|_p, \cdots, \frac{\partial}{\partial w^m}\Big|_p, \frac{\partial}{\partial \bar{w}^1}\Big|_p, \cdots, \frac{\partial}{\partial \bar{w}^m}\Big|_p.$$

Let

(34.14) $$w^k = u^{2k-1} + iu^{2k}, \qquad 1 \le k \le m,$$

where the u^j's are real-valued. Then $dw^k = du^{2k-1} + i\,du^{2k}$; $d\bar{w}^k = du^{2k-1} - i\,du^{2k}$; so that $(du^1)_p, \ldots, (du^{2m})_p$ also form a basis for $CT_p^*(\mathbf{C}^m)$. This fact together with

(34.15) $$(du^j)_p = \sum_{k=1}^{2m} \frac{\partial u^j}{\partial x^k}(p)(dx^k)_p$$

implies

(34.16) $$\det\left\{\frac{\partial u^j}{\partial x^k}, 1 \le j, k \le 2m\right\} \ne 0, \qquad p \in U.$$

Since condition (i) of Definition (34.10) is equivalent to saying that the map $p \to (u^1(p), \ldots, u^{2m}(p))$ of $U \to \mathbf{R}^{2m}$ is one-one, it follows that the functions $u^1, \ldots, u^{2m}$ form a local coordinate system for U in the sense of Definition (15.1).

Conversely suppose that $(dw^1)_p, \ldots, (dw^m)_p$ span the same subspace of $CT_p^*(\mathbf{C}^m)$ as $(dz^1)_p, \ldots, (dz^m)_p$. Then relations of the type (34.12) and (34.13) exist and the above chain of arguments can be followed from there (with p fixed) to yield (34.16), so that $u^1, \ldots, u^{2m}$ form a local coordinate system in some neighborhood of p by Theorem (15.3). This ensures that (i) and (ii) of Definition (34.10) will be satisfied in some neighborhood of p, and if the w^j's are known to be analytic they will form an analytic coordinate system there.

(34.17) Summary. Let $w^j = u^{2j-1} + iu^{2j}$, $1 \le j \le m$, be analytic functions on the open set $U \subset \mathbf{C}^m$ with real parts u^{2j-1} and imaginary parts u^{2j}, respectively. Then the following conditions are equivalent:

(1) $w^1, \ldots, w^m$ form an analytic coordinate system valid in some neighborhood of $p \in U$.
(2) $\det\{(\partial w^j/\partial z^k)(p), 1 \le j, k \le m\} \ne 0$.
(3) $u^1, \ldots, u^{2m}$ form a differentiable coordinate system valid in some neighborhood of $p \in U$.
(4) $\det\{(\partial u^j/\partial x^k), 1 \le j, k \le 2m\} \ne 0$.

Exercises

34.1 Show that there is a unique operator ∂ mapping k-forms on U into $(k+1)$-forms on U and satisfying:

(i) $\partial(a\alpha + b\beta) = a\,\partial\alpha + b\,\partial\beta$ when a and b are constants and α and β k-forms.

(ii) $\partial(\alpha \wedge \beta) = \partial\alpha \wedge \beta + (-1)^{\deg(\alpha)}\alpha \wedge \partial\beta$.

(iii) $\partial^2 = 0$.

(iv) $(\partial f)_p = \sum_{j=1}^{m}(\partial f/\partial w^j)(p)(dw^j)_p$ whenever $w^1, \ldots, w^n$ is an analytic coordinate system valid in a neighborhood of p.

34.2 (Based on Exercise 34.1.) Show that the operator $\bar{\partial} = d - \partial$ satisfies (i), (ii), and (iii) of Exercise 34.1. Show that a function f is analytic if and only if $\bar{\partial}f = 0$.

34.3 Show there is a unique operator J mapping k-forms into k-forms and satisfying:

(i) $J(a\alpha + b\beta) = aJ\alpha + bJ\beta$.

(ii) $J(\alpha \wedge \beta) = J\alpha \wedge J\beta$.

(iii) $J^2 = -1$.

(iv) If f is an analytic function, $J(f) = f$, $J(df) = i\,df$, and $J(d\bar{f}) = -i\,d\bar{f}$.

34.4 Let ω be the 2-form $\omega = d\bar{z}^1 \wedge dz^1 + \cdots + d\bar{z}^m \wedge dz^m$ on $\mathbf{C}^m$. Put $\omega^j = \omega \wedge \cdots \wedge \omega (j \text{ factors})$. Show that $\omega^m = m!\,d\bar{z}^1 \wedge dz^1 \wedge \cdots \wedge d\bar{z}^m \wedge dz^m$ and express this $2m$-form in cartesian coordinates. Show that $d\bar{z}^k \wedge dz^k \wedge \omega^{m-1} = (1/m)\omega^m$.

34.5 (Based on Exercise 34.4.) If the functions $h_1, \ldots, h_m$ are analytic on U and c is a $2m$-chain in U, show that

$$\int_{\partial c}\left(\sum_{j=1}^{m} h_j\,dz^j\right) \wedge \omega^{m-1} = 0.$$

35 Analytic functions of one variable

Let U be an open subset of the complex numbers $\mathbf{C}$. In this case put $z = x^1 + ix^2$, so that the superscript on the z is omitted. A complex function $f = u + iv$ on U is a map $f: U \to \mathbf{C}$ (see Figure 29). The condition for f to be analytic on U, $\partial f/\partial\bar{z} = 0$, becomes

$$0 = \left(\frac{\partial}{\partial x^1} - \frac{1}{i}\frac{\partial}{\partial x^2}\right)(u + iv) = \left(\frac{\partial u}{\partial x^1} - \frac{\partial v}{\partial x^2}\right) + i\left(\frac{\partial v}{\partial x^1} + \frac{\partial u}{\partial x^2}\right),$$

or

(35.1) $$\frac{\partial u}{\partial x^1} = \frac{\partial v}{\partial x^2}, \qquad \frac{\partial v}{\partial x^1} = -\frac{\partial u}{\partial x^2}.$$

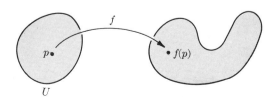

FIGURE 29

Equations (35.1) are known as the Cauchy-Riemann equations and they have an important geometrical interpretation. Notice that

$$f_* \left(\frac{\partial}{\partial x^1} \right) = \frac{\partial u}{\partial x^1} \frac{\partial}{\partial x^1} + \frac{\partial v}{\partial x^1} \frac{\partial}{\partial x^2};$$

$$f_* \left(\frac{\partial}{\partial x^2} \right) = \frac{\partial u}{\partial x^2} \frac{\partial}{\partial x^1} + \frac{\partial v}{\partial x^2} \frac{\partial}{\partial x^2}.$$

It follows from the Cauchy-Riemann equations that

$$\left(f_* \left[\frac{\partial}{\partial x^1} \right], f_* \left[\frac{\partial}{\partial x^2} \right] \right) = \frac{\partial u}{\partial x^1} \frac{\partial u}{\partial x^2} + \frac{\partial v}{\partial x^1} \frac{\partial v}{\partial x^2} = 0;$$

$$\left(f_* \left[\frac{\partial}{\partial x^1} \right], f_* \left[\frac{\partial}{\partial x^1} \right] \right) = \left(\frac{\partial u}{\partial x^1} \right)^2 + \left(\frac{\partial v}{\partial x^1} \right)^2$$

$$= \left(\frac{\partial v}{\partial x^2} \right)^2 + \left(\frac{\partial u}{\partial x^2} \right)^2$$

$$= \left(f_* \left[\frac{\partial}{\partial x^2} \right], f_* \left[\frac{\partial}{\partial x^2} \right] \right);$$

$$f_* \left(\frac{\partial}{\partial x^1} \right) \wedge f_* \left(\frac{\partial}{\partial x^2} \right) = \det \begin{bmatrix} \dfrac{\partial u}{\partial x^1} & \dfrac{\partial v}{\partial x^1} \\ \dfrac{\partial u}{\partial x^2} & \dfrac{\partial v}{\partial x^2} \end{bmatrix} \frac{\partial}{\partial x^1} \wedge \frac{\partial}{\partial x^2}$$

$$= \left[\left(\frac{\partial u}{\partial x^1} \right)^2 + \left(\frac{\partial v}{\partial x^1} \right)^2 \right] \frac{\partial}{\partial x^1} \wedge \frac{\partial}{\partial x^2}.$$

Thus when the Jacobian of f is not zero the vectors $f_*(\partial/\partial x^1)$ and $f_*(\partial/\partial x^2)$ are orthogonal, and have the same length and the same relative orientation as $\partial/\partial x^1$ and $\partial/\partial x^2$ (see Figure 30). In this case if the basis vectors $\partial/\partial x^1|_p$, $\partial/\partial x^2|_p$ are identified with $\partial/\partial x^1|_{f(p)}$, $\partial/\partial x^2|_{f(p)}$, the map f_*: $T_p(\mathbf{C}) \to T_{f(p)}(\mathbf{C})$ can be described as a rotation followed by a positive homothety (a transformation of the form $w \to \lambda w$ where λ is a scalar > 0). A map f with the property that at each point f_* is a rotation followed by a

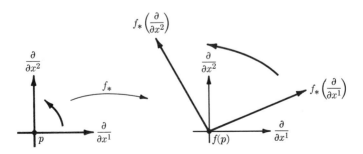

FIGURE 30

positive homothety is called *conformal,* and the content of the Cauchy-Riemann equations or, equivalently, the analyticity of f is that the map $f\colon U \to \mathbf{C}$ is conformal wherever its Jacobian is not zero.

There are some other important reformulations of analyticity.

(35.2) Theorem. f is analytic on U if and only if the 1-form $f\,dz$ is closed, that is, $d(f\,dz) = 0$ on U.

PROOF. $d(f\,dz) = (\partial f / \partial \bar{z})\,d\bar{z} \wedge dz$, which is zero if and only if $\partial f / \partial \bar{z} = 0$. ◆

As a consequence of Theorem (35.2) it is easy to derive

(35.3) Theorem. For a C^1 function f, $\int_\phi f\,dz = 0$ for every 2-chain ϕ in U if and only if f is analytic in U.

PROOF. $\int_\phi f\,dz = \int_\phi d(f\,dz)$, which vanishes for every 2-chain if and only if $d(f\,dz) = 0$ on U. ◆

Theorem (35.3) raises an interesting question: Up to now in order to be analytic a function f had to be C^1 (or at least have partial derivatives) so that analyticity could be defined by the condition $\partial f / \partial \bar{z} = 0$. The equivalent condition $\int_{\partial \phi} f\,dz = 0$ of Theorem (35.3) makes sense as long as f is continuous (actually even weaker conditions will do) and the natural question is: Suppose a function f is said to be *generalized analytic* on U if (1) f is continuous on U and (2) $\int_{\partial \phi} f\,dz = 0$ for every 2-chain ϕ in U, then is every generalized analytic function C^1 on U, and consequently analytic, or are there generalized analytic functions which are not analytic? It turns out that conditions (1) and (2) above are equivalent to the analyticity of f. The fact that they are sufficient to imply f is analytic is known as *Morera's theorem,* while the observation that every analytic function satisfies condition (2) is called *Cauchy's theorem.*

The Cauchy-Morera theorem. f is generalized analytic if and only if f is analytic.

PROOF. The proof of this fact involves several steps of interest in themselves. They are listed below in the order in which they are established later.

1. If U can be deformed to a point, every 1-chain ψ in U with $\partial \psi = 0$ is the boundary of some 2-chain. In fact what is shown is the following: There is a map, $\phi \to \mathrm{cone}\ (\phi)$, of k-chains in U into $(k+1)$-chains in U, such that

(35.4) $\partial\ \mathrm{cone}\ (\phi) - \mathrm{cone}\ (\partial\phi) = (-1)^k\,\phi,$ ϕ a k-chain, $k > 0$.

2. If U can be deformed to a point p_0 and ψ is a 1-chain whose boundary

$\partial\psi = \{p\} - \{p_0\}$, where $\{q\}$ denotes the map $\{q\}(\Delta^0) = q$, define

$$F(p) = \int_\psi f\,dz, \qquad f \text{ generalized analytic on } U.$$

Then F is well defined, C^1, and analytic. Moreover $dF = f\,dz$; so $f = \partial F/\partial z$.

3. If F is analytic on U, the function G defined on U by

(35.5)
$$G(p) = \begin{cases} \dfrac{F(p) - F(q)}{z(p) - z(q)}, & p \in U, p \neq q, \\[2mm] \dfrac{\partial F}{\partial z}(q), & p = q, \end{cases}$$

is generalized analytic on U.

4. *Cauchy's integral formula.* If F is analytic on U, then F is C^∞ on U, $\partial^k F/(\partial z)^k$ is analytic on U for each $k \geq 0$, and

(35.6)
$$\frac{\partial^k F}{(\partial z)^k}(q)\left[\int_c \frac{dz}{z - z(q)}\right] = k!\int_c \frac{F\,dz}{[z - z(q)]^{k+1}}$$

whenever $c = \partial\phi$ is the boundary of a 2-chain in U. In particular, if c is the 1-chain $z \circ c(t) = z(p) + re^{2\pi it}$, $t \in [0, 1]$, bounding the disk centered at p of radius r, $|z(p) - z(q)| < r$, and this disk belongs to U, then

(35.7)
$$\frac{\partial^n F}{(\partial z)^n}(q) = \frac{n!}{2\pi i}\int_c \frac{F\,dz}{[z - z(q)]^{n+1}}, \qquad n = 0, 1, 2, \ldots\ .$$

Results 4 and 2 show that a generalized analytic function f is analytic, because $f = \partial F/\partial z$, which is analytic by 4. These four results are now proved in order.

Proof of 1. The first result is a combinatorial observation. Suppose that $h\colon [0, 1] \times U \to U$ is a differentiable map which deforms U to the point p_0 in the sense of Section 31; that is, $h(1, p) = p$, $p \in U$ and $h(0, p) = p_0$, $p \in U$. Then the associated cone operator, $\phi \to \text{cone}(\phi)$, carrying k-chains into $(k + 1)$-chains is defined by two conditions:

(35.8)
$$\text{cone}(a\phi + b\psi) = a\,\text{cone}(\phi) + b\,\text{cone}(\psi)$$

when a and b are integers and ϕ and ψ k-chains. If $\tau\colon \Delta^k \to U$ is a k-simplex, cone (τ) is the $(k + 1)$-simplex

(35.9)
$$\text{cone}(\tau)(t^1, \ldots, t^{k+1}) = h(t^1 + \cdots + t^{k+1}, \tau(t^1, \ldots, t^k)).$$

Figure 31 should aid in following the argument.

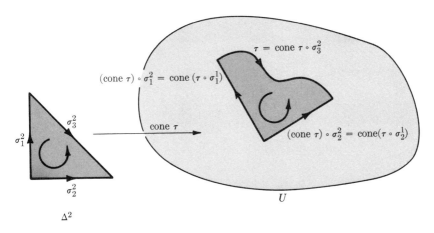

FIGURE 31

Two computations are needed.

$$(\text{cone } \tau \circ \sigma_j^{k+1})(t^1, \ldots, t^k)$$

$$= (\text{cone } \tau)(t^1, \ldots, 0, \ldots, t^k), \qquad 0 \text{ in the } j\text{th position,}$$

(35.10)
$$= h(t^1 + \cdots + t^k, \tau(t^1, \ldots, 0, \ldots, t^{k-1}))$$

$$= h(t^1 + \cdots + t^k, \tau \circ \sigma_j^k(t^1, \ldots, t^{k-1}))$$

$$= \text{cone } (\tau \circ \sigma_j^k)(t^1, \ldots, t^k), \qquad j < k + 2.$$

$$(\text{cone } \tau \circ \sigma_{k+2}^{k+1})(t^1, \ldots, t^k)$$

$$= (\text{cone } \tau)(t^1, \ldots, t^k, 1 - [t^1 + \cdots + t^k])$$

(35.11)
$$= h(1, (t^1, \ldots, t^k))$$

$$= \tau(t^1, \ldots, t^k).$$

Now from these computations it follows when $k > 0$ that

$$\partial \text{ cone } \tau = \sum_{j=1}^{k+2} (-1)^j \text{ cone } \tau \circ \sigma_j^{k+1}$$

(35.12)
$$= \sum_{j=1}^{k+1} (-1)^j \text{ cone } (\tau \circ \sigma_j^k) + (-1)^{k+2}\tau$$

$$= \text{cone } (\partial\tau) + (-1)^k \tau,$$

which together with (35.8) yields (35.4) after multiplying (35.12) with different τ's by the appropriate integers and adding.

Proof of 2. If ψ and ϕ are both 1-chains with boundary $\{p\} - \{p_0\}$, $\partial(\phi - \psi) = 0$ and according to step 1 there is a 2-chain c whose boundary

$\partial c = \phi - \psi.$

$$0 = \int_{\partial c} f \, dz = \int_{\phi} f \, dz - \int_{\psi} f \, dz;$$

so F is well defined. Let C_s be the 1-simplex

$$C_s(t) = p + ts(0, 1), \qquad t \in [0, 1].$$

Then $\partial(\psi + C_s) = \{p + s(0, 1)\} - \{p_0\}$ and

$$F[p + s(0, 1)] = \int_{\psi + C_s} f \, dz = \int_{\psi} f \, dz + \int_{C_s} f \, dz;$$

$$F[p + s(0, 1)] - F[p] = \int_0^1 f[p + ts(0, 1)] is \, dt$$

$$= \int_0^s f[p + u(0, 1)] i \, du.$$

It follows that $(\partial F/\partial x^2)(p) = if(p)$, and a similar argument shows $(\partial F/\partial x^1)(p) = f(q)$. The conclusion of step 2 is now an easy consequence of these relations.

Proof of 3. First suppose U is an open disk,

$$U = \{p : |z(p) - a| < r\} \qquad \text{for some } a \in C \text{ and } r > 0.$$

Put $f = \partial F/\partial z$ and let $b(t) = q + t(p - q)$, $t \in [0, 1]$, $p \in U$. Regarded as a chain, $\partial b = \{p\} - \{q\}$. Since $dF = f \, dz$ and $d(z \circ b) = [z(p) - z(q)] \, dt$,

$$F(p) - F(q) = \int_b f \, dz = \int_0^1 f[q + t(p - q)] |z(p) - z(q)| \, dt.$$

When we compare with (35.5) and use $\partial F/\partial z = f$, it follows that

(35.13) $$\qquad G(p) = \int_0^1 f[q + t(p - q)] \, dt, \qquad p \in U.$$

Now for each $t \in [0, 1]$, let $h_t : U \to U$ be given by $h_t(p) = q + t(p - q)$. $h_t^* \, dz = t \, dz$. If ϕ is a 2-chain, the following computation shows G is generalized analytic:

$$\int_{\partial \phi} G \, dz = \int_{\partial \phi} \left\{ \int_0^1 f \circ h_t \, dt \right\} dz = \int_0^1 \left\{ \int_{\partial \phi} f h_t \, dz \right\} dt$$

$$= \lim_{\varepsilon \to 0} \int_\varepsilon^1 \left\{ \int_{\partial \phi} f \circ h_t \frac{1}{t} h_t^* \, dz \right\} dt$$

$$= \lim_{\varepsilon \to 0} \int_\varepsilon^1 \frac{1}{t} \left\{ \int_{\partial h_t \circ \phi} f \, dz \right\} dt = 0$$

because

$$\int_{\partial h_t \circ \phi} f \, dz = \int_{\partial (h_t \circ \phi)} dF = \int_{\partial \partial (h_t \circ \phi)} F = 0.$$

The proof of step 3 where U is just an open set is deferred until (35.7) has been established.

Proof of 4. Only (35.7) is proved here, (37.6) being left as an exercise. By decreasing U if necessary, one can assume that U is an open disk and still contains the closed disk bounded by the circle c. Then according to the part of step 3 which has been established, the function G of (35.5) is generalized analytic on U, so that in particular

(35.14)
$$0 = \int_c \frac{F - F(q)}{z - z(q)} \, dz$$

or

(35.15)
$$\int_c \frac{F \, dz}{z - z(q)} = F(q) \int_c \frac{dz}{z - z(q)}.$$

To evaluate this last integral let $b: [0, 1] \to \mathbf{C}$ be the map with $z \cdot b(s) = z(q) + \varepsilon e^{2\pi i s}$. b is a parametrization of the circle of radius ε centered at q. Choose $\varepsilon > 0$ so small that the circle of b lies inside the circle of c and let $\omega = [z - z(q)]^{-1} \, dz$ on the complement of the point q in $\mathbf{C}$. It is easily checked that $d\omega = 0$; so according to Example (25.13) (with $b = C_1$, $c = C_2$)

$$\int_c [z - z(q)]^{-1} \, dz = \int_c \omega = \int_b \omega = \int_b [z - z(q)]^{-1} \, dz$$

$$= \int_0^1 \frac{\varepsilon 2\pi i e^{2\pi i s} \, ds}{\varepsilon e^{2\pi i s}} = 2\pi i,$$

and substituting this in (35.15) gives

(35.16)
$$F(q) = \frac{1}{2\pi i} \int_c \frac{dz}{z - z(q)}.$$

Formula (35.7) and the fact that F is C^∞ on U and that $\partial^k F/(\partial z)^k$ is analytic on U now follow on differentiating (35.16) as a function of q, differentiation under the integral sign being allowed in this case because the difference quotients converge uniformly on c.

The remaining part of step 3 follows from this. In fact, let $q \in V \subset U$ where V is an open disk. It has already been shown in the established part of step 3 that the G of (35.5) is generalized analytic on V. By step 2 it is the derivative of an analytic function, $G = \partial H/\partial z$, on V, and by what has just been shown G is then analytic on V. Since G is clearly analytic on $U \sim \{q\}$, the points of U except for q, G must be analytic on U and hence generalized analytic there by Theorem (35.3). ◆

Exercises

35.1 Suppose f is continuous on the disk $|z| < 1$ and that $\int_{\partial c} f \, dz = 0$ whenever the 2-chain c represents integration over a rectangle with sides parallel to the coordinate axes and one vertex at the origin. Show that f is analytic in the disk. [HINT: Show directly that $f = \partial F/\partial z$ where F is analytic.]

35.2 (Based on Exercise 35.1.) Suppose f is continuous on $|z| < 1$ and that $\int_{\partial c} f \, dz = 0$ whenever c represents integration over a rectangle lying entirely in the open upper half disk, $\{z : |z| < 1$, imaginary part of $z > 0\}$, or in the lower open half disk, $\{z : |z| < 1$, imaginary part of $z < 0\}$. Show that f is analytic on $|z| < 1$.

35.3 (Maximum principle.) If f is analytic on U, show that

$$f(p) = \frac{1}{2\pi} \int_0^{2\pi} f(p + re^{i\theta}) \, d\theta$$

and deduce from this that $|f|$ cannot attain its maximum at an interior point of U unless f is constant.

35.4 (Liouville's theorem.) If f is analytic on $\mathbf{C}$ and $|f| \leq M < +\infty$ on $\mathbf{C}$, show using Cauchy's integral formula centered at q (with $r \to \infty$) that $(\partial f / \partial z)(q) = 0$ for each $q \in \mathbf{C}$ and deduce from this that f is a constant.

36 Taylor series

According to Morera's theorem the G that occurs in (35.5) is actually analytic. This allows one to reapply step 3 to G and arrive in this manner at the so-called *finite Taylor development*.

(36.1) Theorem. If f is analytic on the open set U containing q, for each integer $n \geq 0$ there is an analytic function f_n on U with the property that

$$f = f(q) + \frac{\partial f}{\partial z}(q)[z - z(q)] + \cdots$$

(36.2)

$$+ \frac{\partial^{n-1} f}{\partial z^{n-1}}(q) \frac{[z - z(q)]^{n-1}}{(n-1)!} + [z - z(q)]^n f_n$$

on U and $n! f_n(q) = (\partial^n f / \partial z^n)(q)$.

PROOF. (By induction.) If (36.2) holds for a particular n notice that the relation $n! f_n(q) = (\partial^n f / \partial z^n)(q)$ is the result of applying $\partial^n / \partial z^n$ to both sides of (36.2) and evaluating at q. Using step 3 of Section 35 on f_n at q gives

$$f_n = f_n(q) + [z - z(q)]f_{n+1}$$

where f_{n+1} is analytic on U. Substituting this with the value already obtained for $f_n(q)$ in (36.2) yields (36.2) with n replaced by $n + 1$ and completes the proof of the inductive step. The initial step, $f = f(q) + [z - z(q)]f_1$, is a restatement of step 3 in the proof of Cauchy's theorem. ◆

Another important consequence of the Cauchy-Morera theorem is that a uniform limit of analytic functions is analytic.

(36.3) Theorem. If the functions $\{f_n, n = 1, 2, \ldots\}$ are analytic on the open subset $U \subset \mathbf{C}$ and $f_n \to f$ uniformly on each compact subset of U, then f is analytic on U.

PROOF.   If $\tau\colon [0,\,1] \to U$ is any 1-simplex in U, the set $\tau([0,\,1])$ is compact, so that $f_n[\tau(t)] \to f[\tau(t)]$ uniformly for $t \in [0,\,1]$. Applying a well-known property of the integral, we find

$$\int_\tau f_n \, dz = \int_0^1 f_n[\tau(t)] \frac{\partial z \circ \tau}{\partial t} (t) \, dt$$

$$\to \int_0^1 f[\tau(t)] \frac{\partial z \circ \tau}{\partial t} (t) \, dt$$

$$= \int_\tau f \, dz$$

as $n \to \infty$. Now each 2-chain ϕ in U has a boundary $\partial \phi$ which is a sum of 1-simplices like τ with integer coefficients, so that $\int_{\partial\phi} f_n \, dz \to \int_{\partial\phi} f \, dz$ as $n \to \infty$. Using Cauchy's theorem,

$$0 = \int_{\partial\phi} f_n \, dz \to \int_{\partial\phi} f \, dz;$$

so $\int_{\partial\phi} f \, dz = 0$ for each 2-chain ϕ in U and f is generalized analytic. Morera's theorem now shows f is analytic on U.   ◆

(36.4)   Example.   As an application of Theorem (36.3) consider the sequence of partial sums of a power series in $z - a$,

(36.5)
$$f_n = \sum_{k=0}^n a_k(z - a)^k.$$

As polynomials in the analytic function z the f_n's are analytic. Now it is a well-known fact, not proved here, that there is a number r, called the *radius of convergence of the power series*

(36.6)
$$\sum_{k=0}^\infty a_k(z - a)^k,$$

such that (i) $f_n(p) \to$ some number $f(p)$ uniformly on subsets having the form $\{q\colon |z(q) - a| \le \theta\}$, $\theta < r$; (ii) $\{f_n(p)\}$ does not converge if $|z(p) - a| > r$.
Phrased in another manner, $f_n \to f$ uniformly on compact subsets of the disk where $|z - a| < r$; so by Theorem (36.3) the power series (36.6) represents an analytic function on the open disk on which it converges.

Every function f which is analytic in a neighborhood of the point p can be represented in some open disk centered at p by a power series of type (36.6).

(36.7)   Theorem.   If f is analytic in the open set U and the disk $\{q\colon |z(q) - a| \le r\} \subset U$, then

$$f(q) = \sum_{k=0}^\infty a_k[z(q) - a]^k, \qquad |z(q) - a| < r,$$

where

$$a_k = \frac{1}{2\pi i} \int_c \frac{f\,dz}{(z-a)^{k+1}} = \frac{1}{k!}\frac{\partial^k f}{\partial z^k}(a),$$

$c(t) = a + re^{2\pi it}$, $t \in [0, 1]$.

PROOF. The series

$$(36.8) \qquad \frac{1}{z - z(q)} = \frac{1/(z-a)}{1 - \left(\dfrac{z(q)-a}{z-a}\right)} = \sum_{k=0}^{\infty} \left(\frac{1}{z-a}\right)^{k+1} [z(q) - a]^k$$

converges uniformly to the function $[z - z(q)]^{-1}$ if

$$\frac{|z(q) - a|}{|z - a|} \le \theta < 1;$$

in particular this convergence is uniform on the circle c. Theorem (36.7) can be obtained by multiplying both sides of (36.8) by f and integrating over c, using Cauchy's integral formula with $n = 0$ on the left, and integrating termwise using (35.7) on the right. ◆

Exercises

36.1 Suppose f is analytic on the open neighborhood U of p and $f(p) = 0$. Show that p has a neighborhood V such that either (i) f vanishes identically on V or (ii) $f(q) \ne 0$, $q \in V$, $q \ne p$. [HINT: If $f^{(n)}(p) = 0$ all n, Taylor's series expansion shows f vanishes identically on some neighborhood of p. If $f^{(k)}(p) \ne 0$ for some k, use Taylor's finite development [Theorem (36.1)] to show (ii) holds.]

36.2 (Based on Exercise 36.1.) If f and g are analytic on the open set U, show that every accumulation point of the set $S = \{q : f(q) = g(q)\}$ either (i) is an interior point of S or (ii) is in the complement of U.

Answers to
Selected Exercises

Section 2

2.2 $\{p \in \mathbf{R}: 0 \leq p < 1\}$.

2.3 $U_n = (0, 1/n)$ in $\mathbf{R}$.

2.4 $F_n = [n, \infty)$ in $\mathbf{R}$.

2.5 (i) $\bigcap_{n=1}^{\infty} (-1/n, 1/n) = \{0\}$; (ii) $\bigcap_{n=1}^{\infty} (-1/n, 1) = [0, 1)$;

(iii) $\bigcap_{n=1}^{\infty} (-n, n) = (-1, 1)$.

2.6 $\bigcup_{n=1}^{\infty} [0, 1 - (1/n)] = [0, 1)$.

2.11 Let $\mathcal{U}_0 = \{B_\varepsilon(q): \varepsilon$ is a rational number, q is a rational point of $\mathbf{R}^n$, and $B_\varepsilon(q) \subset$ some $W \in \mathcal{V}\}$. $\mathcal{U}_0$ is countable. For each $U \in \mathcal{U}_0$ let $W(U)$ be a specific element of $\mathcal{V}$ chosen so that $U \subset W(U)$. Put $\mathcal{V}_0 = \{W(U): U \in \mathcal{U}_0\}$.

2.12 $B_1((0, \ldots, 0)) = \bigcap_{k=1}^{\infty} B_{1+(1/k)}^{\circ}((0, \ldots, 0))$.

2.13 If $p \in F_\varepsilon$, $d(p, q) < \varepsilon - \delta$ for some $q \in F$, $\delta > 0$. If $p' \in B_\delta(p)$, then $d(p', q) \leq d(p', p) + d(p, q) < \varepsilon$; so $B_\delta(p) \subset F_\varepsilon$.

2.14 If $q \in \bigcap_{k=1}^{\infty} F_{1/k}$, let $q_k \in F$ with $d(q, q_k) < 1/k$. $q_k \rightarrow q$, which implies $q \in F$ since F is closed. The other inclusion follows from $F \subset F_{1/k}$.

2.15 If $p \in U(A)$ let $D(p) = B_\varepsilon^{\circ}(q)$ be an open ball with rational center q and rational radius ε containing at most a countable number of points of A. From Exercise 2.9(b) the class $\mathcal{W} = \{D(p): p \in U(A)\}$ is a subclass of $\mathcal{U}$ and hence at most countable. $U(A) = \bigcup \{D(p) \cap A: D(p) \in \mathcal{W}\}$ is countable because it is a countable union of countable sets.

Section 3

3.2 If D is not closed its complement D^c is not open; so there exists a $p \notin D$ such that $B_{1/k}(p) \cap D \neq \varnothing$ for each k. Choose $p_k \in B_{1/k}(p) \cap D$.

3.3 $p_k = k$ in $\mathbf{R}$.

3.4 Let $\{p_1, p_2, \ldots\}$ be any enumeration of the rational numbers in $(0, 1)$.

3.5 $d(p, q_k) \leq d(q_k, p_k) + d(p_k, p) \to 0$ as $k \to \infty$.

3.8 Let $\{p_k\}$ run successively (with repetitions) through the finite sets A_1, $A_2, \ldots$, where $A_n = \{m/2^n : -n2^n \leq m \leq n2^n, d(m2^{-n}, F) < 2^{-n}\}$.

Section 4

4.5 Let $\{q_k\}$ be a sequence of distinct points in B with no accumulation point in B. Let $C = \{q_1, q_2, \ldots\}$ and for each k let U_k be an open set with $U_m \cap C = \{q_m\}$. Put $\mathfrak{U} = \{[\text{closure } (C)]^c, U_1, U_2, \ldots, U_m, \ldots\}$.

4.6 Suppose the assertion is not true. For each k choose $p_k, q_k \in D$, $d(p_k, q_k) < 1/k$ and $p_k, q_k \notin V$ for any $V \in \mathfrak{U}$. Since D is compact, by passing to a subsequence one can assume $p_k \to p$ and then $q_k \to p$ too. But then $p \in$ some V in $\mathfrak{U}$ and for large enough k, $p_k, q_k \in V$ too, contradicting the original assumption.

4.7 Let $B = \{(a^1, a^2) \in \mathbf{R}^2 : a^1 > 0$ and $a^1a^2 = 1$ or $a^2 = 0\}$; $\mathfrak{U} = \{U_1, U_2\}$ where $U_1 = \{(a^1, a^2) : a^2 > 0\}$, $U_2 = \{(a^1, a^2) : a^1 > 0, a^1a^2 < 1\}$. If $p_k = (k, 1/k)$, $q_k = (k, 0)$, then $d(p_k, q_k) = 1/k$, $q_k \notin U_1$, $p_k \notin U_2$.

4.8 Let $\varepsilon = $ one-half the Lesbesgue number of $\mathfrak{U}$ as a covering of D (cf. Exercise 4.6).

Section 5

5.3 If $c \in [a, b] \cap J^c$, then the relatively open sets $J_1 = (-\infty, c) \cap J$, $J_2 = (c, +\infty) \cap J$, would show that J is not connected.

5.6 The function $f(\lambda) = 1/\lambda$, $\lambda \in (0, 1)$, is not uniformly continuous on $(0, 1)$ because $|f(1/n) - f(1/2n)| = n$ while $|1/n - 1/2n| \to 0$.

5.7 For each $p \in B$ let $U(p)$ be an open set such that $U(p) \cap B = \{q : |f(q) - f(p)| < \varepsilon/2\}$ and let δ be the Lesbesgue number of the open covering $\mathfrak{U} = \{U(p) : p \in B\}$ of B (cf. Exercise 4.6). Alternatively, if f is not uniformly continuous there exist points $p_k, q_k \in B$ such that $|f(p_k) - f(q_k)| \not\to 0$ while $d(p_k, q_k) \to 0$. Since B is compact, by passing to subsequences one can assume $p_k \to p$. Then $q_k \to p$ too and

$$|f(p_k) - f(q_k)| \leq |f(p_k) - f(p)| + |f(p) - f(q_k)| \to 0$$

because f is continuous at p. This contradicts the assumption that f is not uniformly continuous on B.

5.9 (c) Always continuous. (d) $\det (a_m^k) \neq 0$. (e) $\det (a_m^k) \neq 0$.

Section 6

6.3 True for $n = 1$ only.

Section 8

8.2 This is a consequence of the formula in Exercise 6.4 and the fact that the determinant of a matrix product is the product of the determinants of the matrix factors.

Section 10

10.1
$$\det \begin{bmatrix} b_1^1 & b_2^1 \\ b_1^2 & b_2^2 \end{bmatrix} \neq 0.$$

Section 12

12.4 Yes.
12.5 No.

Section 13

13.1 (a) Any vector of the form $a(\partial/\partial x^2) + b(\partial/\partial x^3)$, a, $b \in \mathbf{R}$ with evaluation at $(1, 0, 0)$ understood. (b) Any vector of the form

$$a\,\frac{\partial}{\partial x^1} + b\,\frac{\partial}{\partial x^2} + c\,\frac{\partial}{\partial x^3}$$

where $a - 2b - 4c = 0$ and evaluation at $(1, 2, 5)$ is understood.

13.2
$$X_{C(t_0)} = \frac{\partial}{\partial x^1}\bigg|_{C(t_0)} + \cdots + nt_0^{n-1}\frac{\partial}{\partial x^n}\bigg|_{C(t_0)},$$

$$|X_{C(t_0)}| = [1 + 4t_0^2 + \cdots + n^2 t_0^2]^{1/2};$$

cosine of angle is equal to $3t_0^2[1 + 4t_0^2 + \cdots + n^2 t_0^2]^{-1/2}$.
13.3 (a) $Z = -(\partial/\partial y^1) + 2(\partial/\partial y^2)$ evaluated at $(-1, -1)$; $Zf = -\sin(-1) - 2\cos(-1)$. (b) $c = 0$.

13.5 $\quad Y_1 = \dfrac{\partial}{\partial x^1} + \dfrac{\partial}{\partial x^2}; \quad Y_2 = \dfrac{\partial}{\partial x^1} - \dfrac{\partial}{\partial x^2}; \quad Y_3 = \dfrac{\partial}{\partial x^1} + \dfrac{\partial}{\partial x^2} + \dfrac{\partial}{\partial x^3}.$

13.9
$$Y_j = \sum_{k=1}^{n} \frac{\partial u^j}{\partial x^k}\frac{\partial}{\partial x^k}.$$

13.11
$$Y_1 = \frac{1}{\sqrt{11}}\left(\frac{\partial}{\partial x^1} - \frac{\partial}{\partial x^2} + 3\,\frac{\partial}{\partial x^3}\right);$$

$$Y_2 = \frac{1}{\sqrt{66}}\left(4\,\frac{\partial}{\partial x^1} + 7\,\frac{\partial}{\partial x^2} + \frac{\partial}{\partial x^3}\right);$$

$$Y_3 = \frac{1}{\sqrt{6}}\left(-2\,\frac{\partial}{\partial x^1} + \frac{\partial}{\partial x^2} + \frac{\partial}{\partial x^3}\right).$$

Section 14

14.3 (b) $[X, Y] = \sum_{j=1}^{n} \left[\sum_{k=1}^{n} \left[(Xx^k) \frac{\partial (Yx^j)}{\partial x^k} - (Yx^k) \frac{\partial (Xx^j)}{\partial x^k} \right] \right] \frac{\partial}{\partial x^j} \cdot$

(c) $[e^{x^1} \sin (x^1) + \cos (x^1)] \dfrac{\partial}{\partial x^1} + [\sin (x^1) + \sin (x^2)] \dfrac{\partial}{\partial x^2} \cdot$

Section 15

15.1 $(3 \sqrt{3}/2 + \frac{1}{2})e^3$.
15.2 $-12(dz^1)_p + (dz^2)^p + 4(dz^3)_p$.
15.3 (a) $\omega^1 = dx^1 + dx^2 - dx^3$; $\omega^2 = dx^1 + 3\,dx^2 - dx^3$; $\omega^3 = -dx^1 - 3\,dx^2 + 3\,dx^3$.

Section 16

16.1 $f_1^* = \begin{bmatrix} 1 \\ 0 \\ -1 \end{bmatrix}$; $f_2^* = \begin{bmatrix} -7 \\ 1 \\ 7 \end{bmatrix}$; $f_3^* = \begin{bmatrix} -9 \\ 1 \\ 10 \end{bmatrix} \cdot$

16.2 4.
16.4 $(\alpha^i)^{\#} = X_j$ follows from the relations $\langle (\alpha^i)^{\#}, \alpha^k \rangle = (\alpha^i, \alpha^k) = \langle X_j, \alpha^k \rangle$ all k, and then $(\alpha^i, \alpha^k) = \langle X_j, \alpha^k \rangle = (X_j, [\alpha^k]^{\#}) = (X_j, X_k) = \delta_{jk}$.
16.5 $\phi^*(\alpha_j)(Y_i) = \alpha_j(\phi_*[Y_i]) = (\phi_*[Y_i], X_j) = (X_i, X_j) = \sum_{m=1}^{k} (X_m, X_j)$ $\omega^m(Y_i)$ for each i.

Section 18

18.2 $-5e^1 \wedge e^2 - e^2 \wedge e^3 - 4e^1 \wedge e^3$.

Section 20

20.2 $5e^3$.
20.3 $3e^3 \wedge e^5 - e^1 \wedge e^3$.
20.4 $e^1 \wedge e^4$.

Section 22

22.9 $*d *df = \sum_{k=1}^{n} \partial^2 f/(\partial x^k)^2$.

Section 24

24.1 11/6.
24.2 $c \circ \sigma_1^2 : t \to (1, 1 + 2t)$; $c \circ \sigma_2^2 : t \to (1 + t, 1)$; $c \circ \sigma_3^2 : t \to (1 + t, 3 - 2t)$. Integral = 0.

24.3 −6.

24.4 (a) 0; (b) $\frac{4}{3}\pi b^3$.

Section 26

26.1 $\left[\left(\dfrac{\partial h}{\partial x^1}\right)^2 + \left(\dfrac{\partial h}{\partial x^2}\right)^2 + \left(\dfrac{\partial h}{\partial x^3}\right)^2\right]^{-1/2}$

$$\times \left[\frac{\partial h}{\partial x^1}\, dx^2 \wedge dx^3 + \frac{\partial h}{\partial x^2}\, dx^3 \wedge dx^1 + \frac{\partial h}{\partial x^3}\, dx^1 \wedge dx^2\right].$$

26.2 $N = [(2x^1 + x^2)^2 + (x^1 - 6x^2)^2 + 1]^{-1/2}$

$$\times \left[(2x^1 + x^2)\frac{\partial}{\partial x^1} + (x^1 - 6x^2)\frac{\partial}{\partial x^2} - \frac{\partial}{\partial x^3}\right].$$

Section 29

29.1 (a) $z^1 = r$, $z^2 = \theta$; r, θ polar coordinates. (b) $z^1 = \frac{1}{2}(x^1 + x^2)$, $z^2 = \frac{1}{2}(x^1 - x^2)$.

Section 32

32.2 By Theorem (32.4) $\omega = df_1$ on U_1 and $\omega = df_2$ on U_2. $d(f_1 - f_2) = \omega - \omega = 0$ on $U_1 \cap U_2$, and since $U_1 \cap U_2$ is connected, this means $f_1 - f_2 = c$ a constant on $U_1 \cap U_2$. Define $f = f_1$ on U_1, $f = f_2 + c$ on U_2.

32.3 Outline of solution: Let $C_a: [0, 1] \to U$ be given by $C_a(t) = (a \cos 2\pi t, a \sin 2\pi t)$, $1 < a < 2$. These 1-simplices are all homotopic, so that

$$\lambda = \int_{C_a} \omega$$

is a constant. The 1-form $\beta = \omega - \lambda\alpha$ is closed, $d\beta = 0$, and

$$\int_{C_a} \beta = 0 \qquad \text{for all } a.$$

Now the region $V = U \sim \{(a, 0): 1 < a < 2\}$ can be deformed to a point in U; so there is a function f on V with $df = \beta$. Then the condition

$$\int_{C_a} \beta = 0$$

can be used to show that f extends uniquely to a differentiable function on U with $df = \beta$ there.

Index of Symbols

Index